THE NEW BOOK OF FLIGHT

KW-228-744

(Mr) Timothy Suckling,
"Ancient" House,
Steeple Bumpstead,
N^r Haverhill,
Suffolk.

Christmas 1948.
Christmas 1949
Christmas 1950
Christmas 1951

THE NEW BOOK

OF

FLIGHT

Edited by

C. H. GIBBS-SMITH

Companion, Royal Aeronautical Society;
Author of 'Basic Aircraft Recognition';
'The Aircraft Recognition Manual';
'German Aircraft'; 'Ballooning', etc.

WITH A FOREWORD BY

SIR FREDERICK HANDLEY PAGE

C.B.E., F.R.Ae.S.

Geoffrey Cumberlege

OXFORD UNIVERSITY PRESS

1948

Oxford University Press, Amen House, London E.C.4
EDINBURGH GLASGOW NEW YORK TORONTO MELBOURNE
WELLINGTON BOMBAY CALCUTTA MADRAS CAPE TOWN
Geoffrey Cumberlege, Publisher to the University

To Constance

The frontispiece photograph is reproduced
by kind permission of British European
Airways Corporation.

PRINTED IN GREAT BRITAIN BY
MORRISON AND GIBB LTD., LONDON AND EDINBURGH

455

FOREWORD

by

Sir FREDERICK HANDLEY PAGE

C.B.E., F.R.Ae.S.

AFTER SIX YEARS of concentrated war effort, the rapidity with which the British aircraft industry has geared itself to an impressive peace-time programme is a magnificent feat. Already it is building fine, new civil aeroplanes for the development of world trade and communication.

In many ways, the current position is very similar to that which obtained in 1939. Now, as then, the emphasis is upon an expansive and progressive view in so far as new designs are concerned.

Aircraft which are building or on the drawing-board at the present time will benefit from the great scientific progress which war has brought in its train. In general structure, they will be increased in size and will have improved speed, range and comfort. This finer performance will result not only from improved aerodynamic designs, but also from the installation of more suitable aero engines.

They will be the first fruits of an era which may be described as the turning-point in the technical development of aeronautics. It is a fact that aviation has reached the verge of discoveries and advances almost as significant as the first man-made flight of forty-four years ago. Already, and in so short a time, serious efforts are being made by British research workers and designers in order to conquer supersonic flight.

During the past four decades, there have been periods which have been marked by great advances in aerodynamic design and others which have been characterised by great strides with aero-engine improvements. To-day it is evident that the forthcoming period will be noteworthy for big advances in both spheres.

Of revolutionary importance are the evolution of the jet-turbine engine and current experiments in connection with the high-speed wing. Recent successes in jet-propulsion are the vital indication of an eminently more suitable form of aero-power plant, while there are possibilities of aerofoil drags far lower than could have been envisaged a few years ago.

British aeronautical research workers and engineers are well ahead of other countries in these spheres. Fundamental research continued during the war years despite a natural tendency to reduce such work in order that more time could be devoted to pressing affairs of the moment. New ideas and aerodynamic discoveries which have evolved from the war will make possible this revolutionary progress in aviation.

Resulting from this research are the current designs of new British aircraft. They prove that the mere application of the gas turbine and fruits of other experiments to present-day basic aircraft is not sufficient.

This unremitting effort represents Britain's determination to keep ahead of the world in aeronautical design and, after years of war, to give of the best which widespread research and the benefits of science have made possible.

FOREWORD

I hope that the aeronautical students who read this excellent volume will be inspired by the fine heritage of the British aircraft industry. Great importance attaches to their proper training—and, particularly, to the training of highly skilled aeronautical engineers rather than the aviation research worker.

Enthusiastic young blood is required in the British aircraft industry so that its magnificent traditions and achievements may be enhanced in the coming years when competition in the realms of international aviation will be at a high level.

CONTENTS

CONTENTS

One of the most remarkable of bird photographs. It was taken by the *Daily Graphic* photographer, David Johnson, at 1/10,000th of a second. The bird is a racing pigeon, one of nature's finest airmen. It is constructed for close manœuvre, quick climb, and fair speed (about 40 to 50 m.p.h.). For this all-round performance it has pectoral (wing-moving) muscles which weigh about 50 per cent. of the entire bird ; wings which beat about eight times a second ; and a large tail. This photograph was taken at the extreme stage of the down-stroke, with wings concave and pressing down the air. The characteristic ' slap ' of a pigeon's wings when taking off is caused by the meeting of the wings above the body in the very sharp recovery strokes, not (as has often been thought) in the position shown here. Note also the position of the tail, acting not only as elevator but partial rudder as well.

[*Photo* : ' *Daily Graphic* '

INTRODUCTION

THE PHRASE ' air-minded ' seems almost old-fashioned. It was the crusade to make the world air-minded which one associates with the period following the first world war, when the air and aircraft seemed to have too much of a military atmosphere. To many people the whole subject of the air so often means war, and destruction, and it is the ' many people ' who ultimately support flying, who buy tickets in airliners and pay indirectly for the research and development which the air age demands. Oddly enough, even years before flying was possible (the first man flew in 1783) the prophets associated the air with war and gave the dog a bad name:

' The time will come when thou shalt lift thine eyes
  To watch a long-drawn battle in the skies.'

This prediction was made in 1731. Dr. Johnson, nearly thirty years later, wrote: ' What would be the security of the good, if the bad could at leisure invade them from the air ? ' The most recent war has not improved matters, and it is still chiefly young people who embrace the air age and talk flying.

It is, therefore, essential in every generation, and that, of course, means a continuous stream of new people, that air-mindedness should be encouraged, so that finally (and we are far from it yet) the idea of flying will be as natural and simple to young and old alike as motoring or the railway. There still lingers the old (and once passionately held) idea that if man was meant to fly he would have been provided by the Almighty with wings. It is also important to stimulate even those who do take naturally to the air to see as far and as deeply into the future as they can. England is slowly becoming more dependent upon her brains to hold her own in the modern world, and a large number of those brains must be devoted to the study of the air and its ways if we are to prosper—perhaps if we are to survive.

In this work we have tried to make a balance between the basic subjects of aeronautics—its history, the types of planes in use, the new inventions, the human side of the business, and also the future. The three longest articles deal with the pivotal topic of jet-propulsion, which is now so universally in the aviation news; the controversial and potentially terrible question of the rocket, which has its peaceful and exploratory aspects as well; and the far removed topic of the model aeroplane. Many adults forget that the enthusiasm for the model, in any subject, is a most logical and sensible affair. The model captivates the imagination, involves concentrated interest, and encourages the sort of rational and connected thinking which later on must be applied to the profundities of aerodynamics and mathematics. It is in every sense an exercise; it limbers up the mind as gymnastics develop the body.

The history of aeronautics has been given an honoured place in this volume for two reasons. First, the history of any subject can enlist interest and enthusiasm. Second, in a subject like flying, it is very necessary that those who spend their lives in such work should be able to see themselves as part of a historic chain of events. History, in any subject, provides the mind with a sense of perspective, and perspective is a quality for the lack of which many a modern technician sticks for ever in a narrow groove, unable to see the wood for the trees, unable to see himself and his work in anything like proper proportion.

INTRODUCTION

Perhaps the most interesting to many readers is the reference section of aircraft at present in use over the world's surface. One is thankful, as an editor, that the rate of new production is not as hectic as in war-time. To-day it is just possible, without being too much behind, to keep in sight the main machines which actually do the job of flying the passengers and freight from place to place.

Those readers who are seriously looking forward to a career in one of the many branches of aviation will find a number of articles which tell of what they will find there and the chances provided in the various fields.

C. H. GIBBS-SMITH

Acknowledgments

THE EDITOR wishes to thank the following for many courtesies and much help : Sir Frederick Handley Page ; Mr. John Stroud, for generous assistance and great labour in proof reading and the location of photographs ; the Public Relations authorities at the Admiralty ; the Air Ministry and the Society of British Aircraft Constructors, for the provision of photos ; the Editors of the *New Yorker* ; Mr. E. K. Gann, and Messrs. Michael Joseph and Curtis Brown ; Mr. Cecil Day Lewis and the Hogarth Press ; Major C. C. Turner and Messrs. Sampson Low, Marston and Co. Ltd. Also the Imperial War Museum for kind permission to use their Crown Copyright photographs.

ROCKETRY

by

D. C. Smith, M.A., A.F.R.Ae.S.

Fellow of the Inter-Planetary Society, Assistant Secretary-General, Royal Aeronautical Society

IN 1935 the word 'rocket' brought to mind a firework display; in 1945 it was a deadly weapon of war; in 1955 it may be something entirely different. One thing is certain, however, all people will know of it, for we are rapidly approaching an age when rocket power will be one of the most important sources mankind has available at its disposal.

The purpose of this section is to give briefly the history behind the rocket, to trace its development up to the stage it has now reached, and then to make some reasonable predictions for the future. In this way a background for further advanced rocket study will be available. Only elementary theory is given, although reference is made to sources where the full theory can be obtained.

What is a Rocket ?

Before considering history, it is first necessary to define clearly what is meant by a rocket. Many recent articles have led to some confusion by the statement that rocket propulsion and reaction propulsion are one and the same thing. Examination shows the fallacy of this statement. All propulsion, by its definition, is reaction propulsion and only a special type comes under rocket propulsion.

A rocket motor is essentially a hollow body, closed at all but one point, containing a quantity of combustible or explosive gas, or gas-producing solids. On burning, the pressure increases rapidly, forcing the hot exhaust gases through the orifice.

Consider the state of affairs in Fig. 1 (*a*). Here an internal pressure has been built up, but the body is in stable equilibrium. If a hole suddenly appears in one side, Fig. 1 (*b*), the force (pressure × area) on the one side

is no longer fully balanced and the body therefore moves in a direction opposite to that of the flow of exhaust gases.

The motion is not due to any reaction force between the exhaust gases and the atmosphere outside the motor and thus a rocket motor is even more efficient when it

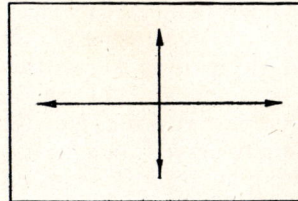

Fig 1a

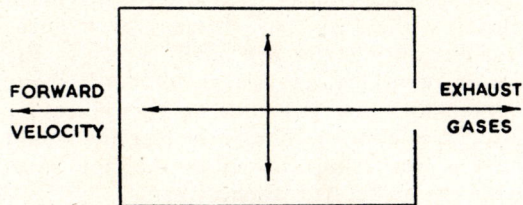

FORWARD VELOCITY   EXHAUST GASES

Fig 1b

FIG. 1.—The basic principle of rocket propulsion.

is working in a vacuum, owing to reduction of air resistance. It is this property which makes a rocket motor supreme in interplanetary travel.

One further point must be emphasised— the rocket motor is self-supporting and does not depend upon oxygen from the surrounding atmosphere for its functioning.

All rocket motors work on these main principles, the main variations between the various motors being the mechanics of the motors themselves, the methods of ignition and control, and the combustible materials which are used.

Early Rocket History

The rocket has a very long history, but its actual discovery, if the word discovery can be applied to what was probably a gradual evolution, cannot definitely be dated. The most that can be said is that there can be little doubt that it was known in China in the early thirteenth century.

The first reference in Chinese documents to the use of rockets indicates that they were known in A.D. 1232. According to this they were used during the siege of Peking by the Mongols. A description is given by the French sinologist St. Julien in his *Journal Asiatique* of 1849. He states:

' The defenders (Chinese) also had " arrows of flying fire ". They attached an inflammable substance to the arrow. The arrow suddenly flew away in a straight line and spread its fire over an area measuring ten steps.'

It is generally agreed that these arrows of flying fire were in fact rockets, as no mention can be found of any method of shooting them. It is probable that they were in fact ordinary arrows with a rocket head fixed to the barb end. This explanation is strengthened by the fact that sketches of Chinese rockets during the last century show the rocket with feathers on it like an arrow. Presumably this was done as an elementary attempt at control, though the feathers would have a very short life once the hot gases from the rocket had reached them.

Although this is the first mention of anything comparing with the powder rocket, it fits in well with von Romocki's theory of the evolution of the rocket. He suggests that the rocket did evolve from the old fire arrow which had been extensively used for many centuries. This was a normal arrow with a small sack of incendiary materials tied to its head. One of the difficulties with these fire arrows was that the fire tended to be extinguished in flight, so efforts were made to make the fire more durable. The Greeks—knowing of the yellow flare from a salt flame—mixed salt with their fire ingredients in an attempt to make the fire hotter. They did not, of course, succeed, but it is

thought that news of this spread eventually to China.

Here, maybe by chance or maybe because saltpetre was the only ' salt ' available, this was added to the mixture instead of common salt. As the incendiary mixture already contained sulphur and charred material, the addition of saltpetre produced a mixture not unlike gunpowder. This mixture filled into hollow wooden sticks—a further method of preventing the mixture from being extinguished in flight—would certainly act as a rocket head to the arrow. The Chinese

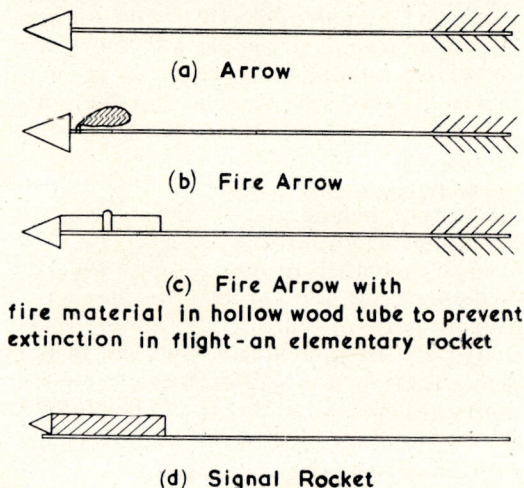

(a) Arrow

(b) Fire Arrow

(c) Fire Arrow with fire material in hollow wood tube to prevent extinction in flight - an elementary rocket

(d) Signal Rocket

FIG. 2.—Probable development of the rocket.

were not unaware of the ' magic ' mixture they had produced, for at the same time as the use of these elementary rockets they had produced exploding bombs.

The news of the discovery travelled fast towards the West, mention of it being made in Arabic and Egyptian history shortly afterwards. By 1249, Roger Bacon in England had described gunpowder in his book *Epistola* and at the same time two other books had been produced on the Continent containing more or less the same information.

From this time rockets were used both for war and display purposes, although for two centuries little advance in efficiency was shown. Then de Fontana, an Italian, produced a series of imaginative designs using rockets as propulsive agents, although no record of any of these machines being made or tried exists. The principles adopted, however, showed an appreciation of the possibilities of the rocket motor.

Throughout these early years no satisfactory attempt had been made to explain just how and why a rocket worked, and it was not until Newton's time that a theoretical basis was possible. The theory of the rocket is in fact an application of Newton's third law of motion. As from this time in rocket history, design was deduced in most cases from theory, it is permissible to interpose a note on theory at this stage.

Rocket Theory

Newton's third law states 'action and reaction are equal and opposite'. This explains the recoil of a gun when it is fired. Quantitatively V, the velocity of recoil, depends upon m, the mass of the shell, v, the velocity of the shell, and M, the mass of the gun. The equation is:

$$M V = m v.$$

In the case of the rocket, M and V are the mass and velocity of the rocket, and m and v the mass and velocity of the exhaust.

For any given velocity, it can be shown that the rocket efficiency varies with the size of the particles forming the exhaust stream, reaching a maximum when the particles are very small. Under these conditions the rocket will reach the speed of its exhaust gases when its weight is 1/2.72 of its initial weight.

The speed of the rocket is not limited to the speed of its exhaust, as when it has reached this speed further particles can be emitted to increase the speed still further. In fact, the velocity will increase as long as the fuel is still producing energy. The efficiency of a rocket also varies with the speed of the rocket. It is very low at the start of the flight, increasing as the rocket gets faster. Thus the performance of a rocket will depend upon

(a) The exhaust velocity. The greater the exhaust velocity the greater the speed and range.

(b) The mass of the exhaust. The larger the amount of exhaust ejected per second the higher the speed.

(c) The percentage of the initial weight of the rocket which is fuel. This is usually defined by the value $\frac{weight\ of\ fuel}{weight\ of\ rocket\ less\ fuel}$ known as the mass-ratio. The more fuel that is available the faster the rocket can go. It has already been shown that with a mass-ratio of 2.72 the speed of the rocket will reach that of its exhaust if that exhaust consists of very fine particles.

In practice the exhaust is usually molecular in size and so almost fulfils this condition.

(d) The aerodynamic shape of the rocket, if part of its flight is to be through

A contemporary caricature (c. 1830) of Mr. Golightly's Aerial Steam-Horse. This drawing has been used frequently in rocket literature, the most recent use being in the special stamps produced for the rocket mail flights of 1934.

the earth's atmosphere. As all rockets have to pass through this aerial barrier this factor in design is important. The drag is particularly crucial when it is realised that all the fuel for later parts of the flight has to be carried over this stage.

The Era of Rocket Gadgets

During the next 200 years many attempts to use rocket motors for power were made.

It was realised that a steam jet would form a reasonable rocket motor and in 1721 a Dutch professor produced a model car which worked. There are, however, no records existing of a full-size car being made.

Large numbers of similar plans were produced in the next two centuries using steam, compressed air, gunpowder and all other means imaginable. These were planned to drive cars, aeroplanes, helicopters, boats, engines and even airships. Inventors rushed to patent their ideas but little was heard of them once the patent was granted.

A caricature of one of the more startling inventions is shown on page 13. This device was patented by Golightly under the name of 'Aerial Steam-Horse' but, needless to say, was never made.

One serious attempt at the use of rockets was, however, made in the period 1790–1820, although in this case they were used for war purposes.

War rockets were first ' re-invented ' with any success in India. The Indians made the cases of iron tubing and fired the rockets, weighing up to 12 lb., at the British troops. This rocket artillery was relatively successful when used in large enough quantities to allow for the inaccuracy of fire.

In the first decade of the nineteenth century Sir William Congreve in England experimented with larger and better rockets and succeeded in forming a rocket corps with the British Forces. The success in action varied considerably, but it is certain that the rocket corps played a very important part in the British victories over Napoleon.

By 1817 Congreve had produced a large range of rockets, explosive, incendiary and shell types up to a weight of 42 lb. with a range of 3,000 yards. The rockets required

no guns to fire them and thus were popular with commanders for their mobility. All his rockets were powder type and remained in use with small modifications for 100 years, the main change being the elimination of the long stick, the directional stability being given by small vanes in the jet of the exhaust.

This history is brief and does not pretend to list all the attempts, some brave and useful, others foolish and valueless, that were made by the many people interested in rockets for their usefulness or stunt value during the years. Fuller details are given in some of the reference books, but a complete history will never be written as so many attempts are lost in obscurity.

The Design of the Powder Rocket

Until modern times the powder rocket, filled with slow gunpowder, has been the main rocket motor available. The design has not changed much in the 700 years of its existence. Essentially the rocket consists of a tube closed at one end and ' throttled ' or fitted with a nozzle at the other. The powder is pressed into the body leaving a cone unoccupied by powder. This can be seen in Fig. 3. The reason for the cone is to

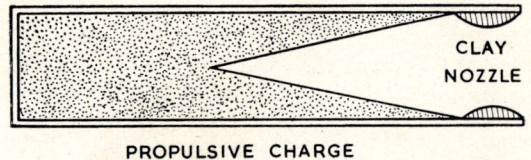

CLAY

NOZZLE

PROPULSIVE CHARGE

Fig. 3.—Schematic diagram of the solid-fuel rocket motor. Note the cone unoccupied by powder to give a larger burning area.

enable a greater area of powder to be burned at one time, thus increasing the quantity and mass of the exhaust gases and the speed of the rocket.

Uses of the Powder Rocket

Other than the war rockets already described, the rocket has been used for many purposes and brief mention will be made of the main classes of use.

ROCKETRY

Life-Saving Rockets

These started as a modification of the Congreve war rocket by the Navy. The standard powder rocket without an explosive head was attached to a length of fine cord and a similar method is used even now. Many thousands of lives have thus been saved by rockets.

Rocket Cars

Early experiments with steam jets had proved that this form of propulsion was not reliable enough to prove a commercial proposition. A few models using powder rockets had in fact been made but nothing of a serious nature was attempted until the much publicised but relatively unsuccessful Opel rocket car.

It was in 1928 that Valier, a rocket enthusiast, suggested a rocket car to Opel, the German light car manufacturer. Opel was probably more interested in the propaganda outlook than the scientific benefits which might be obtained from the experiments, but Valier was genuine in his faith that the car would work.

The rockets used were of two types, bored and solid packed (the solid packed type had no bored cone), and were used in mixed batteries in the rear of the car. The cone-bored type gave a large thrust of 400 lb. for about three seconds, while the solid type gave 45 lb. for nearly thirty seconds, thus a large thrust was available for the start and a lower thrust for maintaining the speed.

In the earlier tests trouble was experienced with the rockets, which often failed to ignite, but eventually complete success was achieved at a public run on a speedway near Berlin, the car reaching 125 miles per hour.

A later model, fitted to run on railway lines, reached 180 miles per hour, but the project was a stunt and was bound to fail eventually. The efficiency of the runs never reached 1 per cent.

Rocket Aeroplanes

Opel, delighted with the advertisement he had obtained from his rocket car trials, tried in 1929 a rocket aeroplane with a battery of rockets in the rear of the cut-off fuselage. The plane flew, but as in the case of the car, was merely a stunt.

Powder rockets are not ideally suited for any propulsion which requires prolonged thrust unless large batteries are carried, the rockets being fired consecutively. An aeroplane fuselage is not a suitable container for such a battery. Thus the first successful rocket aeroplane had to wait for the development of the liquid-fuel rocket described later.

During the 1939–45 war, however, powder rocket motors were used quite extensively to assist the take-off of heavily-loaded aeroplanes. A number of small rockets, usually two, were attached to the aircraft and fired as the aircraft was about to take off. Shorter take-offs were thus obtained. Liquid-fuelled rockets have also been used for this purpose.

Rocket Sleds and Gliders

These were tried in Germany in 1929, but neither were proceeded with any further.

Rocket Missiles

Other than the liquid motor type such as the V.2 and other similarly powered war weapons, several types of solid-fuelled rocket missiles were used in the 1939–45 war. Notable amongst these were the Russian and British rocket guns used against troops and aircraft, the American bazooka, the British Piat and the rocket bombs fired from aircraft.

The Americans also experimented with winged rockets of considerable range, while the Germans had rocket-propelled winged bombs, some controlled by parent aircraft, some from the ground and others flying with pre-set controls.

The various problems which had to be solved in the design of these weapons are given in the sections on the V.2 and other liquid-fuelled rockets.

Mail Flights

From the year 1928 extensive research was undertaken by many enthusiasts during attempts to develop the rocket as a mail carrier. These attempts met with varied success, but there is no doubt that much has been learnt on the behaviour and control of powder rockets.

The first experiments were carried out by an Austrian, Schmiedl, who in 1928 started an extensive programme of research. He began by an investigation of the atmosphere at the various heights at which his rockets would fly, using sounding balloons or small rockets carrying instruments. Having very little personal financial backing he interested several friends and obtained the support he required. Although he had at that time no intention of carrying mail, he included small folded letters in his rockets, giving them to the friends who had made the trials possible.

In later attempts he included a small mail-carrying compartment in his rocket and sold special covers to be carried and posted after the flight. This proved to be a very popular move and from that time it is very difficult to segregate the experimenters who were interested in general rocket research and used mail carrying as a method of subsidy from those who were primarily interested in

A view of one of Schmiedl's rockets in flight. All these rockets were of the powder type.

A very historic cover from Schmiedl's Austrian flights in 1930. This is the message carried in the V.3, the third rocket flight with mail, and is one of the first messages carried by rocket.

rocket mail carrying. Either class was equally valuable in its efforts in improving rocket design.

Schmiedl carried out many valuable experiments. Although the results of his first attempts were not good, the range being low and accuracy poor, later attempts showed great improvement. Flights were carried out at night with success, and a great step forward was made when a parachute with a timed release was attached to the mail container, landing it safely irrespective of the subsequent fate of the rocket. In 1933 he tried a step rocket, consisting of two separate rockets in the same case. On firing, the first step took the whole unit off the launching rack in the usual way. At a predetermined stage in the flight the second rocket was ignited while the first dropped away, the second rocket continuing on its way, having received a considerable starting boost. This rocket was a complete success, and Schmiedl was rewarded by the fact that the Austrian Post Office took a considerable interest in his subsequent flights.

Schmiedl also carried out experiments in Yugoslavia, where he tried a secret and smokeless powder in his rockets in a series of successful flights.

Other experimenters had been working on parallel lines during this period: Tiling and Zucker in Germany being two of the pioneers. Zucker was very energetic and carried out his experiments in several countries, on one occasion attempting unsuccessfully to fire a rocket containing mail over the Straits of

Dover. He also carried out the only flights which were made in England.

It was in 1934 that these little-known flights were made. Zucker came over to England for the Air Post Exhibition and obtained permission to test his rockets. Four flights were made, the first near Brighton when two rockets were fired, the second two in the Hebrides, the last was an attempt to reach the Isle of Wight from Lymington in Hants. None of the results was very good, the rockets being unreliable, with a tendency to explode on firing, and the directional control being poor.

Three other series of experiments should be mentioned; the trials in America carried out by Goddard and Ley and those in India and Australia. Stephen Smith was the driving force in the Indian flights and much good work was done. Flights were made from islands to the mainland, over floods, mountains and rivers. In a list of all rocket mail flights, the Indian trials form a large proportion. In Australia, Alan Young of the Australian Rocket Mail Society organised the flights. His attempts were dogged by bad luck but ten flights were made under varying conditions.

The future of rocket mail flights is much rosier than it would appear from a report of the above flights, as the liquid-fuel rocket has brought almost unlimited range, and the advance of radio almost complete control, for the flights of the future.

A cover carried by one of Zucker's experiments in England. This was the first flight of its type in England and was a limited success.

Meteorological Rockets

It had been realised for some time that until more was known of the conditions in the upper atmosphere, it would be very difficult to predict the flight of rockets. Schmiedl had realised this and had worked on the subject with his balloons, but the possibilities of this method were limited. Reliable results could not be obtained above twenty miles, as this was the ceiling of the balloons, so some other method had to be obtained for the greater heights.

The rocket, with its flight unlimited by the thinness of the atmosphere, in fact being improved by the resultant reduction in drag, was an obvious choice for further investigation of the upper layers of the atmosphere. The system is relatively simple, the rocket carrying the necessary instruments to the required height before either detaching them to fall by parachute or the whole rocket falling by parachute. With liquid-fuelled rockets heights of over forty miles have been attained, with very valuable results. It is at this stage that the structure of the liquid-fuelled rocket should be considered, as the majority of the modern work has been done with this type of motor.

The Liquid-Fuel Rocket

One thing should be emphasised at once. The theory of the liquid-fuel rocket differs in no way from any other type of rocket motor. It is only the mechanics and structure of the actual rocket that are different.

The main difference between the powder and liquid rocket is the fuel used. With the powder rocket there is great difficulty in arranging the continuous feed necessary for a continued flight without the use of stepped batteries of individual motors.

The fuels used vary considerably from motor to motor, but the selection is made from two series of materials, a liquid which burns almost explosively with sufficient oxygen, and an

A photograph of one of the rockets used by Young in Australia in 1935. The size of the rocket can clearly be seen. Four hundred letters were carried in this rocket.

oxygen carrier. The fuel and oxygen carried are pumped under pressure into the motor, where they burn in a semi-explosive manner. The heat produced is reduced by the use of a coolant which in some designs is the fuel itself. The main difficulties encountered in design are the choice of the material for the motor, the intense heat tending to burn through the sides of the motor, causing dangerous explosions ; and the feeding of the two liquids in the correct proportion for complete burning.

Much of the early work on this type of motor was done by Goddard in America and later by Ley, Oberth, Tiling, and others in Germany. Both series of experiments suffered from lack of experience in the control of the rockets, many of the motors performing perfectly on test, while the complete rockets were not so uniformly successful. Goddard was certainly first in the field as he tested one of his first liquid-fuel motors in 1923 and an actual rocket was fired early in 1926.

In most of the early designs the stick of the powder rocket, used entirely for its stabilising effect, was replaced by one or more tubes containing the liquid fuel. Those with one tube were called one stick repulsors, and so on. The fuel was fed to the motor by nitrogen pressure or by the vapour pressure of the liquid itself and in many designs was first passed round the outside of the motor

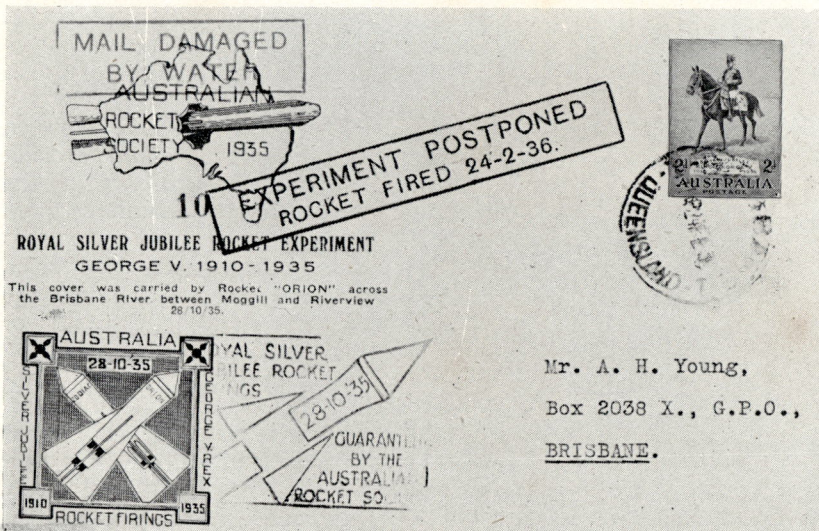

A cover carried in a powder rocket of the type shown in the previous illustration. This rocket fell in the Brisbane River, as shown by the various descriptive cachets.

casing to act as a coolant. This enabled the metal of the motor casing to be much thinner while still resisting the great heat caused by the burning of the fuel.

The fuels used in many of these early experiments were standard petrol and liquid oxygen. The liquid oxygen, though not

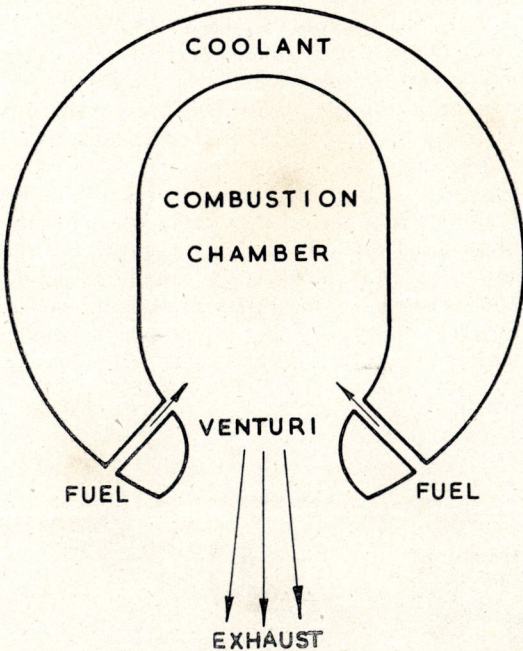

FIG. 4.—Schematic diagram of the liquid-fuel rocket motor.

inexpensive, caused much trouble in the early days as its low temperature encouraged ice deposition on the tubes, casings and valves of the apparatus. In the reports of the early experiments, the statement that the exhaust flame became red and smoky is constantly repeated, indicating sticking of valves with interruption of the oxygen supply.

Although the liquid motor is the more modern type, opinion is still divided as to whether liquid or solid is the more advantageous type. It may well be that the final answer will be given by a motor which is both. Experiments were carried out prior to 1939 on fuels consisting of an oxygen agent in the form of a viscous organic compound containing powdered metals in suspension. These mixtures gave exhaust velocities in excess of those to be expected

from hydrogen and oxygen mixtures and if the difficulties of the mechanics of the system can be overcome this type of fuel, enabling advantage to be taken of controlled feeding, may well be one of the chief fuels of the future.

The apparent advantages of the liquid-fuelled rockets can be summarised as follows:

(a) An individual liquid motor has a longer period of burning than a solid-fuel motor of comparable size, due to the constant feeding.

(b) Higher exhaust velocities are obtainable.

(c) Much easier and greater control can be exercised over the thrust; in fact, the motor can be cut off at any stage.

(d) The exhaust and motor can be situated at any position by suitable design. Thus the motor can be above or below the fuel tanks. With stickless rockets this assists in the design of stable rockets.

Against these points, the following disadvantages must be noted:

(a) The liquid-fuel motor requires weighty accessories such as pumps, fuel lines, tanks, coolant and combustion chambers, which all decrease the possible mass-ratio of the rocket.

(b) There is much more mechanism for potential faults.

(c) The liquids dealt with are often at extremely low temperatures and both dangerous and difficult to handle.

The German Liquid Rocket V.2

Many people have had the idea of liquid-fuelled rockets forced upon them in uncomfortable circumstances in the form of the German V.2.

The Germans had been interested in the potentialities of this type of motor for some time and the Government had stepped in as soon as the work of Ley and his fellow-experimenters had looked promising. Braun began his early work in 1933 when he designed a small rocket, the A.1. Constant improvements in the efficiency of the motor and the size of the rocket were made and the design advanced through several main stages until the V.2 or A.4 was reached. Work on this type started in 1940 and the first operational use was in September 1944. Early experiments had met with mixed success, explosions and failures being frequent. Even in the form in which it was finally flown, failures occurred in from 15 per cent. to 20 per cent. of the firings.

The rocket was forty-six feet long and of body diameter nearly five-and-a-half feet, and weighed 12½ tons when fully loaded. (A table of weights is given in Table I.) It consisted of a light structure of steel sheeting suitably reinforced, entirely enclosing the working parts of the rocket.

The top part of the structure incorporated the war head—the 'pay load' of the rocket weighing nearly a ton. The next compartment, still in the tapering portion of the structure, contained the control instruments. These included an automatic pilot to steer the

rocket over its trajectory. This was quite a complex operation, as the rocket was fired from a vertical position with no launching rack, and during flight it had to be made to turn the rocket in an angle from the vertical, giving the exact direction. Range was obtained by a predetermined cutting off of the fuel during flight.

The instruments regulated direction by movement of four small controls or spoilers in the exit of the jet and four external controls, not unlike aircraft controls, on the fins attached to the rear of the rocket structure.

Wireless control of rockets was also achieved. In this case a receiver and amplifier were included in the instrument bay, impulses from the ground controlling the actions of fuel cut off at the calculated height and velocity. This method, was, however, dropped in favour of an integrating accelerometer.

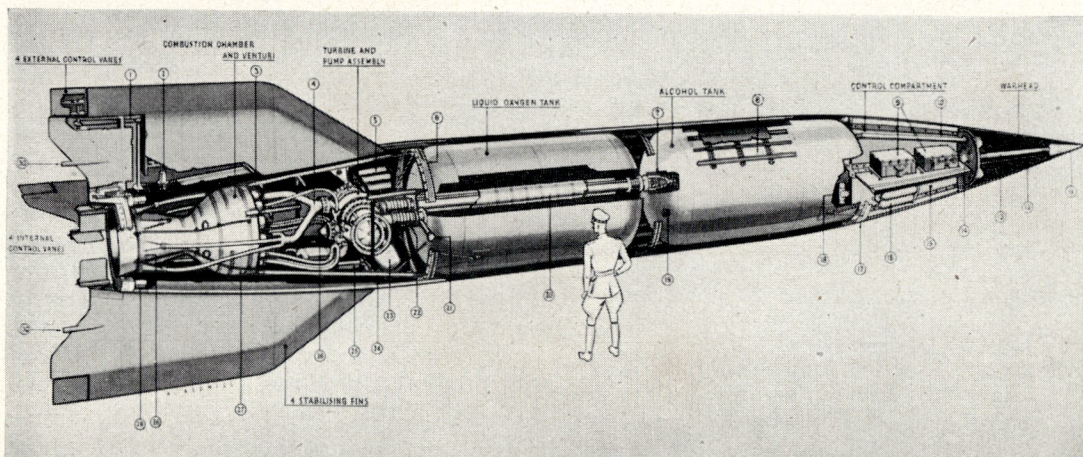

[*Crown Copyright*

Fig 5.   A diagrammatic drawing of the German V.2. rocket.

1. Chain drive to control tabs on external fins from electric motor.
2. Electric motor.
3. Injection nozzles on main combustion chamber.
4. Alcohol delivery piping.
5. Compressed-air bottles.
6. Rear joint ring and lifting point.
7. Servo-controlled alcohol valve.
8. Shell casing support structure.
9. Radio control equipment.
10. Pipe from warhead to alcohol tank.
11. Nose with fusing switch.
12. Conduit for fuse wiring.
13. Exploder tube.
14. Electric fuse for warhead.
15. Plywood support for radio.
16. Nitrogen bottles.
17. Front joint ring and lifting point.
18. Gyros for pitch and azimuth.
19. Alcohol tank filling point.
20. Insulated alcohol feed pipe.
21. Oxygen tank filling point.
22. Expansible bellows connections to alcohol and oxygen pumps.
23. Hydrogen peroxide tank.
24. Tubular support frame for turbine and pumps assembly.
25. Permanganate tank. Hydrogen peroxide and permanganate steam generator for turbine is located behind this tank.
26. Oxygen distributor unit.
27. Alcohol pipes for subsidiary cooling.
28. Alcohol inlet to double wall of rocket motor.
29. Electro-hydraulic servo motors.

Behind the instrument bay were the two main fuel tanks, both built of light alloy, occupying over twenty feet of the rocket length. The first tank contained the burning fuel, in this case a 75 per cent. solution of ethyl alcohol in water, while the rear tank contained liquid oxygen. The alcohol and oxygen were fed through pipes to two special pumps in the rear of the tanks, which delivered the fuel to the burners at a rate of 275 lb. of fuel per second at a pressure of 350 lb. per square inch. Prior to flight, both of the main tanks were pressurised to about 1.4 atmospheres to assist the pump and to reduce stresses on the tank structure.

The feed pump was driven by a special turbine which had its own power supply from small tanks of hydrogen peroxide and permanganate. These liquids were fed by means of nitrogen pressure to a small burner, the hot combustion gases being fed into the turbine.

The fuels were fed to the combustion chamber in the rear of the rocket, the oxygen to eighteen roses fixed in small cups in the dome of the chamber, and the alcohol to an annular ring fixed in the rear of the venturi. The chamber itself, in the form of a venturi closed at the dome end, similar to any other rocket motor, was made from steel with a coolant jacket fitted, the alcohol passing through the jacket before reaching a series of small nozzles round the eighteen cups, where it mixed with the liquid oxygen.

Cooling was very effective and although the internal temperature of the combustion chamber was of the order of 2,500 degrees C. little trouble was experienced.

Behind the venturi opening the four internal controls were mounted, and outside, fixed to the structure, were the four main directional fins. The rocket was designed for mass production and the theory was extremely simple.

Characteristics of V.2 Flight

The rocket was fired by means of a black powder torch which ignited an alcohol-oxygen mixture fed by gravity alone. When this was working the pumps were started by remote electrical control by the firing party, and the main thrust developed. The rocket rose slowly, but with ever-increasing speed, reaching a maximum velocity of 3,400 m.p.h. at twenty-two to twenty-three miles after about one minute's flight. The maximum time of powered flight, limited by the fuel carried, was seventy seconds.

TABLE I

Weight Summary of V.2 Rocket

	Wt. (lb.)	Per Cent Total
Warhead . . .	2,150	7.52
Radio and Instruments .	975	3.41
Structure and Tanks .	1,795	6.27
Liquid Oxygen .	10,940	38.24
Alcohol . . .	8,370	29.26
Structure and Turbines .	1,620	5.66
Auxiliary Fuel . .	399	1.39
Venturi (Motor) . .	1,025	3.58
Controls . . .	1,335	4.67
	28,609	

When the rocket had reached the all-burnt condition, or when the fuel was cut off, the trajectory continued in the form of a free flight parabola, reaching a maximum height of sixty miles. Later experiments have extended this height to over eighty miles though the details of modifications made to the rocket are not known. The maximum ground range achieved by the V.2 was 220 miles, although the average was some twenty-five miles less than this, the entire flight taking about five minutes.

At its peak the motor delivered a thrust of 27 tons and it is estimated that the specific thrust of the exhaust was 220 lb. per second. The amount of oxygen pumped into the motor was about 40 per cent. greater than that of the alcohol and it was estimated that some 5 per cent. of the alcohol was lost due to its cooling functions.

Other German Rocket Designs

In addition to the V.2 the Germans had experimented with or projected many other types of rocket weapon. The majority of these were liquid-motor-propelled, although some were tried using solid fuel. These weapons did not compare in range, speed or size with the V.2 which is the most ambitious rocket that was made prior to 1945.

German Rocket Planes

One of the most interesting of the rocket developments carried out in Germany was in the design of their rocket planes. The best known of these was the Me 163 although other men-carrying rockets were designed.

Work on rocket planes was started in earnest in 1938, but work on the motor was discontinued from 1939–41. When work was again started the progress was rapid and the first flight was made late in 1941. The fuels used in this case were hydrogen peroxide and calcium permanganate.

Several types of motor were tried, some incorporating electric motor starting, but the type in use in the aircraft of 1945, the Me 163C, was a Walter two-motored unit. The large motor, which had a thrust range of 400 to 3,740 lb., was used for take-offs and climb, while the small motor, positioned under the main one, developed a thrust of some 750 lb. and was used in level flight. In this way it was possible to extend the time of flight of the aircraft which, even with this provision, was very short.

The fuels used were T stoff (80 per cent. hydrogen peroxide plus 20 per cent. water) and C stoff (hydragine hydrate, methyl alcohol and water), which were fed by pumps to the combustion chamber, the C stoff being the cooling agent for the chamber.

The aircraft itself was of the tailless type with the ejector openings in the rear. It jettisoned its wheels on take-off and landed on a special skid on the keel of the fuselage. Fifty per cent. of its take-off weight of 11,300 lb. was fuel (mass-ratio 1) and the main feature of the aircraft was its terrific climb, 40,000 feet being reached in just over three minutes. The fuel endurance on full power was only four-and-a-half minutes with a top speed of nearly 600 m.p.h. It is interesting to note that the dry weight of the entire rocket motor was only 415 lb., less than 25 per cent. of the weight of an internal combustion engine designed to give the same thrust.

Projects

The Germans had produced many designs, and in some cases started building a proto-type, for improved types of rocket. They had

[Copyright : Royal Aeronautical Society
A close-up view of the motor and venturi compartment of the V.2 rocket.

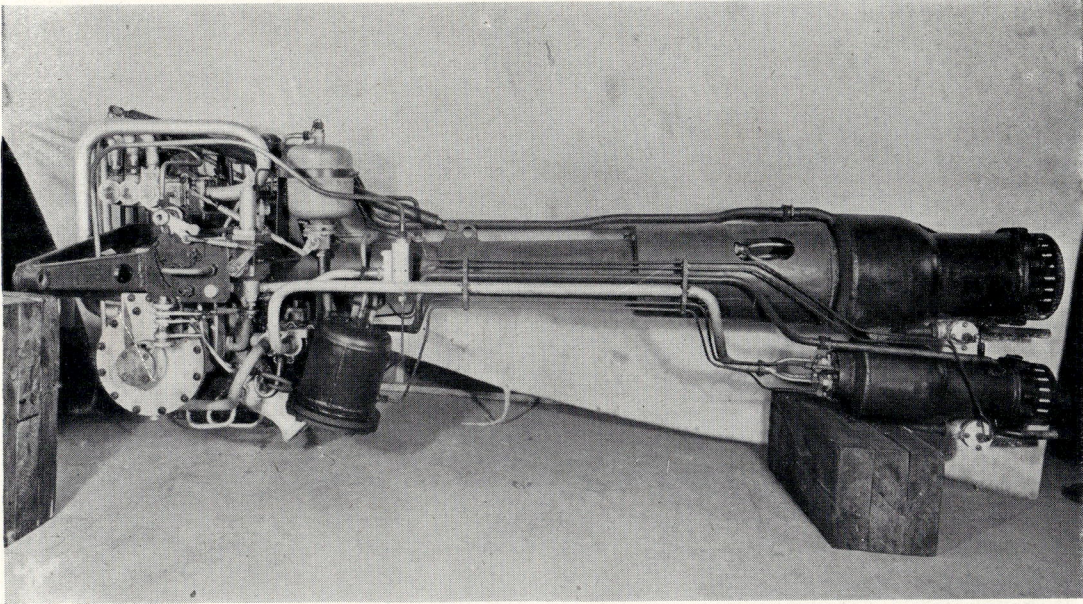

[Copyright: Royal Aeronautical Society

A side view of the Walter motor as used in the German rocket aircraft Me 163.

built a V.2 with short stub wings which was intended to be fired in the same manner as the normal V.2, but which was to include, in place of the war head, a small cabin to contain a pilot. Firing would have been in the normal manner, but after the all-burnt stage, when the rocket reached the top of its trajectory, the pilot was intended to take over complete control of the plane and to bring it down to earth in a glide. It was hoped in this way that a range of some 350 miles would be attained, although the height reached would only be of the order of thirty miles. This reduction in peak height was, of course, due to the extra resistance caused by the wings during the flight in the earth's atmosphere.

At this stage it should be emphasised that there is no danger in piloting a rocket. A rocket is not subjected to large acceleration except on landing and if this manœuvre can be relatively gentle the entire flight would be as comfortable as one in a first-class aeroplane. The human body does not react to velocity; as a matter of fact it is impossible to say what is the normal velocity of every human being on this earth, for at every moment they are moving with a resultant velocity formed by the velocity of the earth's rotation, the velocity of the earth's orbit round the sun, the velocity of the solar system in the universe and any velocity which the universe itself may have through space. Any black-out or bodily harm is caused by acceleration solely.

The Germans had also started project

[Copyright: Royal Aeronautical Society

A close-up view of the exit nozzles of the rocket motor shown in the previous illustration. Note the main and subsidiary nozzles, for full-speed and cruising flight.

23

A half-front view of the Me 163 rocket-motor aircraft.

[Copyright: Royal Aeronautical Society

work on a large booster rocket which was intended to carry a V.2 with wings on the start of its trajectory and then to land by parachute. The V.2 on release would continue under its own power for a further period until all fuel was burnt, the path then being a free flight parabolic trajectory, until the wings enabled it to be controlled in a glide path to the ground.

The range and speed of such a booster rocket is considerably greater than would be obtained from a V.2 of the same total weight as the V.2 plus the booster. The German project, which was known as the A.10, had a booster rocket weighing about 85 tons and carried an A.9, the designation given to the V.2 with wings, up to the all-burnt height prior to its release. With a booster, ranges of up to 3,000 miles become possible and the A.9 was calculated to reach a height of 180 miles and then fall, to reach a maximum speed of 8,250 m.p.h. before starting its glide through the atmosphere to earth.

Wireless Control of Rockets

As has already been mentioned, types of V.2 were tried with wireless control. The control used was never very elaborate, neither can it be said to have been very successful, but if wireless research continues at its war-time speed there is every prospect that satisfactory wireless control will be achieved. It should be possible for a rocket to be fired, controlled in its flight, and landed precisely as required, wireless signals to special receivers in the rocket actuating all the control. The time is rapidly approaching when the whole flight of an aeroplane can be automatic, and it is not a large step to apply this system to a rocket. The results of wireless control will be extremely valuable. It will enable research to be carried out on piloted designs without risking human life and thus enable the safety of rocket flight to be demonstrated to all.

The next stage in rocketry is to fit the second step of a German A.10 with wireless control and fire it over variable ranges. When they have achieved this optimum range of some 3,000 miles it will be possible to transport up to one ton of material from Europe to America in approximately forty-five minutes. The cost would, of course, be great, but it should be possible to carry out this flight as an economical proposition carrying urgent material and urgent mails over this large distance so quickly. A relatively small extension of this scheme would enable rockets to travel all over the earth's surface and no two points of the earth would be more than two hours apart as a result.

A rear view of one of the early type Me 163 aircraft. This type used a motor with no second nozzle.

[*Copyright: Royal Aeronautical Society*

Dreams of the Future

Enthusiasts in rockets are not satisfied with this seemingly bright future. To them the main use of the rocket appears to be in interplanetary travel, the moon being their target number one. Ever since the days of Jules Verne popular stories have dealt with journeys to the moon and many possible and impossible methods of reaching it have been suggested. It can be stated definitely that there is absolutely no future in the shot projectile of Jules Verne. Here, the acceleration on starting is fantastic and not only is it almost impossible to obtain the initial energy, but it is highly probable that any

contents of the shot would be almost entirely disintegrated and human life could certainly not be maintained. The rocket would appear to be the only method of reaching interstellar space and several attempts have been made to design rockets for this purpose.

At present there are several societies whose main aim is interplanetary flight and already one such society has designed a large rocket to be fired by batteries of powder rockets which are arranged to drop off as they are exhausted. The destination of this rocket was to have been the moon. Such designs, however, have existed only on paper at present.

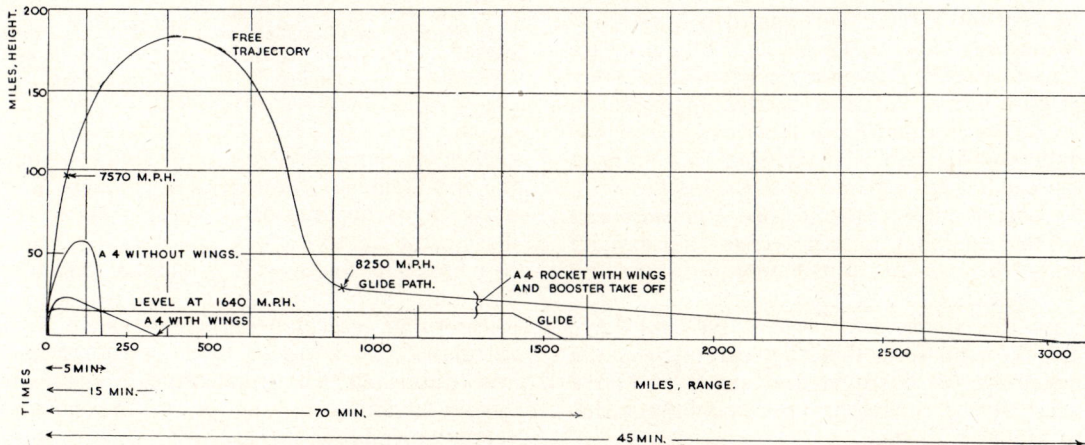

Fig. 6.—Trajectories of rockets with wings, showing flight times and ranges.

The Earth's Field

Before discussing the main rockets in further detail it is advisable to realise what performances will be required. First, there are the forces which have to be overcome to make the flight, of which the main and most extensive one is the gravitational field of the earth. Everybody on the surface of the earth is subject to a force, usually known as its weight, due to an acceleration of gravity. This acceleration varies slightly over the earth's surface, but an average value can be taken at 32.2 feet per second per second. This force decreases as one moves further from the earth's centre and at an infinite distance is zero. Thus, a rocket fired from the earth's surface has to overcome a gradually decreasing force on its motion away from the earth's centre. This force is typical of all planets and on a journey to the moon the rocket has first to overcome the earth's gravitational field up to a point where the attraction of the earth and that of the moon are equal, after which stage the rocket is attracted by the moon. Any rocket passing this point of equal attraction will fall towards the moon; any rocket not reaching this point will fall back upon the earth. Fig. 7 shows a typical gravitational field of the planet. To reach the point of equal attraction between any two planets a certain escape velocity or velocity of liberation is required. In the case of the earth this velocity is approximately seven miles a second.

A second force which has to be overcome is the resistance of the air skin of the earth. This resistance does not persist to any great height, but it has a considerable effect on rocket performances. This can be easily understood when it is realised that it is in the earth's atmosphere that the rocket is of its largest mass and its lowest efficiency and all the fuel that is required for subsequent flight through the interplanetary space has to be carried over this barrier. In fact, both this force and the gravitational force are unfortunate in that they are large at the beginning of the flight and small when the mass of the rocket has become lighter due to using up its fuel.

Flight from the moon would, of course, be against only one of these forces as the moon has no atmosphere. Also, the gravitational forces are much smaller and the escape velocity is only 1.47 miles per second.

TABLE II

Escape Velocities in Miles per Second

Mercury	2.2 miles per second
Venus	6.3 ,, ,, ,,
Earth	7.0 ,, ,, ,,
Moon	1.47 ,, ,, ,,
Mars	3.1 ,, ,, ,,
Jupiter	37.0 ,, ,, ,,
Saturn	22.0 ,, ,, ,,
Uranus	13.0 ,, ,, ,,
Neptune	14.0 ,, ,, ,,

All calculations for projected rockets are usually done in terms of the mass-ratio of the rocket required. This figure is of equal value to that of the actual masses of the

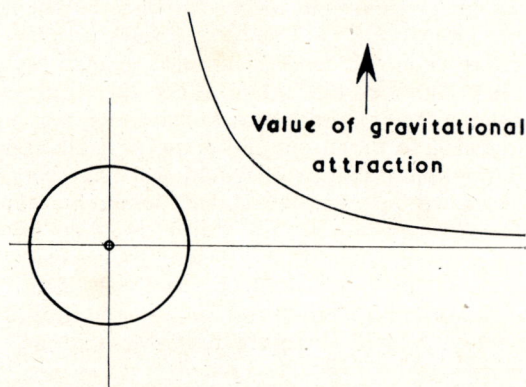

Fig. 7.—Gravitational field of a planet. The force attracting any body to the planet is proportional inversely to the square of the distance from the centre of the planet.

rocket, as the mass-ratio value quickly gives the initial mass of the rocket to carry unit mass to its destination. Thus, a rocket of mass-ratio 2.2, like a V.2, and weight 3.2 tons will finish its flight with a mass of one ton. The mass-ratios of rockets to perform various journeys in interplanetary space have been calculated from theoretical considerations and published for some time. They are always given as a function of the exhaust velocity available, for as will be seen from the theory already given, an increase in the exhaust velocity will give an increase in performance and thus a reduction in the mass-ratio required. Present fuels have theoretical exhaust velocities varying from 2,400 metres per second (1.49 miles per second) in the case of ordinary black powder, to 5,170 metres per second (3.22 miles per second) for hydrogen.

TABLE III

Exhaust Velocities of Fuels (Theoretical)
with Oxygen

Hydrogen	.	.	. 3.22 miles per second
Petrol .	.	.	. 2.77 ,, ,, ,,
Benzene	.	.	. 2.66 ,, ,, ,,
Alcohol	.	.	. 2.60 ,, ,, ,,

With Ozone some 10 per cent increase in values is obtained.

Smokeless Powder	.	.	2.01 miles per second
Black Powder	.	.	1.49 ,, ,, ,,

Practical values with black powder rarely exceed 25 per cent of this value.

The measured exhaust velocity, and thus the velocity obtained in flight, is never as great as the theoretical value and depends considerably on the design of the motor. It is reasonable to expect that in future it may be possible to utilise exhaust velocities up to 75 per cent. to 80 per cent. of their theoretical value.

TABLE IV

Mass-Ratio for Interplanetary Flights

Journey	Exhaust Velocity		
	3,000 m./s. 1.86 mls./s.	5,000 m./s. 3.11 mls./s.	10,000 m./s. 6.22 mls./s.
Earth—Moon .	Over 220	Over 24.5	4.2
Moon—Earth .	1.5	.7	.3
Earth—Moon—Earth .	Over 550	42.5	7

Table IV gives the mass-ratio for various flights against the exhaust velocity available. It will be seen from this table that a rocket does not become practicable unless the higher exhaust velocities are used, and if some value could be obtained giving an extremely high practical exhaust velocity trips to the moon would be assured. These figures show that using matter with an exhaust velocity of 5,000 metres per second (3.11 miles per second) the mass-ratio of the rocket for a

flight from the earth to the moon would be 24.5. With an exhaust velocity of twice this value, the mass-ratio would be 4.2, a much more practicable proposition. If a return were contemplated, these figures would be increased as all the fuel required to bring the rocket back has to be carried on the outward trip. The value for the 3.11 miles per second exhaust velocity would then be just over 40.

Control of Flight

The problems of design of the rockets for a journey from the earth to the moon have been stated. It is useless, even if rockets are designed to cover the journey, if they are destroyed on landing at either end, and a complete plan of operation has already been decided upon. Assuming that a man-carrying rocket is available for a return flight to the moon, stages in its flight would be as follows:

Take-off from the earth is comparatively simple, the only provisions necessary being purely mathematical calculations for the purpose of aiming at the moon. To do this it is only necessary to know the relative positions of the earth and the moon at all stages during the flight.

Directional correction cannot be made by means of external controls as these would rely on a medium such as air for reaction, but control could be obtained by having subsidiary rocket motors placed at certain angles to the main direction of motion which could be fired on control from the cabin, thus providing a component of velocity sufficient to correct the course. The final course of direction would be made in the region of neutral force as it is here that the correction could be made against the smallest external forces. The velocity will decrease as a rocket reaches this point, but after passing it, it will increase under the moon's gravitational field without the expense of any energy. It should be noted that in all such flights the motors are not running continuously and are only supplied with fuel until sufficient velocity has been built up to provide for travel to a point which is just past the neutral point.

The velocity increases as the rocket falls to the moon, and the small control motors are used to turn the rocket round so that the main motors can be used to check the speed of fall. With skilful control of the energy output of these motors it should be possible to make a landing on the moon no more uncomfortable than a ride on a lift.

The start from the moon is accomplished in the same way as the start from the earth. The neutral point is soon reached and the rocket begins to fall to the earth. If it were allowed to fall free it would reach the earth with a velocity approximating to that of the escape velocity for the earth and considerable quantities of fuel would be required to give a retardation velocity. Here, luckily, the earth's atmosphere is beneficial. The scheme suggested for landing on the earth utilises what are known as 'braking ellipses'. The flight of the rocket is decided so that it does not strike the earth but passes round it, entering into the outer reaches of the earth's atmosphere on the side opposite to that of its approach. This will have the effect of slowing it down slightly. The rocket will move off again away from the earth into space with a reduced velocity, performing an ellipse with the earth's centre as one of the focal points. Falling from this ellipse again it will pass even further into the earth's atmosphere and will be slowed down even more, again probably passing into space, this time for a much smaller elliptical flight. The process is repeated and it is thought that on the third flight from the earth's atmosphere the speed of the rocket will be so reduced that it will not again leave this region, but will fall gently to the earth with the help of the control motors and/or a parachute and thus a safe landing on the earth's surface can be achieved.

This method of braking ellipses could, of course, be used on any planet which has an atmosphere, and it is an economical scheme for landing, using the minimum of fuel. First flights to the moon by rockets will, of course, be carried out by the wireless-controlled pilotless type and the first manned rocket will probably be arranged so that it misses the moon entirely, but once confidence and practice in control of rockets has been achieved, the landings should present no difficulty.

Space Stations

It will be seen from the calculations how much easier it is for a rocket to fly from the moon than the earth, and schemes have been suggested whereby intermediate stations should be formed in space to act as 'jumping-off' points for space travel. These space stations would not be motionless, but would in actual fact form small additional moons to the earth. Fuel would be stored in these space stations which would be safely outside the atmospheric section of the earth, and

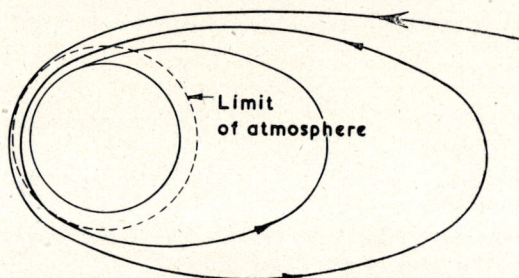

Fig. 8.—Braking ellipses. The figure shows the approach of a projectile from space towards an atmosphere-shrouded planet (*i.e.* the earth). The projectile is successively slowed on passing through the fringe of the atmosphere until it is finally able to land by parachute.

rockets for the moon and other planets would start from there. The stations would be initially fired from the earth and would take up a position in space carefully calculated in position. The space stations would have two velocities, one a velocity of rotation round the earth and the other a velocity of falling towards the earth, while the earth's surface, due to its curvature, was curving away from it at the same speed. Such an orbit is called a synergic curve. While the rocket is in such an orbit no energy is expended and passengers in the rocket would have the feeling of travelling in free space. Fuel would be brought up to the rocket and the personnel would, of course, have to be maintained from the earth. It would be an ideal station for physical experiments as a very large range of temperatures could be obtained down to those approaching absolute zero. The mass-ratio of rockets starting on journeys to other bodies from this station would be much smaller than those starting from the earth, and space travel would be possible in a form of small jumps.

Future Fuels for Rockets

Mention has been made of the great saving which can be obtained by the use of higher exhaust velocities. One of the problems to be solved is the finding of a suitable fuel giving a high velocity, and attention has been directed towards those fuels which would theoretically give such a high velocity. One such fuel would be the hydrogen atom, the reaction used being the association of two atoms to form ordinary molecular hydrogen. The velocity which might be obtained is of the order of 6.22 miles per second, the 10,000 metres per second class of the tables. How this could be obtained has not yet been solved, but if this problem can be properly understood, space travel will be brought much nearer the range of modern rockets.

Another type of fuel which must be considered might make use of reactions of the nuclear fission type. How this could be achieved is difficult to visualise at present. One thing is certain, the normal fission process cannot be used, as firing such a rocket would be equivalent to firing an atom bomb under the rocket, which would be very uncomfortable for any occupants. Other processes of a similar nature are, however, available. The 'pile' process for making Uranium '235' might be used, particularly if some method were used for removing surplus neutrons, as physicists will realise that the 'K' value of such a pile would exceed 1. This might be achieved by special design of the pile. How the energy should be used is still another matter. The neutron beam itself would, of course, supply some energy, but the main function of the pile would be that of supplying heat. If water were brought into a region of such heat, super-heated steam with high exhaust velocity would be produced, although the efficiency would not be very large. The solution of this problem may be reached quite quickly, for considerable energy is being applied to the solution of all atomic matters.

Summary

These are the problems which have to be solved before interplanetary rockets can be designed and made with any hope of success:

(1) The production of a fuel giving a high exhaust velocity and the design of a motor to utilise this fuel in the most efficient way.

(2) The production of rocket designs with a high mass-ratio, a problem closely connected with structural and materials research.

(3) A study of the earth's upper atmosphere and the conditions of interstellar space to ensure that no injurious effects to passengers will arise from the conditions there.

References

'A Review of German Long-Range Rocket Development.' W. G. A. Perring. *Journ. Roy. Aero. Soc.*, vol. 50, p. 483, July 1946.

Rockets. Willy Ley. (Viking Press.)

[Copyright: Royal Aeronautical Society

[Copyright : de Havilland Aircraft Co. Ltd.

A de Havilland Vampire, the Royal
Air Force single-motor jet-fighter.

JET-PROPULSION AND THE GAS TURBINE

by

James Hodge, M.A., A.M.I.Mech.E.

Formerly with Power Jets Ltd., now on the Staff of the English Electric Co.

DURING THE last two years of the war, and since, the attention of everyone interested in flying has been focussed chiefly on the new forms of propulsion which come under the general name of jet-propulsion. This term covers (in its usual meaning) several kinds of prime mover, including the gas turbine, producing a high-speed jet of gases, the athodyd, the V.1 type of engine and the rocket.

There are important differences in the method of production of the jet in all these cases, but the term ' jet-propulsion ' is misleading, in that any form of powered propulsion in the air or on water must be by some kind of " jet." The essential is that some fluid must be given a change of momentum relative to the ship or aircraft—that is, its velocity must be increased in the opposite direction to that in which the vehicle is travelling. This produces a force in the right direction because by Newton's laws of motion, firstly a force must be exerted on the air (confining our attention to aircraft) to accelerate it and secondly, in order to produce this force, there must be an equal force acting in the opposite direction on the aircraft.

Thus an airscrew is a form of jet-propulsion in that it takes a very large quantity of air and pushes it backwards with a slightly increased speed relative to the aircraft. However, ' jet-propulsion ' is usually used to denote a high-speed jet of air or gases rather than the low-speed jet produced by an airscrew or ducted fan.

At the moment the most important method of producing a high-speed jet is the gas turbine whose mode of operation is very simple and will be described later.

Stages in Design

First it is interesting to examine the steps which have led up to the introduction of jet-propulsion. These are quite logical and it is instructive to follow them from the days of the fabric-covered biplanes. These had many obvious disadvantages, the elimination of which provided ready means of obtaining considerable improvements in performance. Chief among these disadvantages were the fixed undercarriage, biplane bracing and struts and the fabric covering, which made it impossible to obtain really smooth aero-dynamic shapes, even had the necessary knowledge for designing the modern ' mathe-matical ' wing profiles been available. Of course, there were exceptional aircraft which had tried to escape from the general trend of design, but these were ahead of their time.

In the 1930's these defects were gradually removed. The biplane largely disappeared and the retractable undercarriage and all-metal stressed skin construction came into general use. The controllable pitch airscrew —finally leading to the constant speed automatically variable pitch type—was also introduced, along with great improvements in engine design. These latter were largely due to the use of a much greater, and con-tinually increasing, degree of supercharging, and greatly improved grades of petrol.

The limitations of this generation of air-craft first became apparent in the fighter types used in the 1939–45 war. The emphasis was placed on speed to a very great extent and as top speeds began to exceed 400 m.p.h. increasing difficulties were encountered in making them still higher. An examination of typical airscrew efficiency curves (Fig. 1) and aircraft weight analyses, shows the main reasons for this.

The total weight of a modern reciprocating-engined interceptor fighter aircraft, with a top speed in the region of 450–500 m.p.h., is divided between the major items roughly as follows:

Percentage

Aircraft structure .	33
Fuel and oil . .	10
Useful load . .	20 (including pilot, equipment, armament, etc.)
Power plant . .	37 (Complete with airscrew, radiators, etc.)

At high speeds, when induced drag is only a small fraction of the total, the drag of an aircraft increases proportionately to the square of its speed. That is, in increasing the speed from 500 to 550 m.p.h., the drag rises by 21 per cent. Since the thrust horse-power required to overcome the drag is proportional to the drag and also to the speed, an increase of thrust horse-power of 33 per cent. is necessary for this increase of speed.

The airscrew is the means of turning the shaft horse-power developed by the engine (which remains practically constant as the forward speed varies) into thrust horse-power. As will be seen from Fig. 1 its efficiency may drop from 69 per cent. to 60 per cent., so that the total increase of shaft power required to increase the speed from 500 to 550 m.p.h. is 53 per cent.

Thus it will be realised that in order to provide enough power to reach really high speeds with a reciprocating engine, there would be very little room or load-carrying capacity to spare for anything other than the engine.

Advantages of the Jet Engine

The jet-propulsion engine, of which the gas turbine is the most important type at present, has several big advantages over the reciprocating engine-airscrew combination in the high-speed range.

First its weight is very much smaller—at 500 m.p.h. at low altitudes it may well be as low as 1/6th that of a reciprocating engine giving the same thrust.

Besides this the variation of power with

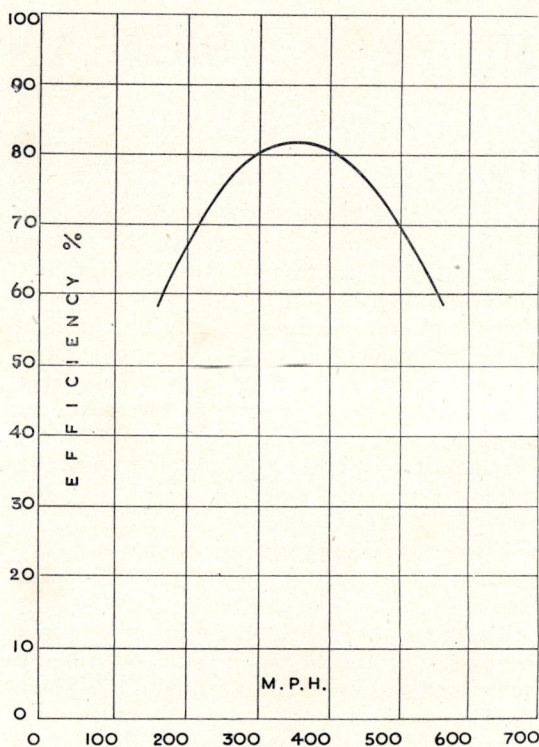

FIG. 1.—Typical airscrew efficiency for a high-speed aircraft.

forward speed of a jet engine is quite different from that of a reciprocating engine (Fig. 2).

The shaft horse-power of the latter remains constant, so that the only change in thrust horse-power with speed is that due to changes in airscrew efficiency. The thrust developed by the jet engine, on the other hand, stays nearly constant at fairly high speeds, so that the thrust horse-power developed is directly proportional to forward speed. This, together with the fact that there is no airscrew whose efficiency can fall at high speeds, means that the increase in engine power and weight needed to obtain a higher top speed is only proportional to the square of the speed —that is, the weight and power of the engine need only be increased by 21 per cent. instead of the 53 per cent. required by the reciprocating engine, in raising the maximum speed from 500 to 550 m.p.h. At low aircraft speeds the high-velocity jet is inefficient, because it needs much more energy to produce

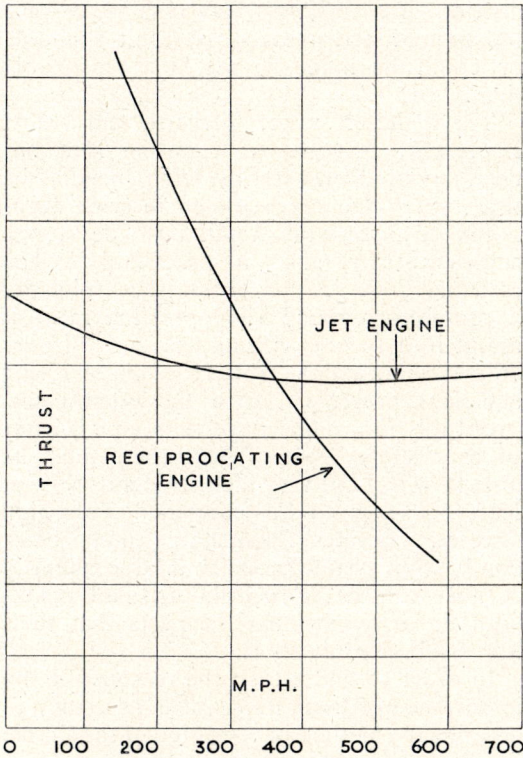

FIG. 2.—Typical thrust curves.

a given thrust than does a low-velocity jet. That is, its efficiency in transforming the energy available in the exhaust gases into useful power, is low except at high speeds.

These are the fundamental reasons for the introduction of the jet engine at this stage in the history of flying. Although in retrospect this seems a perfectly logical and straightforward development, it was not, of course, easy to foresee the need or to determine the means of satisfying it. The pioneer in this country was Air Commodore Frank Whittle. He first became interested in the subject in 1928 while he was a cadet at the R.A.F. College at Cranwell; having to write a paper on a scientific subject, he chose, 'The Future Development of Aircraft', and mentioned in this the possibilities of jet-

propulsion and the gas turbine. He did not at this time, however, envisage the use of a gas turbine for jet-propulsion. This idea came in 1930 and he tried without success to interest the Air Ministry and various private firms. The general view held at that time was that the gas turbine presented too great and too many technical difficulties.

The First Gas Turbines

Some years later, while Whittle was taking an engineering degree at Cambridge, two of his friends succeeded in forming a company known as Power Jets Limited, to develop the jet-propulsion gas turbine. With very little financial backing, this firm went ahead with the practical design of an engine and placed an order for its manufacture with the B.T.H. Company in June 1936. This engine first ran at Rugby on 12th April 1937. As was to be expected, a great deal of work had to be done before a satisfactory performance could be obtained, but in 1939 enough had been done to convince the Air Ministry that the idea was going to be useful and the first aircraft was ordered from the Gloster Aircraft Company. This was the single-engined, single-seat, Gloster E.28/39, which first flew, powered by the Power Jets W.1 engine, on 14th May 1941. The first flights were carried out by the Gloster Aircraft Company's chief test-pilot, Flight-Lieutenant P. E. G. Sayers. No trouble whatever was experienced in this series of flights, which is most unusual with any new prototype aircraft, even without taking into account the completely new type of engine.

Before this, in 1940, sufficient confidence in the new form of propulsion had been obtained for the first fighter aircraft to be ordered, again from the Gloster Company; this was the twin-engined F.9/40, which later became the famous Meteor.

In 1941 a complete set of drawings of the latest Power Jets engine, together with the actual W.1.X. engine which had been used for the first taxi-ing trials of the E.28/39, and three Power Jets engineers were flown to the United States, where large-scale development work was begun immediately.

Besides Power Jets, several other firms in this country were by this time working on the aircraft gas turbine, using both Power Jets designs and their own. In the enemy countries also, a great deal of work was being done, particularly in Germany, where the first flights took place before those of the E.28/39. The Germans were very much limited in the performance they could attain by lack of suitable materials and other handicaps and their engines never equalled the British either in performance, lightness or reliability. The Italians had had a jet-aircraft flying before the war (the Caproni-Campini), but this was not powered by a gas turbine, merely utilising a reciprocating engine driving a small axial flow fan inside the fuselage, and its performance was extremely poor.

Whittle did not actually invent either the gas turbine itself or jet-propulsion. Many forms of the latter have been envisaged since very early times, from the Aeolipile of Hero of Alexandria (which was, incidentally, the first turbine) to Sir Isaac Newton's proposed carriage propelled by a jet of steam, and many others. The gas turbine, too, has been a favourite dream of engineers for many years, as it offers many great advantages, particularly in respect of simplicity, having an entirely rotary instead of a reciprocating motion. Whittle's achievement consisted largely in realising three things—and in having the courage to act on his beliefs—that the time when jet-propulsion would be

needed for aircraft was near; that the best method of producing the required high-speed jet was by means of a gas turbine; and that the necessary pre-requisites for the production of a successful gas turbine, to give the desired performance, were all available or could be made so within a reasonable time.

These latter were, perhaps, the most important, as many a promising idea has been rendered valueless by being ahead of its time, when the necessary engineering technique or material had not been developed sufficiently to make it practicable. The essentials for a jet-propulsion gas turbine are a compressor giving a compression ratio of about four to one with an efficiency of over 70 per cent., and a turbine capable of giving sufficient power to drive the compressor, preferably in a single stage, with an efficiency of over 80 per cent. The turbine must be able to withstand very high temperatures—at least 600 degrees C.—combined with high stresses. Besides these, there must be a combustion system in which a large quantity of fuel can be burned in a small space, without so overheating the parts that their life will be unduly short.

In order to understand the reasons for the importance of these things, it is necessary to describe the method of operation of the simple jet-propulsion gas turbine.

[Copyright: B. T. H. Co., Ltd.

The first model of the Whittle experimental engine assembled for testing.

The third model of the first Whittle engine on test at Lutterworth. (The radiator and petrol tank are for the starting engine, which can be seen in front of the jet engine.)

[Copyright : B. T. H. Co., Ltd.

Method of Operation

First air is taken into a compressor, which increases its pressure and temperature. Then the compressed air is passed to the combustion chamber where fuel is burned in it, increasing its temperature still further—from about 200 degrees C. to about 800 degrees C. These processes are necessary because while burning fuel in air at atmospheric pressure increases the energy content of the air, the energy cannot again be removed from the air to be used as mechanical work in any form. However, when fuel is burned in air at a high pressure, part of the energy can be taken out of the air by expanding it to a lower pressure—the amount of work, or energy, available being dependent on the pressure ratio over which the expansion takes place and the initial temperature. After being heated, the gas passes through the turbine, which drives the compressor. As the available energy has been increased by heating, the expansion ratio through the turbine, which is necessary to give sufficient power to drive the compressor, is lower than the compression ratio. This means that the gases leaving the turbine have a total pressure which is greater than atmospheric and this surplus pressure may be turned into velocity by expanding the gases through an orifice of a suitable size (the jet nozzle).

The compressor efficiency must be as high as possible in order to obtain the required pressure ratio with the minimum expenditure of power. Similarly the turbine must be efficient in order to obtain as much power as possible for the minimum pressure ratio. The combustion temperature must be as high as the materials will stand in order to keep the size of engine necessary, and hence its weight, as small as possible.

Within the framework of the cycle outlined above many variations of detail design are possible, and these may have major effects on the performance of the engine.

As gas turbines consume much greater quantities of air than reciprocating engines (an engine of a size suitable for the Meteor consumes something of the order of 35,000 cubic feet of air per minute at ground level), reciprocating compressors would be far too large and heavy. There are two types of rotary compressor in general use in gas turbines to-day—the centrifugal and axial. A comparison of their relative merits is very involved and as is usually the case where different solutions are available to the same problem, each type has its own special field of usefulness, which will become more clearly

35

defined as further experience and knowledge are gained. Most of the compressors in actual use in this country so far have been centrifugals, but the tendency in the immediate future will probably be to use axials or a combination of both.

Gas Turbine Design

The combustion system may take several different forms and at the moment design is more of an art than a science. Unlike the reciprocating engine, combustion in the gas turbine is continuous and once it has started no ignition system is necessary. Among the different layouts used so far have been a single annular chamber, or several smaller cylindrical chambers each dealing with a portion of the total flow. The prime requirements of the combustion system are that it must burn the required amount of fuel in as small a space as possible and with as small a drop in pressure as possible. It must also be capable of working with widely varying pressures and fuel and air flows, brought about by changes in altitude, engine r.p.m. and aircraft speed. To meet such a stringent specification much time must be spent on painstaking development work for each new design.

Considerable experience was available on turbine design although steam turbines differ considerably from gas turbines. Nearly all jet-propulsion turbines are of the single stage axial flow type instead of having many stages as in steam turbines. Also the stresses and temperatures are usually much higher in gas turbines and the velocity of the gases leaving the turbine is much higher. This is permissible because the energy thus carried away, instead of being wasted, forms part of the energy of the propulsive jet. This makes it possible to obtain very large powers from small high-speed turbines by passing through them very large quantities of gas—a typical turbine of about eighteen inches overall diameter can develop about 5,000 shaft horse-power.

Although it has been said earlier that when Whittle began his work the necessary prerequisites for the construction of a successful gas turbine were available, this does not mean that all the information necessary for design could be obtained immediately. The knowledge existing at that time had, however, advanced to a stage where the remaining steps could be taken without departing a very long way from existing practice. This meant that the amount of development work necessary could be expected to be of reasonable proportions and would not take too long.

For instance, the highest compression ratio which was known to have been attained in a single stage centrifugal compressor at that time was about 2.5 and efficiencies were very low. By degrees the compression ratio was raised to 4 and the efficiency from well below 70 per cent. to about 80 per cent.

New materials were available for the turbine, but until a considerable amount of testing had been carried out it was impossible to determine exactly how much stress and how high a temperature these would withstand in actual use.

These and similar problems involved the expenditure of much time and money and if the attempt to solve them had been made too early, this might easily have proved overwhelming.

Jet and Reciprocating Engines Compared

It is impossible to make a direct comparison between a jet engine and a reciprocating engine as their power outputs cannot be measured in the same way unless an aircraft speed is specified. However, taking engines of roughly equivalent power the major differences between the two types become apparent.

The jet engine is generally smaller than the reciprocating engine itself, and the latter also has several appendages which make it considerably larger, such as radiators, oil coolers and the propeller. As was stated previously, the weight of the jet is a great deal less than that of the reciprocator, and the power varies very differently with forward speed.

The fuel consumption of the jet is about twice as much at ground level, but improves with altitude until at about 36,000 feet it is only 1.5 times as much. It increases slightly with aircraft speed due to the increased air flow through the engine brought about by the ram effect.

The most informative comparison of overall efficiency is given by an examination of curves of 'specific' fuel consumption—that is, pounds of fuel per hour per pound of thrust (Fig. 3). This shows how greatly the jet benefits by high forward speed and by high altitude. Another important point is that the jet engine gives its highest efficiency (lowest specific consumption) at its maximum power, whereas the reciprocating engine is uneconomical at maximum power and is at

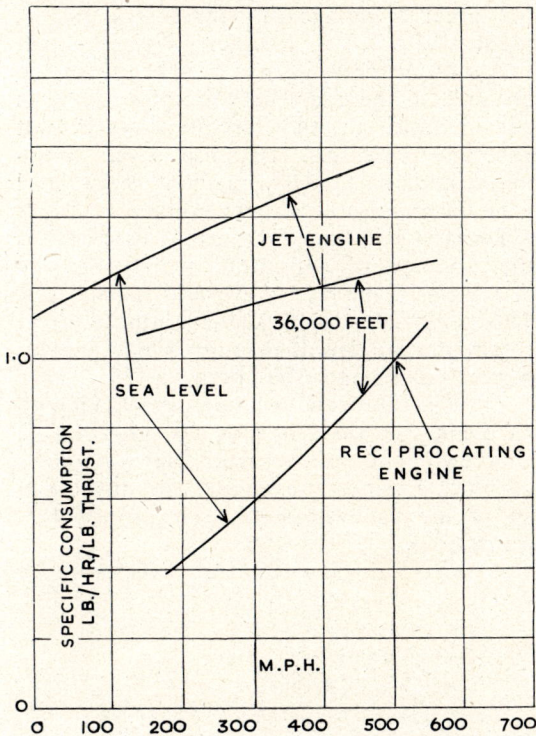

FIG. 3.—Typical specific fuel consumptions.

its best at something like half power. There is no counterpart in the jet engine of the rated altitude of the reciprocating engine, whose power falls off continuously with increasing altitude instead of remaining practically constant up to the rated altitude.

No electrical equipment is needed on a jet engine except for starting—this gives greater simplicity and reliability and eliminates any trouble due to interference with radio. No difficulty is experienced in starting even on the coldest day and no warming-up period is

required. The engine can be started and accelerated from its idling speed to full speed in a few seconds. This feature is particularly valuable when it is necessary to be able to take-off at short notice. No fuel need be wasted in keeping the engine warmed up so as to enable this to be done.

The instruments and controls required for a jet engine are also very simple. No boost or mixture controls are necessary and apart from a starter button and fuel shut-off cock, the pilot's only control is a throttle. His engine instruments consist only of r.p.m. indicator, jet temperature gauge, fuel pressure gauge, fuel contents, oil pressure and possibly one or two more. This not only makes jet aircraft very easy to fly and less tiring for the pilot, but installation and maintenance times are much reduced. Lack of airscrews, radiators and other appendages is also, of course, a major factor in this respect.

Gas turbines will burn practically any liquid fuel from diesel oil to hundred octane petrol and the grade of fuel has no effect on performance. Usually fuels similar to ordinary paraffin have been used. Oil consumption is very small—usually under a pint an hour.

The introduction of the jet engine has resulted in several major modifications in aircraft design. An immediately obvious point is that the undercarriage can be much shorter, as no ground clearance for propellers has to be provided. This results in a saving of weight and stowage space, which latter is much more important than is generally realised. The undercarriage is nearly always of the tricycle type. Not only does this keep the hot jets from playing on the ground, which might damage runways, but this type is more suitable for the high landing speeds of modern aircraft, and for blind landing.

The tail must be kept clear of the jets, either by discharging the jets behind the tail, as in the E.28/39, by putting the tailplane high on the fin as on the F.9/40, or by some other method. Apart from the bad effects of the heat on the tail, there would also be serious buffeting if the jets were allowed to impinge on the tail, making control of the aircraft very difficult.

The lack of airscrews removes a considerable element of danger to those on the ground, as it is very easy to walk into a fast rotating airscrew. On the other hand, the consumption of air is so large that the intakes are much bigger than those of a reciprocating engine and objects such as hats, coats and even people have been drawn into the intakes, which have to be provided with gauze guards.

Engine Position

In a jet aircraft the pilot is practically certain to have a good view even in a single-engined aircraft, as it is extremely unlikely that there will be an engine in front of him. One reason for this, in the single-engined type at least, is that with the engine in front the pilot would have to sit above the jet pipe, which is likely to be very hot. Another reason is that, with a given length between the air intake and the end of the jet pipe, it involves a smaller loss of performance to have the engine well back, with a long intake duct and short jet pipe than with a short intake and long jet pipe. This also involves less difficulty with the structure in supporting the hot parts which may easily have a bad effect on the strength of the adjacent light alloy airframe. The latter reasons also apply to wing-engined aircraft.

The position of the engine as determined from these considerations has a considerable effect on the problem with which the airframe designer is faced in laying out his aircraft. First the engines are much lighter than those to which he is accustomed and also they are further back. This means that his ideas on how to get the centre of gravity of the aircraft in the right place, relative to the wings, have to undergo a considerable change. Another factor affecting this is that in a jet aircraft there is usually a greater weight and volume of fuel, for which stowage space must be found near the centre of gravity of the aircraft, otherwise there will be too great a change of trim as the fuel is used.

Although the noise which is heard on the ground, if there are jet aircraft about, is considerable, in the aircraft this is not generally the case. The noise is very directional and, particularly in front of or level with the engines, it is quiet inside.

Perhaps even more important than this is the absence of vibration, which can be extremely tiring for crew and passengers. This great advantage is due to the entirely rotary motion of gas turbines which enables perfect balancing to be obtained.

There is no torque reaction associated with jet engines as there is with a single-rotation airscrew. This follows from Newton's laws of motion, since the engine, in pushing a jet of air backwards, is itself pushed forward.

With an airscrew the air, besides being

The Gloster E.28/39 experimental aircraft in its original form.

[*Crown Copyright*

[Crown Copyright

A later picture of the E.28/39. Note the additional tail fins to give increased stability at high speeds.

accelerated straight backwards, is given a spinning motion, which means that there must be an equal and opposite torque acting on the aircraft. With a contra-rotating airscrew the second row of blades cancels out the spin imparted to the air by the first row, so that this effect is absent, as it is with a jet engine, in which the air leaves the engine practically without spin. This is important, particularly at take-off with high-powered single-engined aircraft from a confined space (an aircraft-carrier for example). Here the swing of an aircraft due to torque is liable to cause the pilot considerable difficulty.

The absence of slipstream from an airscrew (which causes sufficient airflow over the control surfaces to enable manœuvring to be carried out on the ground) makes necessary a different technique in the case of jet aircraft. Steering while taxi-ing must be done largely by means of differential operation of the wheel-brakes rather than by means of the aerodynamic controls.

As was previously stated, the installation of jet engines is very simple. In addition, as the aircraft is so low on the ground, the engines are easily accessible without high staging; and by special attention to details

of design some extremely short times for changing engines have been obtained. On the other hand refuelling takes longer than with reciprocating engines as there is usually a larger quantity of fuel to handle.

Jet Performance

The differences between the performance of aircraft powered with jet-propulsion gas turbines and those having reciprocating engines are mainly due to a few differences in the characteristics of the engines which have been mentioned previously. The more important of these are the fact that the thrust of a reciprocating engine is fairly independent of forward speed at a given altitude and r.p.m.; the lighter weight but higher fuel consumption of the jet, and the improvement in the efficiency of the jet with increasing altitude, forward speed and r.p.m.

Bearing these factors in mind, and also remembering that a strictly fair comparison is difficult to make because of the magnitude of the differences between the two types, the main features of aircraft performance can easily be deduced.

Take-off and rate of climb at low speed

immediately after take-off are not generally as good with jets. The reason for this is the first mentioned above—that is, while the airscrew gives a very large thrust at low speeds, falling off rapidly as the speed increases, the jet only gives slightly more thrust at low speeds than at high speeds and thus does not perform very well until fairly high speeds are reached. The same reasoning applies to acceleration of the aircraft, for example when opening up to 'go round again' after a balked landing.

The rate of climb of jet aircraft, however, when they have reached their best climbing speed, can be quite as high as that given by reciprocating engines. Aircraft powered by the latter have their maximum rate of climb at the forward speed corresponding to the minimum horse-power requirements of the aircraft for level flight. Since the thrust horse-power developed by this type of engine remains practically constant with speed, this is the speed at which the power available for

climb—that is, the difference between total available power and that required to overcome the aircraft drag in level flight—is a maximum. On the other hand, the thrust horse-power developed by the jet engine increases almost directly proportionally to the forward speed, so that maximum power is available for climb at a higher speed. Also this speed is not fixed entirely by the aircraft design (speed of minimum power requirements for level flight). Rather it bears some relation to the top speed of the aircraft. These points are illustrated in Fig. 4. The combination of a rate of climb comparable with that of a reciprocating-engined aircraft and a much higher climbing speed, means that the jet aircraft has a flatter climbing angle. On the other hand, its high speed enables it to do very spectacular and prolonged zoom climbs. The ceiling of a jet aircraft is generally considerably higher than that obtainable by means of conventional engines and can be made very high indeed if required. This is because as the altitude increases it is necessary to fly faster to obtain sufficient lift to support the aircraft in the thinner atmosphere. This, of course, suits the jet engine. Also as gas turbines are so light, a very great deal of power can be packed into an aircraft, giving it a very high performance in all respects. This amount of power would be quite impossible to install by means of reciprocating engines as they would be far too heavy. For instance, the Rolls-Royce Derwent engines used in setting up the world speed record of 606 m.p.h. in the Meteor in 1945 were developing between 5,000 and 6,000 thrust horse-power each, at this speed. Even assuming an airscrew efficiency of 70 per cent., which could not be attained with present-day knowledge, at such a high speed, this represents the equivalent of about 7,500 shaft horse-power each. Reciprocating engines which would produce this amount of power, supposing they could be made in such a size, would weigh about 10 tons for the two—almost twice the weight of the complete aircraft fitted with jets!

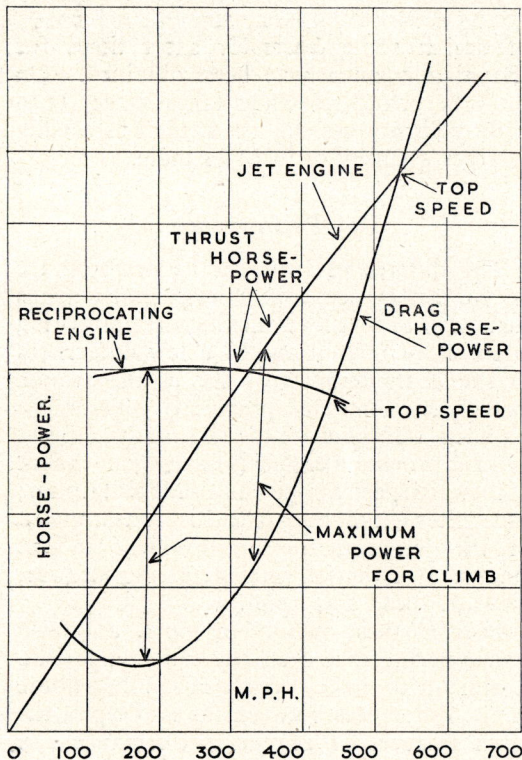

Fig. 4.

High Speeds and the Airframe

This is sufficient illustration of the now well-known fact that top speeds can be very high indeed when using jet engines. The main point of interest in this connection is that the limit to top speeds is now quite definitely imposed by the aircraft rather than by the engine. The stresses which must be borne by the airframe at such high speeds are very great, but much more important than this is the effect of compressibility on the drag of the aircraft. Compressibility effects are those due to the speed of the air passing over some part of an aircraft approaching the speed of sound and they result in very great increases in drag and often in dangerous changes in the control characteristics of the aircraft. The first parts of a normal aircraft to run into this trouble are the tips of the airscrew blades. Not only do these move forward with the aircraft, but they also have a high rotational speed. The two combined result in a very high speed relative to the air and when this exceeds the speed of sound, a rapid decrease in airscrew efficiency results, together with a great deal of noise, long before the aircraft itself is flying anywhere near the speed of sound.

However, the further increase of top speed brought about by the use of jet engines, brings the velocity of the air over parts of the wings and fuselage up to sonic speed, so that in order to increase aircraft speeds still further either means must be found to reduce the resulting rise of drag, or a very large amount of extra power must be provided to overcome it. Several methods are available in order to do the former, which is obviously greatly preferable. These include improving the wing section and the shape of the aircraft generally, making the wings thinner and sweeping them back. All these can help considerably, especially the latter, which was developed in Germany during the latter stages of the war, but they only serve to postpone the time when it will be necessary to make an aircraft which will fly faster than the speed of sound (see p. 226). This will necessitate radical departures from accepted standards of aircraft and engine design and the result will probably look quite different from any aircraft hitherto seen. It will have very thin wings, probably with very sharp, instead of rounded, leading edges. Assuming a single-engined aircraft, the fuselage will be completely taken up by the power plant and

fuel tanks, leaving just sufficient room for the pilot, probably in an almost prone position. The engine will certainly produce a high-speed jet, but whether it will be a boosted form of gas turbine or a rocket is problematical. The aircraft will have a very short endurance at supersonic speeds (a matter of a few minutes) and will attain these speeds at a very high altitude.

Long-Range Flying

To return to the performance of present-day aircraft—the remaining most important

[*Crown Copyright*

The rotor of the Power Jets W2/700 engine, showing the compressor impeller and the turbine. This is the only moving part of a gas-turbine jet engine except the accessories.

aspects are the range and optimum speed for long range of jet aircraft. In spite of the high fuel consumption of the jet-propulsion gas turbine, very considerable ranges can be covered by these aircraft under suitable conditions. The most important of these is that the flight should be carried out at an altitude near the ceiling of the aircraft, in fact at the ceiling using cruising power. The engines are more efficient at high altitudes, because of the lower atmospheric temperature. The aircraft must fly faster in order to obtain the required lift, but the drag is reduced; and the engines must operate nearer to their full power, which is more economical.

In these circumstances the fuel consumption of jet engines is not unduly greater than the best possible with the reciprocating type. Further, as the weight of the jet engines is so much less, a greater load of fuel can be carried, and for moderate ranges this difference can compensate for the increased consumption. The cost of fuel is not generally as important as might be imagined. In civil operation it constitutes only a fairly small proportion of the total cost of operating an airline, and in military flying, cost is generally subsidiary to other considerations. Although paraffin might be expected to be very much cheaper than high octane petrol, this is not the case. The difference in cost is quite small as very large facilities for the production of this petrol are now available, and a large part of the cost is due to the cost of transport of the fuel to the refuelling bases where it is required, cost of transport being practically the same for any liquid fuel.

Although the economics of airline operation is a very complicated subject, one further point in favour of high speeds is worthy of mention. There is a maximum number of hours in a year during which an aircraft can be engaged in actual passenger- or freight-carrying flights. The limit is set by many factors : for example, the need for overhaul of the aircraft, refuelling and loading times. It is the object of all operators to raise this limit to as high a value as possible, as this increases the amount earned by an aircraft, while many other expenses, such as ground organisation, aerodrome maintenance, advertising and other overheads, remain constant, independently of the number of flying hours. Having decided on a maximum number of flying hours it is also advantageous for each aircraft to carry out as many profit-making flights during this time as possible. This again increases the amount earned by the aircraft without increasing the overhead charges. So that even though the direct costs, such as fuel, may increase with a rise of speed, this can be largely offset by the increased earning capacity of the aircraft. The increased reliability and life between overhauls which should be obtainable with gas turbines should prove to be of great advantage in increasing the proportion of flying hours.

The important factor affecting the range of any aircraft is neither the weight of the engines, nor that of the fuel, but of both together, and a light engine can to a large extent compensate for a high fuel consumption. The fuel weight is, however, likely to be predominant on very long-range flights.

With the same total weight of engines and fuel, the aircraft with the heavier consumption has a certain advantage in that its weight is reduced to a greater extent in the course of the flight, making landing easier. This may, in some cases, permit this aircraft to be loaded more heavily at take-off, while the loading at landing drops to the same value as that of the type with heavier engines and lower consumption.

Gas Turbine Driving an Airscrew

The jet engine is only one means of making use of the gas turbine. Even more important in the immediate future is likely to be the gas turbine driving an airscrew. This works in the same way as the jet type, except that some of the energy which went to form the jet is utilised as shaft power. This may be done in the same turbine which drives the compressor, perhaps by increasing the number of stages to two or three, or by using a separate turbine. The proportion of the total available power which is turned into shaft power can be varied to any desired extent to suit the aircraft operating speeds for which the engine is intended. The highest efficiency is obtained by reducing the jet velocity to such an extent that at the cruising speed of the aircraft for which the engine is designed, the jet efficiency is the same as that of the airscrew.

By this means the fuel consumption can be reduced, at high altitudes, to a value at least as low as that of any reciprocating engine, while the weight of such a gas turbine remains considerably lower than can be attained by the latter. This gives the gas turbine of this type a clear advantage in load-carrying capacity irrespective of range, but this is still largely dependent on flying at fairly high altitudes. This feature is inevitable with any type of gas turbine—it is fundamental that their specific fuel consumption decreases with reduction of atmospheric temperature.

There is, therefore, a very strong incentive to develop satisfactory pressure cabins—much stronger than was the case with piston engines ; but even if these were used,

[Copyright : Rolls-Royce Ltd.
The Rolls-Royce *Derwent I* engine as used in the record-breaking Gloster-Meteor.

this problem would have to be solved in the near future as it is at least desirable to be able to fly at moderate altitudes—say above 10,000 feet, in order to be able to avoid much weather trouble and so to increase the comfort and regularity of services. As passengers of all types have to be catered for, and some would find such altitudes uncomfortable, the pressure cabin would become a necessity. Although, no doubt, some trouble will yet be encountered in its development, this is already well advanced.

Another form of gas turbine drives a ducted fan. This is very similar to the airscrew type, giving its useful work largely in the form of shaft power. Instead of utilising this to drive a normal airscrew, a ducted fan is used. This is a large, low compression ratio axial flow compressor, having one or more stages. Alternatively it can be regarded as an airscrew with a large number of small blades. As would be expected, its characteristics are intermediate between those of the pure jet and the airscrew —it is, in fact, a medium-speed jet, whereas an airscrew is a low-speed jet. The ducted fan has advantages which may make it useful in the speed range where the airscrew

and jet give about equal performance, and where it may be better than either. As nobody has yet flown a ducted-fan gas turbine, this is difficult to predict with any certainty.

The 'Athodyd' or Ram Jet

An even simpler form of jet 'engine' than the gas turbine, is the 'propulsive duct' or 'athodyd' (ram jet). The cycle of operations is the same, but the engine has no moving parts such as compressor and turbine. Compression of the air is achieved by the ram effect due to the forward speed of the aircraft. That is, the air is diffused, its velocity relative to the aircraft being transformed into pressure. This effect is also made use of in the gas turbine, but it is then subsidiary to the compression provided by the rotary compressor. After this compression the air is heated and expanded through the jet nozzle, no turbine being needed as there is no compressor to drive.

This system has the obvious advantage of extreme simplicity, but does not work except at very high speeds. For instance, even with 100 per cent. efficient recovery of the velocity

43

energy, the compression ratio at 500 m.p.h. is only 1.21. However, at speeds at or above the speed of sound, the obtainable compression ratios are high enough to make it quite an attractive scheme. Even then it is not economical and is only justified by its simplicity and lightness. By virtue of these qualities it may prove very useful as a booster at high speeds. For example, a

The V.1 Engine

Another variant is the V.1 engine. This is fundamentally different as it operates intermittently. In this case, after ram compression, the air is admitted to the combustion chamber through a bank of non-return valves. Combustion takes place explosively as in a reciprocating engine, but as there is

A Meteor equipped with Rolls-Royce *Trent* gas turbines driving airscrews. This was the first gas-turbine airscrew aircraft to fly in Britain.

[*Copyright: Rolls-Royce Ltd.*

fighter aircraft which has a normal top speed of 550 m.p.h. could carry an athodyd, without much extra weight, to be used in case of emergency to give it an extra burst of speed, at the expense of a heavy fuel consumption, for a short time. This might be a better method than providing extra power in the main engines, which would then have to be run at low power for normal flight.

Several variants of the athodyd are also possible. Some of these may be termed supercharged athodyds, in which the pressure is raised rather above the ram pressure by some means before the fuel is burned, thus making it possible to get some power at low speeds and improving the efficiency at high speeds. One way of doing this is to burn fuel behind a ducted fan; another is to burn fuel in the exhaust of a jet engine before expanding the air through the jet nozzle. Both these schemes provide means of obtaining extra power in an emergency, as the plant can be operated economically for normal flight without burning the extra fuel.

no piston, the pressure generated pushes against the air in the jet pipe. When the pressure in the combustion chamber drops as the air is forced out through the jet pipe, more air is admitted through the valves and the process is repeated. This engine again represents a certain sacrifice in simplicity in order to obtain greater economy and to make possible operation at relatively low speeds. However, it seems unlikely that engines of this type will find any considerable use in peace-time, as the gain in efficiency is not sufficient to make them really useful at low speeds and they have no great virtues at very high speeds.

There are other means of boosting the power of a jet-propulsion gas turbine, some of which are particularly useful to give increased thrust at take-off. Two of these are the injection of water or some fluid such as liquid ammonia into the compressor intake. The consumption of this additional fluid is in both cases high, so that only short-period operation is feasible.

Rocket Assistance

A method of assisted take-off which has been widely used is the rocket, which is equally applicable to aircraft with any type of power plant or even to gliders.

In addition rockets were used during the war to propel pilotless missiles, such as the British rockets fired from aircraft and the German V.2 weapons, and also the German Me 163 rocket aircraft. This is yet another form of jet-propulsion, but has fundamental differences from all the types yet considered. Chief of these is the fact that no air is needed for the operation of a rocket. In order to burn fuel of any sort whatever, oxygen must be present, as burning is simply the chemical combination of some other element with oxygen. In all the engines so far examined the oxygen used has been provided by the atmosphere; in a rocket, on the other hand, the oxygen is carried internally, not always as free oxygen, but sometimes as a chemical compound. The Germans used liquid oxygen in the V.2 and hydrogen peroxide in the Me 163.

Thus the two main differences of rockets from all other forms of propulsion are that they are completely independent of the atmosphere and can continue to operate even in a complete vacuum, and that the total weight of combustibles which has to be carried is far greater than when using atmospheric oxygen.

Rockets generate a very high-velocity jet and are thus only suitable for very high speeds. The endurance of aircraft with this form of propulsion can only be very short with the rockets in operation, though a long glide may improve the range considerably. A very great deal of power can be packed within a small frontal area and as the amount of power generated is independent of altitude, while drag decreases with altitude, very high speeds at high altitudes are obtainable by means of rockets.

Future Developments

Having briefly discussed the main variants of the gas turbine and of the other forms of jet-propulsion, it is interesting to speculate on probable future developments in the field of aircraft propulsion. One prophecy which

may be made with considerable confidence is that the gas turbine, in some form, will within a few years replace the reciprocating engine as the power plant for all aircraft (except perhaps those having very low power or ultra high speeds—that is, above the speed of sound). This is generally agreed by the aircraft and engine industries, and a point worth noting is that the Germans had come to

The German V.1.

the same conclusion at the beginning of 1945, when all new work in Germany on piston engines was stopped in order to concentrate on gas turbines and jet-propulsion.

One result of this almost universal adoption of gas turbines should be very much closer collaboration between the airframe and engine designers. This can bring very great advantages to both and will probably come about largely because gas turbine engines, and in particular jet engines, can be designed and built very much more quickly than piston engines. The result will be that the engines can be 'made to measure' for a particular aircraft, in cases where a new engine design is justified. The performance and weight of gas turbines are predictable with considerable accuracy, and some simple jet engines have been designed, built and tested within a period of six months, or even less. On the other hand, reciprocating engines take much longer to bring to a suitable state of development to enable them to be used. The more complicated types of gas turbine, such as those driving airscrews, will, of course, take longer to produce, but even so, should take less time than reciprocating engines. Gas

[*Crown Copyright*
Launching a V.2.

turbines can also be made to develop much larger powers in a single unit than is possible with the older type, which is limited, probably, to about 3,000 or 4,000 horse-power by considerations of complication, possible sizes of cylinders, and so on. It is a relatively easy matter to make a much larger gas turbine than this, and once having made one of any size it is also easy to make a scaled-up version, without a great deal of re-design.

The choice of a particular type of gas turbine will be dependent on the cruising or top speed of the aircraft. For speeds up to about 450 m.p.h. an airscrew drive will be used—the top limit for this type of propulsion will depend largely on the ability of the airscrew designers to increase their efficiencies

at high speeds. There may then be an intermediate stage from perhaps 450 m.p.h. to 550 m.p.h. where the ducted fan will be used, and above this speed the pure jet engine (though this may well be used at lower speeds as well—above 400 m.p.h. perhaps).

Cruising speeds for ordinary civil operation will undoubtedly rise, as they have done continuously from the beginning of air travel. It is difficult to estimate the extent of this rise in the immediate future, until some experience has been gained in routine operation with the new power plants. However, 400 m.p.h. is very probable and 500 may be used in special cases—for example inter-continental mail services. It is unlikely that cruising speeds much above 500 m.p.h. will become common in the immediate future, as there is comparatively little to be gained by their use. The time taken to cross the Atlantic at 500 m.p.h. is roughly five hours. An increase of speed to 600 m.p.h. would save less than an hour.

By increasing the weight and complexity of the power plant by one of several methods, considerably greater fuel economy could be achieved. Specific consumptions could be reduced to three-quarters of the lowest values so far attained by any aircraft power plant. This would only be economical when very long ranges are required, and as there is little likelihood of a demand for ranges much in excess of the equivalent of a single-stage Atlantic crossing, there will be little incentive to develop such engines for aircraft use. For land and marine work these developments will undoubtedly take place as, in these applications, engine weight is subsidiary in importance to economy of operation. Among the means of obtaining such high efficiencies may be mentioned the combination of the gas turbine, in the form of an enlarged turbo-supercharger, with the reciprocating engine.

Alternatively the efficiency of the gas turbine can be improved by adding intercoolers between the compressor stages (as in the Rolls-Royce Merlin engine with two stage supercharger), and heat exchangers to return some of the waste heat from the exhaust gases to the air entering the combustion chambers. Advances will certainly be made by raising the compression ratio and the combustion temperature, as better materials become available, and these will not involve a great sacrifice of weight.

Aircraft in the normal speed class may well begin to take on unfamiliar shapes, as full use is made of the characteristics of the new power plants and modern aerodynamic knowledge. Airscrews when used are likely to be placed behind the wing in order to minimise the disturbance of the flow over the wing. This has recently become particularly necessary as new wing profiles have been designed, having a greatly reduced drag. These are the laminar flow wings and they depend on having a smooth airflow over them.

With increasing size of aircraft the all-wing type may well acquire fresh prominence or in some cases ' tail first ' designs, like the Miles Libellula, which have many advantages when using jet-propulsion.

In the light aircraft range it is at present rather doubtful if gas turbines can be made sufficiently efficient to be worth while. An engine of this type developing 100 shaft horse-power would be only a few inches in diameter and would be light enough to pick up ! Construction of such an engine would need almost a watchmaker's technique, and compressor and turbine efficiencies might well be very low, by reason of the aerodynamic effects of the small size.

At the other end of the scale—the supersonic aircraft—rockets will probably be used to begin with at any rate. The problems of supersonic flight are likely to be solved in the near future as a great deal of research is now being directed to this end. As the power required will almost certainly remain very large indeed, the endurance of supersonic aircraft will be limited to a few minutes, although the eventual development of power plants which are rather more economical than rockets, such as boosted athodyds, may bring about some improvement.

For very high speeds indeed, of the order of the 3,000 m.p.h. reached by the V.2, rockets must be used, with wings to enable a prolonged glide to be made. It is possible that such rockets might be used for passenger and mail carrying, but the usefulness and necessity for this seems very doubtful, until the time comes, as it may well do, when man attempts interplanetary flight.

It is extremely unlikely that for many years it will be practicable to use atomic energy for aircraft propulsion, as the weight involved would be prohibitive, in spite of the attractions of a non-existent fuel consumption, but even without this it is clear that there will be far-reaching advances in aircraft of all kinds.

THE LITERATURE OF FLIGHT

The First Aerial Voyage

21st November 1783

A letter written by the Marquis d'Arlandes, who accompanied Pilâtre de Rozier on the first aerial voyage in history. They took off in a Montgolfière hot-air balloon from the Château de la Muette, Paris, and having crossed the city landed some five-and-a-half miles from their starting-point after twenty-five minutes in the air.

WE set off at 54 minutes past one o'clock. The balloon was so placed that M. de Rozier was on the west and I was on the east. The machine, says the public, rose with majesty. I think few of them saw that, at the moment when it passed the hedge, it made a half-turn, and we changed our positions, which, thus altered, we retained to the end. I was astonished at the smallness of the noise and motion among the spectators occasioned by our departure. I thought they might be astonished and frightened and might stand in need of encouragement, so I waved my arm, with small success. I then drew out and shook my handkerchief, and immediately perceived a great movement in the yard. It seemed as if the spectators all formed one mass, rushing by an involuntary motion towards the wall, which they seemed to consider as the only obstacle between us.

At this time M. de Rozier said, 'You are doing nothing, and we are not mounting.' 'Pardon me,' I replied. I threw a truss of straw upon the fire, stirring it a little at the same time, and then quickly turned my face back again; but I could no longer see La Muette. Astonished, I looked at the river. M. de Rozier then said, 'Behold, there is the river, and observe that we descend. Well then, my friend, let us increase the fire'; and we worked away. But instead of crossing the river, as our direction seemed to indicate, which carried us towards the Invalides, we passed along the island of Cygnes, reached to the principal course of the river, and advanced as far up as the Port de la Conférence. I said to my intrepid companion, 'Behold, there is the river, etc.' I stirred the fire, and took with the fork a truss of straw, which, no doubt from being too tight, did not take fire very easily.

I lifted and shook it in the middle of the flame. The next moment I felt as if I were lifted up by my armpits, and said to my dear companion, 'How we mount, etc.' At the same time, I heard a noise from the top of the machine, as if it were going to burst; and I looked, but did not see anything.

However as I was looking up, I felt a shock, which was the only one I experienced. The direction of the motion was from the upper part downwards. I said then, 'What are you doing? Are you dancing?' 'I didn't stir,' said he. 'So much the better,' I replied; 'it is at last a new current, which I hope will carry us away from the river.' True enough, for when I turned in order to see where we were, I found myself between l'Ecole Militaire and Les Invalides, beyond which place we had already gone about 2,500 feet.

M. de Rozier said at the same time, 'We are over level ground.' 'Yes,' said I, 'and we advance.' 'Work on,' he said, 'work on.' I then heard another noise in the machine which appeared to be the effect of a rope breaking. This fresh admonition made me examine attentively the interior of our habitation. I saw that part of the machine, which was turned towards the South, was full of round holes, many of which were of a considerable size. I then said, 'We must descend,' and at the same time I took the sponge and easily extinguished the fire, which was round some holes that I could reach; but leaning on the lower part of the linen, to observe whether it adhered firmly to the surrounding circle, I found that the linen was easily separated from it, on which I repeated that it was necessary to descend. My companion said, 'We are over Paris.' 'Never mind that,' I said, 'but look if there appears any danger for you on your side —are you safe?' He said, 'Yes.' I examined my side, and found that there was no danger to be apprehended. Farther, I wetted with the sponge those cords that were within my reach. They all resisted, except two, which gave way. I then said, 'We may pass over Paris.' In doing this, we approached the tops of the houses very sensibly; we increased the fire, and rose with the greatest ease. I looked below me, and perfectly discovered the Missions Etrangères. It seemed as if we were going towards Saint-Sulpice, which I could perceive through the aperture of our machine. On rising, a current of air made us leave this direction, and carried us towards the South. I saw on my left a sort of forest, which I took to be the Luxembourg; we passed over the Boulevard, and then I said, 'Let us now descend.' The fire was nearly extinguished; but the intrepid M. de Rozier, who never loses his presence of mind, and who went forward, imagining that we were going against the mills that are between Petite Gentilly and the Boulevard, admonished me. I threw a bundle of straw on the fire, and shaking it in order to make it inflame more easily, we rose, and a new current carried us a little towards our left. M. de Rozier said again, 'Take care of the mills': but as I was looking through the aperture of the machine, I could observe more accurately that we could not meet with them, and said, 'We are there'. . . . The moment we touched the ground, I raised myself up in the gallery, and perceived the upper part of the machine to press very gently on my head. I pushed it back, and jumped out of the gallery and on turning myself towards the machine, expected to find it distended, but was surprised to find it perfectly emptied and quite flattened.

Cierva C.40 Autogiro making a jump start.

[Photo : ' Flight '

HELICOPTER STORY

by

B. J. Hurren

On the staff of the Fairey Aviation Co.   Formerly Lt. Commander in the Fleet Air Arm.

AVIATION IS news.   The world's press seizes upon almost every item of aeronautical activity and—frequently with a lack of discrimination, especially as regards accidents —displays man's encroachment on the natural realm of flight with unabated enthusiasm.

This fever has been running for nearly forty years.   It broke out virulently when Blériot made his sensational flight across the English Channel in 1909.   And thereafter, particularly in the years 1910–14, every aeronaut became invested with a halo, was described as an ' ace,' an ' intrepid airman,' a derring-do fellow to be justly held in awe by lesser, earthbound mortals.

In this spate of air news and doings, it may come as a surprise to the everyday man in the street to learn that man's first gropings towards sustained flight in heavier-than-air vehicles were concerned with rotating-wing aircraft. Thus, that incredible genius Leonardo da Vinci, peerless among inventors, left sketches which technical experts to-day, with hundreds of years of scientific knowledge behind them, declare to be sound in principle and potentially capable of being interpreted as designs for a helicopter. This effort, which may be fairly described as a Big Idea, did not proceed beyond that stage:

[Photo : ' Flight '
Fairey Gyrodyne.

and whilst homage must be accorded the great inventor we must qualify this by the fact that it remained no more than an idea.

Without examining subsequent ideas for aircraft, particularly in the early nineteenth century (for all of them can be found in the excellent and authoritative book *Aeronautics* (*Heavier than Air Aircraft*), by M. J. B. Davy of the South Kensington Science Museum, it can be stated that the *idea* of rotating-wing flight has never faltered, even if it remained dormant for decades. Indeed, looking back on the flimsy contraptions which were passed off as aeroplanes at the famous aeronautical meeting at Rheims in 1909, it is surprising that so much development work was concentrated on the fixed-wing aircraft—development which has led to a ten-fold increase in speed in less than forty years.

Rotating Wings

The helicopter, by comparison, is still in its earliest experimental stages. The helicopter of the future may bear as much relation to the present helicopter as the modern Gloster-Meteor to Santos Dumont's nightmarish box-kite.

Two widely divergent views exist about the helicopter. There is the roseate view, taken by the public at large, of a Wellsian future with aerial buses and cabs flying over and along the great thoroughfares of a metropolis. Alternating with this optimism, which is of the most generalised character, is a slough of technical pessimism which is of a specialised character and may not be anywhere near as justifiable as the optimism. To-day's defeats in science are so often to-morrow's victories of technical achievements.

The rotating-wing aircraft gives many advantages over the fixed-wing, but it carries compensating disadvantages. It may become evident, soon, that in fact the two broad categories of aircraft are quite distinct and do not overlap each other's spheres of transportation.

That word ' transportation ' is the key word in aeronautics. Whether its load is bombs or passengers and freight, the function of the aeroplane is to carry from one point to another. The fixed-wing aircraft covers, infinitely better than the rotating-wing aircraft, certain categories of air transportation ; and *vice versa*. Where it is a question of speed from one point to another, the fixed-wing aircraft has an incontestable advantage. Already the speed of fixed-wing aircraft exceeds five times the highest speed attained by any rotating-wing aircraft. In altitude (always remembering that the world's height record is still held by a balloon !) the fixed-wing aircraft completely outclasses the helicopter. In range the advantage is even more apparent since a fixed-wing four-engined bomber has unofficially flown 10,000 miles without alighting, whilst the world distance record for a helicopter is claimed by America as 430 miles in a five-hour flight (1946). Whilst from day to day new records are in reach for the helicopter, it may be taken that 120 m.p.h. is at present (1947) at the top of the speed range and 20,000 feet the ceiling.

It is evident, then, that for transporting goods or passengers by air from, say, London to New York or Capetown or HongK ong, the helicopter is quite outclassed by its fixed-wing rival. It can be dismissed entirely from such journeys, since the new forms of power available to designers of fixed-wing aircraft will enable them to travel at supersonic speeds which, for technical reasons, are outside the scope of the rotating-wing aeroplane.

The Advantages

There are, nevertheless, categories of air transportation in which the helicopter is immeasurably superior to its fixed-wing rival. The advantages of the helicopter derive from the fact that aerodynamically it can do something that no fixed-wing aircraft can do; it can hover, remain poised in space, without forward motion. Given this quality, it can patently descend or rise vertically. It can also move slantwise, crab-wise, and even fly backwards—though this is rather a pointless parlour trick of the pilot.

This ability to move in the vertical plane can be over-stressed; for, in practice, the need to move in this manner, without any forward or backward motion, is rare indeed. This is an important, yet often overlooked, point which will be returned to on the subject of the autogiro.

Different Types

There are so far three varieties of rotating-wing aircraft. They are (1) the rotaplane, (2) the helicopter and (3) the gyrodyne.

The rotaplane is the official British title of that aeroplane which is far more commonly known as the autogiro. The name autogiro is a proprietary word, the copyright being invested in the Cierva company which, quite rightly, asserts its full claim to the title. Hence the official word rotaplane (in America, rotorplane).

Rotaplanes

The autogiro is quite distinct from the helicopter. It has a fuselage and is sustained in flight by rotating blades—they are hardly to be classed as wings—but thereafter the similarity vanishes. At the forward end of the fuselage is an orthodox aero engine which drives an orthodox airscrew. The airscrew is caused to rotate by the engine,

just as with an ordinary aircraft, and the slipstream set up by the airscrew causes the free blades to rotate. The action, then, in this current of air is closely similar to the action of a sycamore pod gyrating as it floats to the ground.

You will note that with the rotaplane class the flow of air starts from *below* the rotating blades, passes through the disc circumscribed by the revolving blades, and on *upwards* to spill into the free air again.

[*Photo: ' Flight '*
Weir Rotaplane.

The immediate technical advantage of this system from an air transportation viewpoint is that should the engine fail then the pilot can cause the stream of air to flow *upwards* by manœuvring his controls for glide descent, thus causing the aircraft to remain airborne on its blades. This is an important factor for safety.

The Cierva autogiro dates from 1925 in Britain, and since that date has been successfully flown continuously by rotating-wing pioneers. Much of the limelight of these flights fell on Captain Brie, R.F.C., who made many brilliant and spectacular flights. In 1935, for example, he made the first take-offs and landings with an autogiro from a small platform erected over the stern of the Italian cruiser *Fiume*. These experimental flights were made with the ship motionless and at various speeds up to 24 knots. With the advent of war in 1939, an autogiro unit was established in France; but contrary to the expectations of many proponents of rotating-wing flight the autogiro did not take any prominent part

51

in reconnaissance work—certainly nothing like the work performed by the orthodox aircraft. Nor was it snapped up commercially to the degree which had been predicted: for frequently technical advances in aeronautics hang fire for no apparent reason and are later enthusiastically adopted for even less reason.

The autogiro cannot rise or descend vertically in still air. But since 'still air' is a rare phenomenon, and the number of occasions when an immediate vertical movement is required even more rare, the autogiro achieves almost everything in flight that the helicopter can do. By means of a jump device, take-off is very rapid and the ascent at an acute angle; whilst, headed to wind, the autogiro can in effect hover over a point on the ground. If, for example, the widely held belief that one day air taxis will use the roof of a railway station were to come true, then the autogiro could certainly operate from such a confined space, where no normal light aeroplane and certainly no airliner could.

Helicopters

The helicopter is an entirely different kettle of fish. In direct contradistinction to the autogiro, the blades of a helicopter are caused to rotate by a direct drive from the engine. The power plant is normally housed inside the aircraft, and drives the blades round.

A moment's reflection will show that, as opposed to the autogiro, the flow of air is thus from *above*, then through the orbital disc of the blades, and *downwards* to free air. The blades can be set at different angles of incidence; but the important point is that the change of pitch through several degrees is considerable when the pilot wishes to move them from their normal position of thrust into the autorotative position. In different words, if the engine should fail, the pilot must quickly alter the pitch into the autorotative position, so that, as with the autogiro, the aircraft can plane down like the sycamore pod. Note that this involves a transfer of the air flow from one direction to another: that takes time, which means loss of height, and therefore the helicopter

has not the high safety factor of the autogiro.

However, potentially, if not factually so far, the helicopter is capable of development to big aircraft which would be an extremely difficult line of advance for the rotaplane type of aircraft.

Gyrodynes

The gyrodyne combines the virtues of both autogiro and helicopter. In design it is in the helicopter category, but its blades are set in such an attitude during normal flight that they are virtually in the autorotative position. Hence, if the engine fails, the gyrodyne assumes almost immediately the characteristics of a powerless autogiro.

Dr. Bennett, one of the foremost rotating-wing engineers in the world, gives this description of the gyrodyne of the Fairey Aviation Co. Ltd. 'The helicopter is propelled by inclining the rotor disc with respect to the flight path. As a result, the axial flow through the rotor increases with forward speed. To compensate for the reduced angle of attack caused by the increased axial flow, the blade angle has to be increased. At a high forward speed it is generally greater than the maximum value at which the rotor would autorotate in power-off flight. Hence the safety of the aircraft is impaired, because in the event of engine failure the blade angle must be quickly decreased to prevent the blades from losing their kinetic energy, and stalling. The provision of automatic pitch reduction may ensure that the worst consequence of power failure is temporary loss of lift until the aircraft reaches a steady sinking speed in autorotative flight.

'Not only is the safety of the aircraft impaired by the increase in axial flow with forward speed, but also the smoothness and efficiency of the rotor. A change in axial flow does not alter the blade angle of attack equally from root to tip, but affects the tip portion of the blades least. Consequently, when the collective pitch is increased to compensate for the increased axial flow, the blade angle at the tip is excessive: it may even approach the stall cyclically at high transitional speeds where the angle of attack on the retreating blade is already high due to blade flapping or feathering.

' Hence the helicopter rotor becomes inherently rough and inefficient with increase in forward speed.

' The autogiro rotor is also inclined with respect to the flight path; but the axial flow is substantially constant over the entire

smooth and as efficient in forward flight as the autogiro.'

The interpretation of these ideas has already resulted in some extremely diversified helicopters. In America, so far, there are more than eighty designs in hand and each tackles the problems differently. A major problem is the torque (' A twisting moment, in Mechanics ') set up by the rotation of the blades. The

Bell Model 42 4-passenger helicopter.
[Copyright: Bell Aviation Co.

speed range. Hence the relative smoothness of the autogiro or of the helicopter in power-off flight—compared with the high-pitch operation of the helicopter in powered flight.'

Dr. Bennett goes on to say that the rotor of the gyrodyne has a backward inclination—as in the autogiro—at take-off. This backward inclination decreases with increase in forward speed; until, at maximum speed, the tip-path plane is only slightly inclined forward or backward with respect to the flight path—but it is never inclined excessively forward as in the helicopter.

' It is therefore unnecessary to exceed the maximum autorotative blade-angle to compensate for an increased axial flow. The gyrodyne should therefore be as safe, as

present most common helicopter, the Sikorsky R.4, has a stabiliser mainly for torque counteraction rigged out on a boom aft of the main fuselage, and rotating in the vertical plane. Other ideas include two sets of rotors, either rigged outboard, or in tandem, or one above the other, revolving in opposite directions so that the torque set up by one cancels out the torque of the other.

A German Success

The first successful helicopter was the German Focke-Achgelis, FW 61, which in 1938 made a remarkable flight demonstration *inside* the Deutschlandhalle, Berlin. This aircraft had two rotors mounted on outriggers, driven by a 160 h.p. engine.

Cierva W.9 helicopter.

[*Photo : John Stroud*

Air Taxis

Most aerodromes are distant from the centres of population. Britain's star civil aerodrome, at Heathrow, is twelve miles from the centre of London. Transit to and fro is tedious, along congested main roads. The idea of a commuting air taxi, collecting passengers at their hotel roofs and taking them direct to the flying field, has many attractions.

Furthermore, many present journeys that take hours, and sometimes days, can be cut to a matter of minutes. For example, the Greek Islands, the jagged coasts of Scotland and Norway, and the cross-water trips typified by the Bristol Channel and the Solent seem to be begging for the sort of air service the helicopter taxi offers.

There are two points to note about this. First, if instead of orthodox wheels the helicopter undercarriage is fitted with 'boots' in the shape of air-inflated pontoons, the aircraft can be flown with equal facility from land, water, snow, ice or mud swamp.

It must be stated that this, and many comparable flights were, in a sense, artificial. As outlined above, the air flow is downwards, and consequently when the helicopter is near the ground a buffer or cushion effect is created as the air flow impinges against the ground and strives to spill free. This gives a hidden lift characteristic; and it is likely that many of the designs announced or projected would not rise far clear of this artificial assistance to lift.

The forward speed of the FW 61 was in the region of 80 m.p.h., and few helicopters exceed 110 m.p.h. maximum.

Apart from the technical aspect, the helicopter has many possibilities for special-duty flying, doing work that could not be done efficiently by orthodox fixed-wing aircraft.

Secondly, no expense is incurred in laying out great aerodromes. It is very nearly true to say that the helicopter can operate from anywhere; it is entirely true to say that to pick up or set down passengers and freight the helicopter does not necessarily have to land at all, since a ladder can be lowered whilst the aircraft is still airborne near the ground. Hence, with special communities, not even the expense of an alighting stage is required.

An example of this can be seen in such districts as the tea plantations in Assam, where planters' houses and estates are set among the terraced hillsides. Here no adequate open space is available for orthodox aero-

Cierva C.30 Autogiro.

[*Photo : John Stroud*

drome construction; nor would such aero-dromes be serviceable during the periods of heavy rains. But a door-to-door air delivery service is entirely practicable for helicopter aircraft.

Photography

Whilst at present the vibration is unsatisfactory, there is no doubt that when this technical difficulty is overcome, air photography by helicopter will be in increasing demand. The hover characteristics are of immense importance for this class of work, and the studies of town planners and such authorities as harbour boards will be considerably eased. The helicopter can, obviously, play an important rôle in geological air survey for oil and minerals.

Agriculture

In America, particularly, where great plantations extend, the helicopter has been called in for pest control. Special sprays eject protective fluid, and farmers' work that once took days can be completed with ease in a morning with greater accuracy and more overall efficiency than by any other means.

Likewise, in districts where the great forests extend, and where a comprehensive fire-guard service is in being, the ranging helicopter performs an invaluable duty. Clearly, to tackle an outbreak of fire in the forest before it has seized a hold by spraying the affected area with fire-extinguishing chemicals, is of first interest to forestry commissioners.

Postal Services

The tremendous advantages of direct accessibility to zones at present isolated and remote can be conferred by the helicopter. Many districts in the world are periodically cut off, by flood

Bristol 171 4-seat helicopter

waters or heavy snow in particular, but this isolation can be banished readily. The helicopter can not only facilitate and speed up the postal links; it can ensure their continuity.

Incidentally, this also applies to medical services, in either taking the patients to hospital or else bringing the doctors and nurses to outlying districts.

Police Patrol

The marshalling of crowds and the control of heavy volumes of road traffic come within the orbit of helicopter work.

Ship and Shore Contact

The delivery of ship pilots and such officials as customs and health authorities to ocean

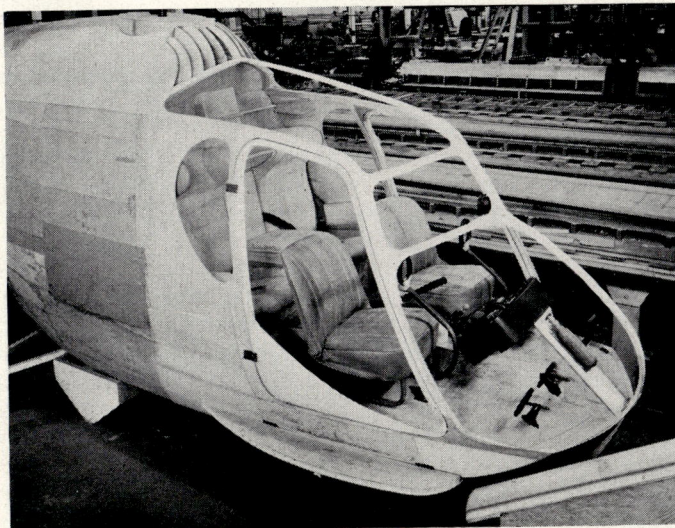

Mock-up of the Bristol 171 helicopter

[Photo: Rudy Arnold

Sikorsky S.51 3-passenger helicopter.

and to fly a helicopter is undoubtedly a professional attainment in which ability to fly by instruments with intense concentration is an essential. The idea of happy-go-lucky flying in a rotating-wing aircraft is quite divorced from reality. However, development work to simplify controls is well in hand, and technical progress should soon result in considerable improvements in this direction.

Jets for Helicopters

The 'jet' engine, which has revolutionised fixed-wing flight, has also an effect on rotating-wing aircraft. The basic idea is to have the issue of the jet at the blade tips; and although this sounds simple, in fact the technical difficulties are formidable. Nevertheless, Doblhoff in 1945 built and successfully flew in Austria a helicopter using a jet-driven rotor.

It is not difficult to find objections to the helicopter; but these must be viewed in the light of the history of development of orthodox aircraft. In the years 1909–19, a number of extraordinary fixed-wing aircraft were produced, and some flew very successfully, but it was not until two decades later that the absurdities of many of the early aircraft became apparent. There are grounds for hope that the helicopter, now going through an awkward stage of development, may triumph over the present checks and flourish like the green bay tree.

I do not think this an ill-advised term. There are many who serve devotedly at the altar of the god of Science, but there are equally many who consider the results of aeronautical science should be carefully controlled. The possibility of having the air buzzing with the hum of helicopter taxis is not one of undiluted joy, for the noise and interference attendant upon such a state would be intolerable to many. Incidentally,

liners can obviously be carried out by helicopter. These aircraft have already landed on and taken off from ships under way. In a busy harbour such as Portsmouth, routine of contact between warship and shore base can be expedited.

With the helicopter offering so many possibilities, it may be somewhat ungenerous to say that as a pilot of orthodox aircraft for many years, and an air passenger of wide experience in almost every type of military warplane and civil airliner, there is no doubt in my mind that the fixed-wing aircraft is preferable purely as a means of flight. This is obviously a personal prejudice akin to the aversion that can be felt to tram travel, but it is a strong one. It may be added that those who take to rotating-wing flight seem to become entirely obsessed with the idea.

At present, the controls are complicated

the strong down-draught caused by the rotors would make short work of any flower gardens, so that the idea of 'back-garden' aviation is not likely to be popular.

Unfortunately there is a fly (even a large bluebottle!) in the balm of the helicopter dream. At present the law restricts the field of helicopter flight to areas free from crowds. Thus, the idea of the town air taxi can be technically accepted, but the civil aviation authority has still to get legal permission for such operations. A compromise, offering landing stages or pontoons on the River Thames, seems to provide a possible solution for London, but the law grinds slowly.

To sum up: At this date, the helicopter is on the verge of appreciable technical improvement, but in its present form it is far from perfect. Its commercial possibilities are exceedingly wide, but are not yet developed. Rotating-wing aircraft are opening up new fields of aviation rather than entering upon the preserves of the longer established fixed-wing aircraft. The law will have to be altered before many of the dreams of the man in the street concerning helicopters can come true.

THE LITERATURE OF FLIGHT

The First Aviator

Orville Wright's own account of the first sustained flight in a powered aeroplane. This flight, in a very real sense, changed the whole course of history.

DURING THE night of 16th December 1903, a strong cold wind blew from the north. When we arose on the morning of the 17th, the puddles of water, which had been standing about camp since the recent rains, were covered with ice. The wind had a velocity of 22 to 27 m.p.h. We thought it would die down before long, but when 10 o'clock arrived, and the wind was as brisk as ever, we decided that we had better get the machine out. . . .

Wilbur having used his turn in the unsuccessful attempt on the 14th, the right to the first trial belonged to me. Wilbur ran at the side, holding the wings to balance it on the track. The machine, facing a 27-mile wind, started very slowly. Wilbur was able to stay with it until it lifted from the track after a forty-foot run.

The course of the flight up and down was exceedingly erratic. The control of the front rudder was difficult. As a result, the machine would rise suddenly to about ten feet, and then as suddenly dart for the ground. A sudden dart when a little over 120 feet from the point at which it rose into the air, ended the flight.

This flight lasted only twelve seconds, but it was nevertheless the first in the history of the world in which a machine carrying a man had raised itself by its own power into the air in full flight, had sailed forward without reduction of speed, and had finally landed at a point as high as that from which it started.

The Spell Of Flying

BEFORE TAKE-OFF, a professional pilot is keen, anxious, but lest someone read his true feelings, he is elaborately casual. The reason for this is that he is about to enter a new though familiar world. The process of entrance begins a short time before he leaves the ground and is completed the instant he is in the air. From that moment on, not only his body but his spirit and personality exist in a separate world known only to himself and his comrades.

As the years go by, he returns to this invisible world rather than to earth for peace and solace. There he also finds a profound enchantment although he can seldom describe it. He can discuss it with others of his kind, and because they, too, know and feel its power they understand. But his attempts to communicate his feelings to his wife or other earthly confidants invariably end in failure.

Flying is hypnotic and all pilots are willing victims to the spell. Their world is like a magic island in which the factors of life and death assume their proper values. Thinking becomes clear because there are no earthly foibles or embellishments to confuse it. Professional pilots are, of necessity, uncomplicated, simple men. Their thinking must remain straightforward, or they die—violently.

E. K. GANN—*Island in the Sky*, 1945

Up In A Balloon

I AM in a very small balloon over Surrey on the last day of a beautiful May. So light is the wind that on that little voyage three hours and a half were taken to travel sixteen miles, from Roehampton to Betchworth. There is scarcely a cloud in the sky.

Very slowly I approach a big wood. It would rather express the situation were I to say that very slowly a big wood comes nearer to the balloon, for there is no sense of movement, and the earth below seems to be moving slowly past a stationary balloon. As the wood comes nearer I watch the aneroid and get a bag of ballast ready. For I know that over the wood the air will be slightly cooler, with probably a slight down-draught due to convection, and that the balloon will immediately begin to descend; and I shall have to check that descent by throwing a little ballast.

Fifteen hundred feet up and almost absolute silence, broken occasionally by the barking of a dog heard very faintly, or by a voice hailing the balloon, and by an occasional friendly creak of the basket and rigging if I move ever so slightly. Then quite suddenly I am aware of something new.

The balloon has come down a little already, and I scatter a few handfuls of sand and await the certain result. But my attention is no longer on that, it is arrested by this new sound which I hear, surely the most wonderful and the sweetest sound heard by mortal ears. . . . It is the combined singing of thousands of birds, of half the kinds which make the English spring so lovely. I do not hear one above the others; all are blended together in a wonderful harmony without change of pitch or tone, yet never wearying the ear.

By very close attention I seem to be able at times to pick out an individual song. No doubt at all there are wrens, chaffinches, blackbirds, thrushes, hedge-sparrows, warblers, greenfinches and bullfinches and a score of others, by the hundred; and their singing comes up to me from that ten-acre wood in one sweet volume of heavenly music.

C. C. TURNER—*The Old Flying Days*, 1927

United States Navy K-class Goodyear non-rigid airship.

AIRSHIPS

by

Lord Ventry

Founder and Hon. Editor of 'The Airship'. Formerly in the R.A.F.
Hon. Air Commodore No. 902 (County of London) (Balloon) Squadron.

AIRSHIPS ARE of three main types, non-rigid, semi-rigid and rigid. As at the moment all existing airships are non-rigid or semi-rigid, more attention will be given to this class of ship.

The non-rigid consists of a streamline envelope. Below the envelope is slung the car or cars, and on the stern are the stabilising and control planes. At high speeds the nose may blow in. To prevent this, stiffeners, like the ribs of an umbrella, stiffen the bows. The engines are either in the car, or more often outrigged from it, driving the propellers direct. If a breakdown should occur when in flight they are accessible to the engineer.

Non-rigid and semi-rigid airships depend on the maintenance of internal pressure inside the envelope for form and rigidity. If pressure should fall seriously the ship becomes uncontrollable and may break up.

Airships have both dynamic lift derived from movement through the air, and static lift from the gas. Thanks to the former, a ship can leave the ground and fly when heavier than air, and be forced to earth when lighter than air.

Non- and semi-rigids can be constructed in all sizes from some 6,000 cubic feet up to probably 2,000,000 cubic feet, but the semi-rigid cannot be constructed in such small volumes as the non-rigid, owing to the weight of the keel. This keel, which differentiates the semi-rigid from the non-rigid, is slung between car and envelope.

We will now consider how designers have tackled the various problems involved in the construction of non-rigid airships.

The Envelope

The envelope must combine lightness and great strength with good gas-holding properties. In the past gold-beater's skin (made out of the lining of the intestines of oxen), silk and oiled cotton have all been tried. To-day a woven material of cotton proofed with rubber is normally employed. The plies are laid on at a bias to each other. This adds strength and prevents a tear from spreading, but even so it cannot prevent some of the fast-moving hydrogen molecules from escaping. Lengthwise threads are known as warp, and cross threads as weft.

When a fabric has been in use it stretches, and the bigger the volume the greater the tendency to do so. Distortion may also occur, though much of the latter can be overcome by careful design of the car suspension. If very large non-rigids are to be constructed, something other than woven fabric may have to be developed. Internal pressure increases with diameter and this entails a heavier fabric and a certain loss of lift.

The shape of the envelope must be such that it combines maximum lift and minimum

drag. It must not have too high an internal pressure, for this shortens the envelope's life and also decreases the lift. The envelope must also be easily stabilised, and to combine all these points means a compromise. The length of the present-day American non-rigid is a little more than four times its diameter. The ballonets which are inside the envelope and take care of differences of pressure will be considered under aerostatics.

Car Suspension of Modern Airships

The modern Goodyear non-rigids are all of circular section, which is the best from a drag point of view. Two or more catenary curtains of fabric edged with wire hang down inside the envelope. They are attached on each side of its top longitudinal centre line. The bridles of the car suspensions are attached to these curtains. The car itself is slung some three feet below the envelope, and the main suspensions are led upwards through gas-tight glands in the bottom of the envelope. These suspensions terminate in the bridles. Outside the envelope and above the car is an external catenary band. A secondary suspension system is attached to this, which relieves the top of the envelope of some of its load. The car is so close to the envelope that all the external suspensions can be faired in.

Thus the car load is well distributed and car and envelope virtually form one unit, so reducing resistance. The main suspensions are taken from points near the top of the envelope and owing to their length their angles are quite moderate, so the envelope is not submitted to an undue compressive load.

The ship is kept as low as possible, thereby giving good air and ground handling qualities and at the same time housing-shed height is reduced.

Stability

A streamline envelope has little sense of direction or stability and as speed increases it begins to pitch and yaw. To counteract this, designers soon found themselves obliged to add fins.

Between 1906 and 1910 French designers

U.S.NAVY L

U.S.NAVY G

U.S.NAVY K

U.S.NAVY M

PROPORTIONALLY IN SCALE

Four types of United States non-rigid naval airship.

tried out gas-filled fins, placed on the stern of the envelope. These were not very effective and caused much drag. The British airships *Baby* and *Gamma* (1909 and 1910) originally had these gas-inflated stabilisers, but they were soon abandoned for the more efficient planes.

The French began by placing the stabilising planes on the car girder, but by 1911 it was found that they were very much more effective if placed on the envelope.

The shape of the envelope affects its stability. The longer it is in relation to its diameter the less the lift. The stabilising surfaces, however, may be smaller and are more effective. The modern non-rigid can attain a speed of close on 80 m.p.h. and has excellent stability.

Control

An airship has two sets of controls: dynamic, consisting of elevating planes and rudder, and static, for the gas and water ballast. When moving under power, both sets of controls may be used at once. When the motors are stopped the ship becomes a free balloon, and altitude is governed by discharging ballast to reduce weight and gain altitude or valving gas to reduce lift and lose altitude.

From the beginning rudders were employed for directional control. At first these were usually placed on the stern of the car frame, but it was soon found that their proper

French Astra airship 1907 *Ville de Paris* (non-rigid) showing inflated stabilisers.

position was on the stern of the envelope itself.

Various methods of vertical control have been tried. One of the earliest was to shift weights forward and aft. The early Parseval ships were made to climb or descend by filling one or other of the ballonets. Control was sluggish, and when pressure height was reached and the ballonets were empty, gas had to be valved if a descent was decided on.

In fact, up to 1907, pilots carried on with their well-tested free ballooning methods. To ascend they let go ballast and to descend they valved gas. The length of flight depended on the amount not only of fuel, but of ballast. Relying on this method of control was very wasteful especially in summertime when the sun was constantly in and out of cloud, causing expansion and loss of gas due to heating.

In 1907 the French Army began to use elevating planes on their third airship, the semi-rigid *Lebaudy Patrie*, and, as they were placed each side of the car, they were not

Bow stiffeners on Goodyear non-rigid airship.

very effective. They lifted the ship bodily, but they did make it possible to rise and descend without loss of gas and ballast.

In 1912 the British Army moved the elevating planes on H.M.A. *Gamma* from the stern of the car frame to the stern of the envelope. They were then very effective, for by tilting the ship they altered the angle of propeller thrust. This arrangement was gradually adopted in all airships. The elevating planes, if they work in the propeller slipstream, can be made very effective even when placed on the car, if they are not too near the centre of the ship.

Swivelling propellers were developed by the British pioneers Beedle and E. T. Willows, and they were used on all six ships designed by Willows, as well as on the British Army airships, *Gamma*, *Delta* and *Eta*. These propellers could be swung so that their thrust could force a heavy ship vertically up off the ground, or bring a light ship down vertically. They enabled ascents to be made from very restricted places and it was possible to land in the same way and without outside assistance, but their use involved shafting and loss of efficiency, so they were abandoned.

Jet control has not yet been thoroughly tried out on airships, but one successful experiment was made in the last of the Italian semi-rigid *Forlanini* ships in 1931. When the main 150 h.p. engine was declutched from the propeller it drove blowers, which were connected up to valves placed on the extreme bow and stern of the envelope.

Power Plant and Transmission

The first man-carrying airship was the *Giffard*, which ascended on 24th September 1852. She had a 3 h.p. steam-engine and a speed of 5½ m.p.h. Renard's *La France* was driven by an electric motor of about 9 h.p. at a speed of some 15 m.p.h., but steam and electric motors were far too heavy and no real progress was possible until the light petrol motor appeared. The German, Woelfert, pioneered the use of such a motor. His ship first ascended on 24th June 1896 with an 8 h.p. Daimler motor. But in an ascent in 1897 it caught fire and the crew were killed.

Santos Dumont was the first to make successful flights with the new power, between the years 1898 and 1903, in France. After this, power increased and weight was reduced, until by a slow process of development we have the fine motors of to-day.

Airship motors must be flexible, capable of slow running, and easy to start and stop in the air. Great care must be taken to insulate petrol motors with fireproof bulkheads, and the exhaust pipes must be kept well clear of anything combustible, and led downwards from the envelope.

Up to 1915 propellers were always shaft or chain driven, the motors being in the car. The propellers were usually raised above the car to bring the centre of thrust nearer to the centre of resistance. The propeller brackets, however, caused drag, and the drive a loss of power.

The small British airship, *S.S.1*, in 1915 was the first non-rigid to have a direct drive, and since then direct drive and out-rigged motors have become almost universal.

Speed and Lift

The 635,000 cubic feet M class of the U.S. Navy (1943) with 1,100 h.p. are the largest and fastest successful non-rigids yet constructed. Their maximum speed is about 80 m.p.h. Short of revolutionary forms of power units, much greater speeds seem unlikely so far as non-rigids are concerned.

When the speed is doubled, resistance is

British *S.S.* of 1915 (non-rigid) showing later design of stabilisers.

four times as great, and when it is trebled, the drag increases nine times, therefore the higher the speed the greater the pressure the envelope has to withstand. Drag has now been cut down virtually to a minimum, and transmission losses (the loss of power between the motors' output and the thrust asserted by the propeller) have been practically eliminated. If, however, the propeller were on the stern of the envelope, speed would be still further increased.

Goodyears have a new fabric available, which has the same strength as the present fabric, but is one-third lighter. This will mean still more lift.

The airship will always be much slower than the aeroplane, but have much greater lift. If the dimensions of an airship are doubled the lift is eight times as great, and the weight increases about four times. Therefore the bigger the airship the more the lift, and lift is the very life-force of the airship.

Airships can remain in the air independently of motor power and have a speed range from zero to about 80 m.p.h. They can land in and take off from places inaccessible to aeroplanes and fly with safety in the thickest of fogs, and without the aid of elaborate ground installation.

The most important duty a non-rigid airship can perform is to escort convoys against mines and U-boats in war-time. The fastest convoy moves at about 15 m.p.h. If an airship can cruise for fifty hours or more at 50 m.p.h., with a maximum speed of about 80 m.p.h., she is quite fast enough.

Ballonet Theory and Aerostatics

For every inch the barometer rises or falls, both air and gas contract and expand about 1/30th of the volume of the airship. They also contract or expand approximately 1/500th for each degree F. the temperature falls or rises. The volume of the gas inside the envelope therefore varies with alterations of pressure and temperature.

Air balloons known as ballonets inside the envelope can be inflated and deflated to compensate for these variations.

If the airship rises with ballonets empty, and with air and gas at the same temperature, the gas expands some 1/30th for each 1,000

feet she climbs. Therefore 1/30th of the gross lift is lost. If, however, there is air in the ballonets, no lift is lost. Then air is valved instead of gas. In both cases air is blown into the ballonets.

The safety and controllability of a non-rigid depends on the maintenance of pressure inside the envelope. This is achieved by air-inflated ballonets within the envelope. If the pilot sees that the pressure is rising unduly he can valve air from one or other of the ballonets. If pressure falls he blows in air if need be. Automatic valves are fitted which open at a lower pressure than the gas valves, and non-return valves insure that air does not leak away. When the ship is in the shed or moored out, the ballonets are connected via a hose to an electric blower, for on no account must pressure fall below a certain figure.

If an airship ascends with ballonets empty, gas is valved throughout the climb. On descending, air is blown in to compensate for this loss of gas. The larger the ballonets, therefore, the higher the ship can climb. The ballonets as we have noted may also be used for trimming purposes.

Effect of Pressure on Lift. Ballonets empty

An airship is about to climb to 5,000 feet from her station at mean sea-level, and there is no air in the ballonets. The average height of the barometric pressure at mean sea-level is thirty inches, but for every 1,000 feet the airship climbs, the barometric pressure falls about one inch.

The airship will, therefore, lose about 1/30th of her gas per 1,000 feet, or 5/30ths, that is about 1/6th, when she reaches 5,000 feet. In other words she has lost roughly 1/6th of her lift, less the weight of fuel consumed.

On descending, air is blown in, and she lands with 1/6th of her volume made up of air, and so with only 5/6ths of her original lift, the loss being slightly offset by the fuel consumed.

Pressure and Lift with air in the Ballonets

The airship takes off again, and climbs to the same height. This time air valves instead

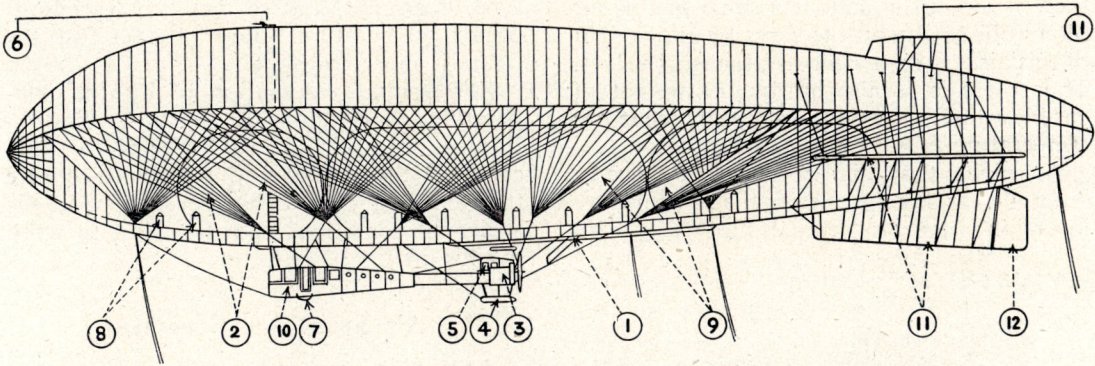

Arrangement of N.S. non-rigid airship, Type No. 7 to 12.

1. Water ballast bag.	2. Internal rigging.	3. Power units.
4. Floats.	5. Engineer's cabin between motors.	6. Gun position.
7. Trail and grapnel ropes.	8. Petrol tanks slung inside envelope.	9. Ballonets.
10. Control cabin.	11. Stabilising Fins.	12. Rudder.

Crew 8; Capacity of envelope 380,000 cubic feet; Overall length 262 feet; Overall height 68 feet 9¼ inches; Overall width 57 feet 9 inches; Motors—two 260 h.p. Fiat; Maximum speed 50 Kts.

of gas, so her lift at 5,000 feet is the same as it was on the ground, with a slight addition for the fuel consumed. Her gas volume has increased by 1/6th, but the air displaced is 1/6th less in weight than it was at mean sea-level. Provided, therefore, there is air in the ballonets an airship can ascend and descend without the lift altering except for the weight of the fuel consumed.

The height at which the ballonets are full of gas is the pressure height and if the airship ascends above this height, gas blows off and so lift is lost.

If the ship is flying at a constant altitude and the barometric pressure rises, both air and gas increase in density and weight. Lift, however, will remain the same, for the volume of air displaced decreases at the same rate as its weight increases.

If pressure falls and there is air in the ballonet, again there is no alteration in lift. The gas expands and air valves, but as the volume of air displaced increases its weight decreases. If, however, there is no air in the ballonet the expanding gas blows off.

Temperature and Lift, Air and Gas Temperatures Equal

So far we have ignored temperature changes, or rather it has been assumed that the temperature of air and gas are the same.

Gases expand and contract roughly 1/500th for each degree F. that the temperature rises and falls. When air and gas temperatures are the same, temperature changes have the same effect on lift as changes in barometric pressure.

If the ballonets are empty and the temperature rises 10 degrees F., 10/500th or 1/50th of the gas is valved; 1/50th of the lift will, therefore, be lost. If, however, air blows off instead of gas, the lift remains the same. Although the volume of air displaced has increased by 1/50th its weight is 1/50th less.

If the ship is in flight and the temperature drops 10 degrees F., then both air and gas are compressed by 1/50th. That volume of air must be blown into the ballonets so the lift is unchanged. Although the air displaced is 1/50th heavier the volume of air displaced is 1/50th less.

Lift when Air and Gas Temperature are different

So far it has been assumed that air and gas temperature are the same. This is seldom the case in practice. Hydrogen is about seven times as good a conductor of heat as air. During the day, therefore, the sun tends to superheat the gas above the air temperature. This causes the gas to expand. If

E

there is air in the ballonets some of this air blows off, so the lift increases by the weight of this air. If there is no air, then gas valves. Thus there is a false lift by the weight of gas blown off. False lift disappears when gas temperature falls.

At night time the reverse may occur. After a clear day there is often a temperature inversion; that is, temperature rises with

Effect of loss of pressure in a non-rigid British coastal airship of *Astra Torres* type, 1915–18.

height instead of falling. This means that the airship may fly in a layer of air warmer than the gas inside the envelope. Thus gas contracts, air is blown into the ballonets and the ship loses lift. This is known as latent lift, for when the gas takes up the same temperature as the surrounding air, lift is regained.

Variations of Temperature with Height

This leads up to the consideration of how the lift is affected by the usual temperature variations with height. Temperatures of both air and gas vary with altitude. The average fall in temperature in the damp atmosphere over Britain is about 3 degrees F. per 1,000 feet. This is known as the lapse rate. Hydrogen, being drier, has a lapse rate of about 5 degrees F. per 1,000 feet. The air figure varies near the ground, especially in daytime. Solar radiation varies with the

type of ground, and so there are variations of air temperature. Over 10,000 feet the figure is more constant.

For accurate estimation of lift the temperature of air and gas must be known. In large ships air and gas thermometers are carried. Slide rules and tables which give the weight of 1,000 cubic feet of air and gas under all conditions help the pilot to work out his lift.

Air Speed and Superheat

An airship superheats more quickly when on the ground or flying slowly, than when moving fast through the air. The aluminium colour of the envelope, by reflecting the sun's rays, helps to keep the gas cooler. A black-coloured envelope such as was used for night work by army airships of 1914–18 was the worst from a flying point of view. Such ships were very sensitive, particularly in hot weather when broken clouds were about.

Times of Starting and Landing

If a long flight entailing a heavy load is undertaken it is usual to start between sundown and dawn. Then there is more lift owing to lower air temperature, and no superheat to cause a loss of gas when rising.

If the ship has been flying high and comes down fast the gas temperature will gain 2 degrees more per 1,000 feet than the air. This will increase the lift. Thus in descending from 4,000 feet, air temperature will increase by some 12 degrees F. by the time the mean sea-level is reached, and the gas temperature may gain as much as 20 degrees. This must be added to any superheat the ship may have started with. This means the valving of a lot of gas when ballasting up to land. A pilot brings a light ship down slowly, to give time for the air and gas temperatures to equalise as much as possible.

With a light ship the time to land is about sunset. The sun has then lost most of its power, but the ground is still radiating warm air, and so reduces the lift when approaching the ground.

A heavy ship lands at such a time as the sun can superheat the gas, thus giving a

*S.S.*40 non-rigid with black envelope for use over the lines in France, 1916. She superheated very quickly owing to the colour of the envelope. The gondola is an adapted aircraft fuselage.

false lift, but before the ground has had enough time to warm up the air. A landing soon after dawn would then be best.

Gas Purity

All the time that an airship is inflated there is a tendency for gas to escape and air to be sucked in. As a result the purity of the gas slowly deteriorates. If the purity of a hydrogen ship falls, say, to 87 per cent., 13 per cent. of the lift has been lost. It is then time to deflate, for when the purity falls to about 85 per cent. there is so much oxygen mixed with the hydrogen, that an explosive has formed. Hydrogen is the lightest known gas, but it is inflammable when pure, and dangerously explosive when mixed with oxygen. The purity can, however, be restored if it has not fallen too low by blowing in large volumes of fresh hydrogen.

Helium has the great advantage of always being safe. It cannot burn or explode. Moreover the gas in helium ships can be purified while the ship is still inflated at a loss of about 10 per cent. of the gas during the process. Helium weighs about twice as much as hydrogen. For design purposes it is best to assume that hydrogen will lift about 65 to 68 lb., and helium about 60 to 62 lb., per 1,000 cubic feet.

Piloting Non-Rigids

The ship leaves the ground with a known weight on board, and a known lift. Air and gas thermometers are fitted, and the barometric pressure and gas temperature are logged. As the ship rises, the pilot keeps a sharp eye on the manometers and pressure gauges. If the pressure rises too much, he valves air, usually from the aft and then the fore ballonet in turn.

In small ships the pilot controls the ship himself, steering with his feet. By his side is an elevator wheel, mounted in a fore and aft direction, which takes the place of the joystick in an aeroplane. Close at hand are the engine controls and draw nobs, or toggles, for working the ballast, air and gas controls.

Airships carry the same instruments as aeroplanes, with the addition of manometers and other forms of pressure gauges, inclinometers and a super-sensitive instrument called the statoscope. A variometer may also be carried, for this gives the actual rate of rise and fall.

In larger airships a steering coxswain, with compass in front of him, steers the ship and keeps her on her course, by a wheel. Close by, the height coxswain has his hands on the elevating wheel. He has a large-scale altimeter, variometer and inclinometer to assist him. The height coxswain has the hardest job, and under bumpy conditions it takes some experience to keep an airship at a given height. All depends on the equilibrium and trim, and the pilot has to keep an eye on those points throughout the flight, as well as on the pressure.

As a ship flies on, she tends to become light through the burning of fuel. A light ship has to be kept from rising by flying down by the bows, so using the motors, which may mean increased engine speed. This in turn increases fuel consumption, with the result that the ship becomes lighter still. When on a long flight, the pilot has to watch this tendency and make use of cloud by day to keep the gas from superheating. Thanks to his knowledge of aerostatics, and to his air and gas thermometers, an airship pilot makes the utmost use of local meteorological conditions. He knows how much fuel the motors are consuming, and therefore the exact weight of his ship, so he can keep a pretty accurate tally of his lift.

Small variations of pressure are countered by the height coxswain and it is often only in landing that air is blown into the ballonets. In small ships, where weight is a consideration, there is no auxiliary blower, and pressure is kept up by lowering an airscoop behind the propeller. In a large ship there is usually a blower worked from either of the motors. Better still, the blower may be driven by a small auxiliary motor and if the main engines should fail, pressure can then be kept up.

Landing

If a large ship has made a flight of any length the pilot must ballast up carefully before landing. He has a pretty good idea of the lift through the feel of the ship, and her angle of flight. He has a record of all weights on board and knows how much fuel he has burnt and how much ballast and gas he has let go. It is a great help if he has ballasted up every few hours while in flight.

The air and gas thermometers and his lift tables and slide rule are of great use in enabling

him to bring his ship down in the correct trim and lift. He obtains the ground pressure and temperature so that he can make allowance for these, brings the ship into the wind, slows down and centralises the controls.

Dynamic lift now disappears, and by watching the statoscope, variometer and inclinometer he finds out the exact static condition of the ship. Ballast or, more probably, gas is valved and air blown if necessary into one or other of the ballonets. The ship is now in horizontal trim and probably a little light.

A wide circle is made, and the ship descends, heading towards the V-shaped landing party. The apex of the V points into the wind. If he comes down on the long bow guys, these trail the ground and are seized by those on the open end of the V. As the car nears the ground the remaining men wait under it to stop it from bumping.

Sometimes the trail rope is dropped about twenty yards ahead of the landing party and from a height of from fifty to a hundred feet. If a trail rope landing is made, the landing party must never run in under the ship, but must keep ahead of her; otherwise her head will be pulled down towards the ground. When a landing is made on the guys, which is usually preferable, these must be run out at right angles to the ship. The pilot must never forget his pressure, and the coxswain must keep the ship dead into the wind and, with the height coxswain, aid the landing party by efficient use of rudder and elevators.

Once on the ground the bow and stern guys are manned, and the car party hold on to the car handling rails. Pressure is built up if necessary and ballast substituted for any of the crew who leave the car. The ship is then walked back to the shed.

Once anchored down in the shed the ballonets are immediately connected up via a fabric hose pipe to an electric blower and a hand known as the gas guard is left on watch. His job is to

Inside car of experimental airship *Eta II* of 1916. Note two motors and steering wheel. Elevator wheel is on port side of steering wheel.

H.M.A. *S.S.Z.55* (semi-rigid) making a trail rope landing, 1918.

see that the pressure is kept within a certain range as ordered.

Mooring of Airships

If an airship is to work away from its shed the problem of mooring out has to be considered. To survive heavy weather, airships must either be pegged down behind trees or in some convenient shelter, such as a chalkpit, or else mooring masts must be provided.

Mast Mooring

The ideal method of mooring out all types of airships to-day is mast mooring, which the Americans have brought to high efficiency. British airship officers, however, were the first to invent and use a mooring mast, and four names deserve to be mentioned: Admiral Sir Murray Sueter, R.N., Air-Commodore E. A. Masterman (late R.N.), the late Wing-Commander C. M. Waterlow, who was a Sapper, and the late Major G. H. Scott, killed in H.M.A. *R.101*, who devised the present masthead and method of handling. Omitting experiments with H.M.A. *No. 1*, with which the first two officers were concerned, as she was a rigid, the first non-rigid to use a mast was H.M.A. *Beta 1*, on 19th February 1912, at Farnborough. Her nose

had been strengthened, and a mooring cable was attached to its extremity. *Beta*, with a crew of three, made a short flight and approached the mast up wind, with the mooring cable trailing on the ground. This cable was shackled to a cable leading out of the cone-shaped top to the lattice mooring mast. The winch, at the foot of the mast, then hauled the ship up to the mast until the ship's nose was safely home in the umbrella-like masthead.

The cone was free to turn, so the airship was always head to wind. *Beta* remained out for about twenty-four hours, a rope-ladder connecting the airship's car to the ground. Only three men kept watch, and no gas was put in.

This was a great step forward, but later experience proved that the ship's nose soon became damaged in gusty weather when the ship had to swing to a variable wind. To remedy this, many other experiments were tried out between 1914 and 1918, until winds of 50 m.p.h. could be ridden out.

In 1920–21 the late Major Scott solved the problem with H.M.A. *R.33* and the American non-rigids use the same basic method to-day. Scott eliminated the masthead cone, substituting a telescopic tubular arm, capable of being pulled in any direction, and topped by a hollow cup. On the ship's nose is a

S.S.Z. ships in a woodland bay, 1918. Natural shelter mooring.

hinged cone hanging downwards and the wire from this cone is shackled to the mast's cable. When the two cables are connected up the airship is pulled down to the mast until the cone can be locked into the cup on the masthead. The airship is then free to

The *R.100* (rigid) moored to the mast at St. Hubert aerodrome, Montreal, Canada.

head into wind, and there is no wear and tear on the airship's nose. The U.S. airships can be taken out of and put into their sheds while still on the mast, and have survived 70 m.p.h. gales while so moored.

Semi-rigid Airships

Semi-rigid airships differ from non-rigid only in that they have a keel between the car or cars and envelope. The first true semi-rigid was the *Lebaudy*, a French ship, which made her first ascent on 13th November 1902 at Moisson. Like the British-built *Alpha*, formerly *Nulli Secundus* of 1907 and 1908, and the German M ships of the same date, the keel was external to the envelope.

With the exception of the *Usuelli*, all the Italian semi-rigids, and the U.S. airship *RS.1*, had their keels either built into the envelope or, if external, slung from internal rigging directly under it. The same was also true of the later French Zodiacs. This greatly reduced drag.

Thanks to the keel the weight of the car is very well distributed and a lower envelope pressure is possible. This means a lighter envelope which largely offsets the keel weight. Bow stiffeners and fins can be built into the keel. The keel, however, is a complication, and is liable to make inflations and deflations more difficult. The Goodyear suspension system has made it possible to construct non-rigids up to at least 750,000 cubic feet, and experienced designers consider that ships of over 1,000,000 cubic feet can be constructed on the non-rigid principle.

The Russians have semi-rigids designed so far as is known on the Italian N class, which were some of the best semi-rigids. At least one of these Russian semi-rigid airships was used successfully during the war. It is believed that a Russian semi-rigid is being employed on a long-distance route as a passenger carrier.

The famous Norwegian polar explorers, Amundsen and Riiser Larsen used an Italian ship, the *N.1*, to explore the North Polar regions in 1926. Their ship, renamed *Norge*, with its designer Nobile as pilot, flew over the North Pole on 12th May of that year. They started from Svalbard, and landed at Teller in Alaska after a flight of nearly four days.

Italo-Norwegian semi-rigid *Norge* at Oslo mooring mast, 1926. The keel is external, but faired into envelope.

S.R.1 (semi-rigid), an Italian M ship bought by Britain, 1918 ; note the rudders carried on outriggers.

Rigid Airships

Rigid airships have no need of ballonets to keep up pressure. Their hull is made up of transverse frames or rings, joined together by longitudinal girders. Between each main transverse frame there is a space called a bay and in each bay is a gas bag. Over the whole streamlined hull is a fabric cover. There is, therefore, an airspace between the outer cover and gas bags. This air space is ventilated, so that the temperatures of air and gas are more equalised, and the draught created when the airship is under way minimises the risk of pockets of gas forming.

Inside the hull there are usually one or more keels which provide access to various parts of the ship and may add to its strength. The heavy weights, such as fuel and water ballast, are spaced along the keel, at the junction of keel and main transverse frames. On the extreme bow is a mooring cone of the same type as that on a non-rigid, and on the

stern are the great stabilising and control planes. Both mooring cone and planes are built into the hull, to obtain the utmost strength for these members. The control car is also built into the hull, and abaft are the small cars, each containing a motor. Those outrigged are termed wing cars, and an engineer is carried in each. The gas bags each have their own valve, usually automatic, and they can also be operated from the control car where all the controls are centred.

The piloting of a rigid is somewhat similar to the handling of a big non-rigid. The main difference is that the rigid pilot has no worries relating to pressure, as the hull itself takes care of this, and there are no ballonets. From an aerostatic point of view a rigid with flabby gas bags is in the same condition as a non-rigid with air in the ballonets, and the same laws apply. To balance this advantage the rigid pilot has to take care not to put heavy loads on his long hull. In other words he must take great

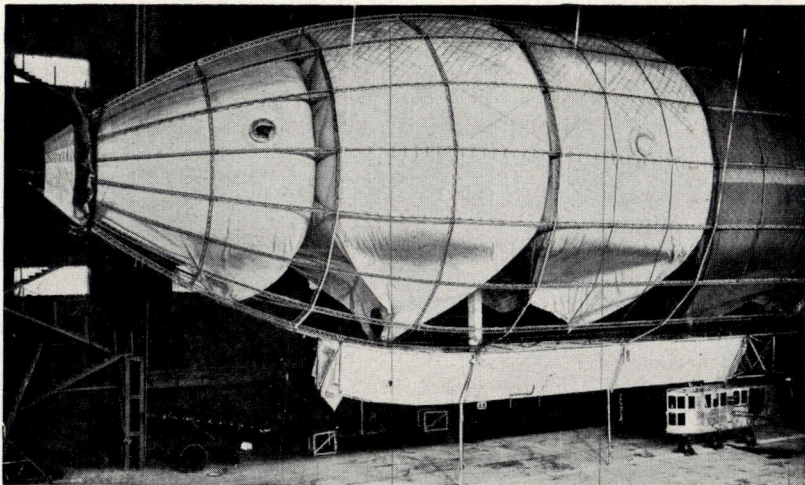

H.M.A. *R.9*, a rigid airship with outer cover removed, showing gas bags, longitudinal and transverse girders, external keel and control car.

Internal keel of Zeppelin *Hindenburg*, with petrol tanks.

care to equalise the loads by taking ballast and fuel from the right tanks. In so doing he keeps his ship in good horizontal trim. Ballast and fuel can be pumped from one part of the ship to another, and the exhaust gases can be turned into ballast which prevents the ship from becoming light.

The German Zeppelins have been the finest rigids constructed so far and the *Graf Zeppelin* and *Hindenburg* between 1931 and 1936 carried out a service across the North and South Atlantic. Their payload was much greater than the largest aeroplanes of to-day, and they gave their passengers vastly superior comfort.

The United States are still interested in airship development, and some details are given below of a projected giant Goodyear rigid :

Volume	10,000,000 cubic feet
Length	950 feet
Diameter	142 feet
Motors	Six 1,050 h.p.
Maximum speed	90 m.p.h.
Normal speed	75 m.p.h.
Crew	60
Payload for 6,000 miles	85,000 lb.

Britain's Contribution to Airships

The last British airship to fly was H.M.A. *R.101*. Since then Britain has done nothing in the airship line. Before closing this article, however, it must be made clear that in the past British airship officers and designers played a leading part. Here is a short list of British contributions to airship design and development.

1906   *Willows I* had swivelling propellers.

1910   H.M.A. *Beta I* first airship moored in pits and the lee of trees.

1911   H.M.A. *R.1* was the first airship to have direct drive and was also the first airship to carry a water recovery apparatus for the manufacture of ballast in flight.

1911–12 Mooring mast for both rigid and non-rigid airships invented and developed in England.

1912   H.M.A. *Beta II* was the first non-rigid airship to have all control surfaces on the envelope.

1913   H.M.A. *Eta* was the first airship to have patch system of suspension.

1913   On 24th August, H.M.A. *Eta* towed H.M.A. *No. 2*. This was the only time that one airship towed another.

1914   First use of airships to convoy ships, and hunt submarines and mines in war-time.

1914   First towing of an airship by a warship—the airship was H.M.A. *No. 3*.

1915   First use of propeller slipstream for pressure control in non-rigid airships thereby saving weight and complication in small-type airships. The airship was the *SS. 1*. This was also the first non-rigid airship to have direct drive.

AIRSHIPS

1915   H.M.A. *Delta* used in first experiment with a transporter mooring mast.

1915   *SS.* airships first to use wheels and take-off like aeroplanes.

1916   *SS.* airships first to land on bow guys i.e. without tail ropes.

1917–18 First experiments with transporter mooring mast and rigid airships.

1918   H.M.A. *R.23* first airship to launch an aeroplane in flight.

1919   H.M.A. *R.34* made a double crossing of the North Atlantic.

1929   H.M.A. *R.101* first rigid airship to have diesel motors.

1930   H.M.A. *R.100* first aircraft of any kind to fly from Britain to Canada and return.

[*Copyright ' Flight '*

The *R.33*, showing fighter aircraft suspended from the hull.

[*Copyright : de Havilland Aircraft Co. Ltd.*

The de Havilland Hornet 2-motor fighter is **among** the world's fastest airscrew - driven aeroplanes.

RADAR IN AVIATION

by

G. O. Lace, D.F.C.

Squadron Leader, R.A.F.

INVENTION MAKES the greatest strides in time of war. Needs must when the Devil drives; and a man, or nation, is never so ready to think out new shifts as when life itself is at stake. With Discovery it is different, for that is a matter of natural growth in highly fertile minds; Invention, which is the application of Discovery to the needs of life, flourishes best when those needs are most insistent; its fruits, however, remain for our use long after the urgency has passed.

So it has been with Radar. The discovery on which it is all based was made in peace-time; but had it not been for the stimulus of war, the development of this new science would not have been so rapid or so extensive. As it is, there exist innumerable Radar devices, capable of anything from the destruction of flying bombs to keeping a ship off an iceberg; but, owing to the speed at which some of them were made, they cannot yet be considered perfect. Those that were made to help, and not to hinder, need little adaptation to the needs of ordinary life; while even those that were designed for destructive purposes may prove useful in some other way.

The glamorous secrecy that shrouded Radar during the war, and the romantic, and often nonsensical, revelations that have followed, have combined to create a false idea in the mind of the ordinary man, who has been left with the impression that this is a subject both more mysterious and more perfected than is the case. What is true of the ordinary man is also true of the ordinary aviator; ask a dozen pilots of assorted vintages what are their views on Radar; some will tell you that it is unnecessary ('We got on without it in the old days') and others will show that they rely on it too much ('Gee packed up, but we got there'). In neither case is the opinion based on much knowledge, owing to the effects of secrecy and hurried training. If one is to have a true picture of the possibilities of Radar in aviation, it is necessary first to get a general idea of how it works, what sort of things it can do, how well it can do them, and what it may reasonably be expected to achieve in the future.

Perhaps the best way to introduce the subject is to give a short account of the main stages by which Radar has progressed from the discovery of the principle itself to the most recent inventions, using as little technical language as possible, and letting brevity do as little violence to the truth as we can. The story will be told, of course, mainly in terms of the air; but we must remember that the uses of Radar are not limited to that element.

All Radar is based on a device known as the cathode-ray tube (hereafter CRT), and you must have an idea how it works. Imagine a radio valve, eighteen inches or so in length, and six to twelve inches in diameter, lying on its side with the top facing you. Inside the tube, at the back (see Fig. 1), is the usual arrangement of filaments and plates, by means of which a stream of electrons is propelled towards the front of the tube. This front is made of fluorescent glass (usually green), and glows when it is 'bombarded' by the stream of electrons, whose presence and behaviour can thus be observed. Now the stream, which leaves the back of the tube as an unruly torrent, can be controlled as it flows along the tube, by means of potentials applied to plates at the sides, so that by the time it arrives at the front of the tube it is canalised into a fine jet of the desired strength, which, as it bombards the fluorescent 'screen', creates a small and well-defined spot of green light. The potentials used to achieve this result are adjusted by the operator by means of two controls known, usually, as 'brilliance' and 'focus'.

Having organised a bright and clear little

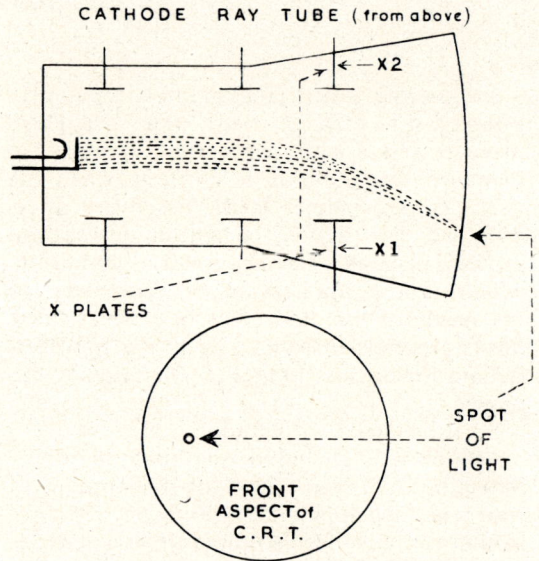

CATHODE RAY TUBE (from above)

Electron Stream

Plates controlling Brilliance and Focus

SCREEN

SPOT OF LIGHT

SCREEN

FRONT ASPECT of C.R.T.

FIG. 1.—Cathode-ray tube.

words, consists of a succession of movements from left to right, so rapid and so frequent as to appear continuous. This line is known as a 'trace', or 'timebase', and the frequency at which the spot crosses the tube is known as the 'trace speed'; this speed is normally many hundreds a second, and is controlled by special valves.

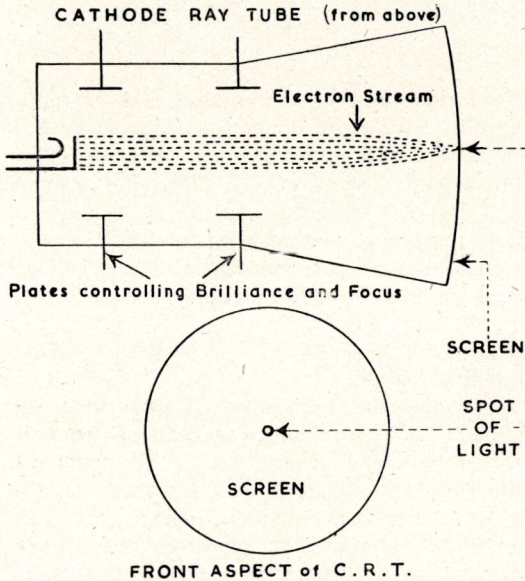

CATHODE RAY TUBE (from above)

X2

X1

X PLATES

SPOT OF LIGHT

FRONT ASPECT of C.R.T.

FIG. 2.—Deflection of electron stream to left of screen.

spot of light in the centre of the screen, the next stage is to fit two more plates inside the tube; these are known as the 'X' plates, and are shown as X_1 and X_2 in Fig. 2. Now if a positive potential is applied to one, and a negative to the other, the electron stream will be attracted by one and repelled by the other, and the spot will move across to one side of the screen. Reverse the potentials, and the spot will nip smartly to the opposite side. If, then, you apply a rapidly alternating current to the plates, the spot will dash from one side to the other so fast that you will not see a spot at all, but a continuous line; the effect is much the same as when you twang a whippy knife. There is one difference, however, in the CRT; for reasons that will appear later, the spot moves back from right to left much faster than it crosses from left to right, and the return movement is not seen by the observer. The line, in other

Similarly we can add two more 'Y' plates, on the upper and lower sides of the tube (see Fig. 3), with the aid of which it will obviously be possible to raise or lower the spot on the screen. By applying a steady potential, instead of an alternated one as in the case of the X plates, we can move the trace itself up or down. Both these methods are used as required.

Now the currents that produce the green spot, control it, and turn it into a trace, are all provided within the set itself, and do not depend upon the reception of signals from outside. But, naturally, Radar systems work by the use of radio signals, and we must consider these next. An ordinary radio signal consists of a continuous wave travelling (at 186,000 miles a second, the speed of light) in all directions from the point at which it is transmitted. A Radar signal consists, on the other hand, not of a continuous wave, but of a series of very short pulses, separated by comparatively long intervals, which are of absolutely even length, thus : — — — — — — — — —. Of course, the whole process is so rapid that when these signals are made visible by a CRT, they appear continuous. The human eye cannot distinguish anything so fast as these separate pulses.

Suppose for the sake of argument that we make a CRT with a trace speed of 100 a second, and a receiver with which we pick up pulses that are being transmitted at the rate of 100 a second, and that last each for 1/1000th of a second. What will happen on the screen? Fig. 4 will help us to see. The spot starts off from the left-hand side of the screen, takes 1/100th of a second to cross over to the right (ignoring the infinitesimal time that is used in the return journey, or fly-back) and repeats this *ad lib*. Now since the pulses from outside are arriving one every 1/100th of a second, it follows that once during each crossing of the screen the

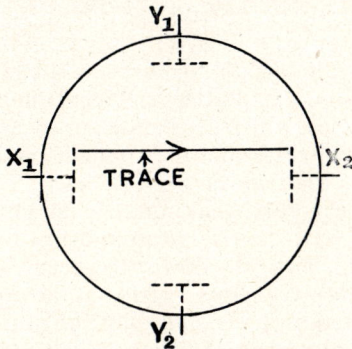

FIG. 3.—Front aspect of Cathode-ray tube with trace produced by X plates, and raised by Y_1. The plates are, of course, not seen by the viewer; their position is shown by — — — — —.

spot will be attracted, for as long as the pulse lasts, towards whichever Y plate the incoming pulses are being fed onto by the receiver. Assuming this to be Y_1, the spot will be deflected upwards, and as the pulses are lasting 1/1000th of a second, this upward deflection will appear on the screen for 1/10th of the length of the trace. Now each individual pulse lasts so short a time that we cannot see the effect of it on the screen;

it is only because the trace speed and the frequency of the pulses are exactly the same that the spot is attracted upwards at the same point of its crossing; so the observer sees no longer a straight trace, but one with

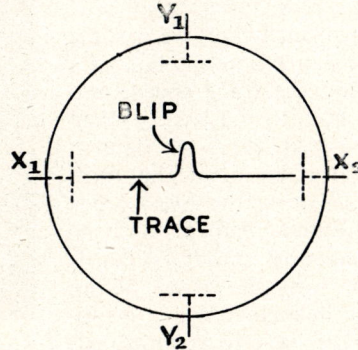

FIG. 4.—Front aspect of Cathode-ray tube with blip produced by pulse on plate Y_1.

a kink in it; the kink appears continuous, just as the trace does; but in reality it consists of a series of kinks, which are occurring at the rate of 100 a second. This kink is called a 'blip'.

Now suppose that the pulses are *not* arriving at exactly the same repetition rate as we intended, but at 101 a second. What happens now? The second pulse after we switch on will reach the Y plate, and attract the spot, a fraction of a second *before* the spot reaches the point of its travel at which it was affected by the *first* pulse, and the third one will come a little earlier still. In other words, the blip will be seen to move very slowly to the left along the trace; when it reaches the left-hand edge, it will disappear and start again on the right-hand edge. If, on the other hand, the pulses were arriving at 99 a second, the blip would move to the *right*. If the pulse repetition rate were too far different from the trace speed, nothing but a continuous blur would appear. It is, in practice, desirable to be able to move the blip to and fro along the trace, and this is accomplished by inserting in the CRT a control which slightly varies the trace speed. If, therefore, we want to move the blip to the left, we twiddle this knob to the left; this has the effect of *de*creasing the trace speed; the pulse rate (over which we have

The bulge under the fuselage of this Avro Lincoln heavy bomber houses the H2S Radar. This type of Radar reproduces a plan of the country over which the aircraft is flying.

[*Photo : Avro*

no control but which we assume to be constant) therefore becomes *faster* than the trace speed, and the blip goes to the left. When we have got it where we want it, we turn the knob to the right enough to bring the two speeds into absolute agreement, and the blip obediently stands still. It won't be long, however, before this very delicate balance is upset, and we have to keep adjusting the trace speed to keep the blip in the desired place.

This is one of the most vital principles of the cathode-ray tube, and if you cannot follow it you cannot understand how Radar works. Before we leave the CRT, however, there are two points of detail that it will be misleading to omit. The first is that, whereas the presentation has so far been described with the trace horizontal, this is not always the case; there are Radar sets with vertical traces and horizontal blips. The second point is that it is not essential to have separate plates at all; if a ring is placed round the inside of the CRT, and the incoming signals are fed onto this by a method that incorporates direction-finding, then the screen will give indications of bearing as well as of distance.

*　　*　　*

This very cursory description of the mechanical means used in Radar enables us to pass next to the practical ways in which it is employed. The main purpose of Radar is to enable someone to find out the position, and other particulars, of something that he cannot hear or see (except in the Radar sense). Now the CRT measures distance by means of time; and the way it does it is best shown by a practical example. Imagine a station equipped with a pulse transmitter, a receiver and a CRT (which, with its attendant controls, is called an indicator), and situated in the middle of a flat desert. When the transmitter is switched on, it will radiate pulses in every direction. The receiver will pick them up and pass them to the Y plate in the indicator, and as long as the pulse rate and trace speed are identical a stationary blip will appear on the screen. The pulses, however, radiating from the station, will strike a cloud or an atmospheric layer, and *bounce back*, again in all directions. (Incidentally, the reason why Radar uses very high radio-frequencies, which are handicapped by having a short range, is that they bounce much more strongly than lower frequencies.) The only part of the pulse that concerns us now is the bit that went vertically up and has bounced, therefore, vertically down, and been picked up by our receiver. It is arriving at the right rate, so it makes a *second* blip on the trace, though a weaker one than was made by the 'direct' signal, and easily distinguishable from it. Of course, this signal can go on bouncing up and down *ad lib*, and as long as it has any strength left in it will produce yet further blips; but the direct signal, and the first reflection are all that we bother with.

Now we can move the direct blip along to the left-hand end of the trace, and make it stand still there; the other blip will of course move with it, as its rate is the same whatever happens. It is next necessary to measure how far along the trace the reflected blip occurs. Let us keep to our trace speed and pulse rate of 100 a second, and suppose that the gap between the two blips (to be exact, between their left hand or ' leading ' edges) is 1/12th of the length of the trace. Then the reflection is arriving 1/1200th of a second after the direct signal, and must have spent half that time in reaching the object from which it has bounced. As we know the speed at which it has travelled (186,000 miles a second) we can easily do the sum. The object is 77½ miles away.

We placed our station in a flat desert, because in practice there would have been reflected blips from other and nearer objects, such as chimneys, hills, boys' kites, and so on. This difficulty can be largely overcome by directing the pulses only into the sector that it is desired to study; even so, skill and experience are needed to interpret the many blips that will appear, and to select the right one or ones to use.

But to obtain the critical measurement of the interval between the blips, estimation or a foot-rule won't do. After all, to be right even within one mile, it is necessary to measure within 1/93,000th of a second, which will amount to precious little in terms of inches on the screen ! So by a highly ingenious circuit, the CRT is made to produce a system of ' calibration pips ' along the trace. A typical display of these pips is shown in Fig. 5, and you will be able to imagine the kind of way in which they are used.

Before we proceed, it must be made clear that the system must be so timed that the spot that makes the trace does not have time to make one complete crossing *before* the reflected blip arrives ; that would wreck everything ; but its prevention is not difficult ; a Radar pulse, travelling to its extreme range and back, can hardly be gone longer than 1/400th of a second. So as long as the trace speed is not faster than that, the spot cannot complete a cycle before the reflected blip returns.

*   *   *

The measurement of the height of the various layers of the atmosphere was, in fact, one of the earliest uses to which the cathode-ray tube, in this its simplest form, was put. The story runs that when, many years before the war, a team of scientists were engaged on this task, they were much

put out to find an unwanted blip that moved about along the trace independently of the ones that, to them, mattered ; it followed that the object from which it was bouncing must itself be moving ; so that one of them, happening to look out of the window, saw an aeroplane flying over, and realised that the intruding blip was reflected from that. In due course it was seen that here was possibly a method of ' seeing ' aircraft that were out of direct sight and earshot ; and, in fact, the immediate results of this were the construction of a chain of Radar stations round parts of our coast, and the stoppage of all mention of the CRT and its uses, except as a military secret. The chain of stations was designed to give notice of approaching aircraft, and an indication of their range, direction and height.

But not, unfortunately, of their intentions. To do this, it was necessary to arrange that friendly and hostile aircraft gave different types of reflection. This was done by fitting into our own aircraft a receiver/transmitter

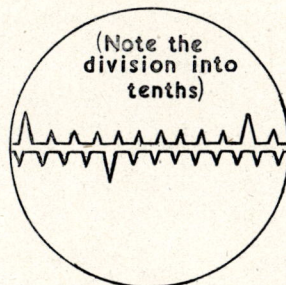

FIG. 5.—Typical show of calibration pips.

which, every time it received a pulse from the ground station, automatically transmitted one of its own, which was much stronger than a mere reflection ; and thus the CRT operators on the ground could tell whether they were dealing with friend or foe. Further, by fitting in the aircraft a means of regulating the *duration* of the signal it sent out, it was possible to arrange that an SOS could be sent by transmitting a longer signal, which appeared as a broader blip on the screen on the ground. The process whereby a signal arriving from outside causes the transmitter to operate automatically is known as ' triggering '.

Naturally, if the enemy had been able to capture one of these responders intact, they could have worked out from it the radio-frequency as well as the pulse-recurrence rate, of the whole system, and have their own aircraft with similar responders; so each set had inside it enough explosive to destroy it in the event of a violent or unpremeditated landing. Or, of course, if a Radar mechanic got clumsy with his fingers; in that case it might be, for him, the last time.

The Battle of Britain was won partly because the men on the ground who directed the defending aircraft (and the guns) had this advance warning of the enemy's attacks, and so had time to put the fighters into the best position to deal with the attackers. The system worked very well by day, but at night the fighters could not be brought near enough to the target to see it; and this difficulty was met by fitting in the nose of the fighter a miniature Radar set, complete with transmitter, receiver and indicator. This equipment (known as AI) had a limited range, so that the procedure was as follows: the ground controller brought the fighter into AI range of the enemy; as soon as the radio observer (AI operator) could 'see' the enemy on his indicator, the controller was informed, and faded out, though he still watched the proceedings on *his* indicator; the observer then guided the pilot on to the target until the pilot could see it with his

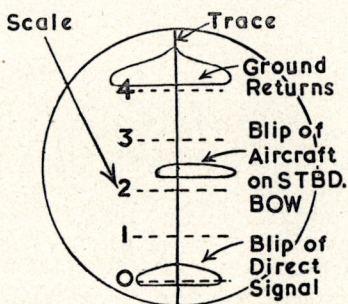

Fig. 6.—Appearance of screen on typical search equipment.

own eyes; the rest was up to him. A successful interception was always regarded as a joint kill by all three men; and, indeed, all three needed to be very skilful to bring one off.

DOTTED LINES = MASKED PULSES
CONTINUOUS LINES = UNMASKED PULSES

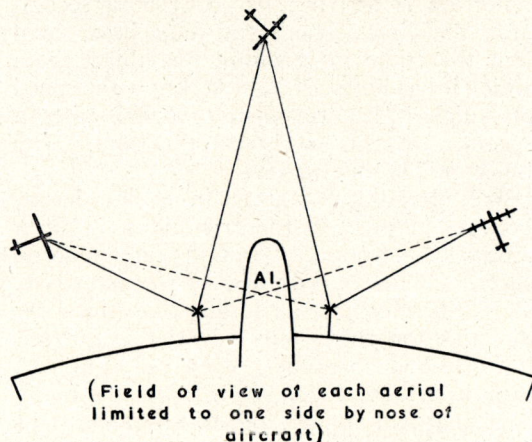

(Field of view of each aerial limited to one side by nose of aircraft)

Fig. 7.—AI. Directional plan of aerials.

As this installation had many features that are fundamental in many types of Radar, we must consider how it worked (see Figs. 6 and 7). The trace was vertical, travelling from bottom to top. The aircraft carried two receiving aerials, one on each side, so placed that pulses coming from the starboard side were picked up by the right-hand aerial only, the left-hand one being masked from them. Similarly, the starboard aerial could not receive the pulses that came from anywhere on the port side. Meanwhile, a switch-motor inside the set connected the starboard aerial to the right-hand Y plate, and then the port aerial to the left-hand Y plate, in rotation; but, as usual, it did it so fast that the eye saw both blips all the time; of course, if the target were on the port beam, there would be no blip at all on the right-hand side of the trace; if it were dead ahead, there would be equal blips on both.

The procedure was then as follows: as soon as the set was switched on, the transmitter sent out pulses which created a direct signal (fixed at the bottom of the trace), and, if they encountered any object in range, a second blip higher up the trace. A printed scale showed the range of the target; the relative strength of the two halves of the blip (left and right) showed whether the target lay to port or to starboard. The operator would order an alteration of course to whichever side was necessary, until the blip was evenly balanced. The fighter was now after its prey, and assuming that it had the higher speed, the blip would be coming slowly down the trace. This was AI in its simplest form; and there was, of course, one object that the pulses were bound to be reflected by; this was the earth, and a great nuisance, too. For if the aircraft was, say, at 10,000 feet, then a very powerful blip would appear at about two miles range on the screen, so powerful as to swamp everything else at that range or higher. In other words, the operator could only see blips from objects that were nearer to the aircraft than the ground was. Low-flying aircraft were therefore practically immune from AI.

This difficulty, of ground returns, was in due course largely overcome; but in passing it should be noted that we have here the germ of the Radar altimeter, which is, in principle, the most simple of all Radar devices. 'Simple' is perhaps an odd word to use of a gadget which, if it is to measure height with an accuracy of ten feet, must be able to measure a fiftieth of a millionth of a second.

*　　*　　*

The AI principle has obvious applications to peace as well as to war; it could be used, for instance, either by ships or by aircraft, to find lifeboats at sea; especially if the latter were fitted with responders on an internationally agreed frequency and pulse rate. But there are two more advanced developments of the idea, which have a direct value to peace-time flying; though, as they were first made under the urge of military need, they are not yet perfected. They are called, 'Rebecca-Eureka' and 'Babs'.

The former of these, 'R-E', consists of two parts. The aircraft carries a transmitter-receiver-indicator, known as Rebecca, which gives to the operator the range and direction of the target in the same way as AI; but a responder beacon, Eureka, sited on the ground at the point to which it is desired that the aircraft shall home, is triggered by the pulses from Rebecca, and sends back pulses of its own, but on a *different* frequency. As Rebecca is therefore receiving and transmitting on two different frequencies, the ground returns are not picked up, and the range is greatly increased. A number of frequencies are available, so that more than one Eureka can be worked at one time in a small area.

This is a very useful idea for homing aircraft to their own bases in bad weather; to make matters easier, the pulses sent out by Eureka can be made to blink, in the morse code, the letters of the airfield, and this should prevent any confusion; it also gives an aircraft that is lost a valuable hint of its rough position. But in war-time it was not so simple; Rebecca-Eureka was devised to meet the requirements of the Airborne Forces, who had to drop men and supplies very accurately for them to be of any use. An Airborne Division scattered over fifty square miles is useless; but put down just where it is wanted, it may be effective. The catch was, of course, that the Eureka itself had to be dropped by parachute, with the men to work it, just before the main force arrived; and the small and select body of paratroops who did this job, and the R.A.F. crews who dropped them, carried between them a heavy load of responsibility for the success of the operation. Eurekas were also provided to the Resistance movements, and used to guide our supply-dropping aircraft.

'Babs' (*B*lind *A*pproach *B*eam *S*ystem) is a refinement of Rebecca-Eureka, and is a landing approach aid. The same installation is used in the aircraft, with the exception that only one receiving aerial is used, the signal being fed to one side of the trace only; it doesn't matter which. The aerial has no directional properties. The ground equipment, however, is much larger and more complicated than Eureka. It consists of a responder-beacon, triggered by the signals from the aircraft. It is placed at the upwind end of the runway (see Fig. 8), and when triggered sends out *two* signals (as usual they appear to be simultaneous but are in fact alternated). One of them, which is of very short duration, is transmitted only into a sector (the 'Dots Sector') which extends from the line of the runway (produced) through about 40 degrees clockwise, so that it fills the air which is on the *left* of an aircraft making a correct straight approach to land. The other, which lasts twice as many

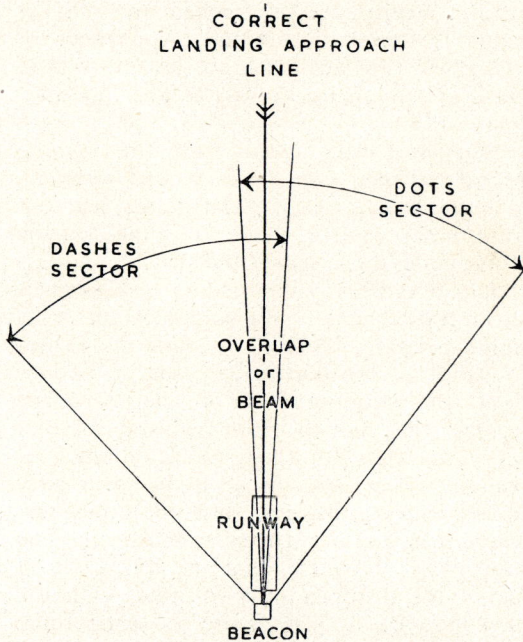

FIG. 8.—System of Babs transmissions. (Width of beam exaggerated.)

millionths of a second, is transmitted into the corresponding area on the right of an approaching aircraft. The two overlap very slightly (by less than one degree) along the approach line, and each spills over a little into the other's sector. The principle is the same as in the original Radio Blind Approach, where the pilot heard dashes when he was on the right and dots when on the left, the two adding up to a continuous signal when he was 'on the beam'. The terms 'dots and dashes' have been retained, but with Babs it is a matter of seeing, not hearing (see Fig. 9).

Since one pulse lasts twice as long as the other, it will appear twice as broad; as the trace is vertical, it may be regarded as *taller*. If the aircraft is on the straight line of approach, or within half a degree of it, both signals will be received at equal strength, and will appear as in Fig. 9 (A), both being of equal amplitude and, of course, at the same range. But if the aircraft is to port of the beam, the dots sector will appear stronger than the dashes, as in Fig. 9 (B). An aircraft can be brought very accurately into its landing position with Babs. But the

indications of range are not considered good enough to justify completely blind landings; these would in any case need a very accurate Radar altimeter; granted *that*, there is no reason why you should not land blind on a runway of 3,000 yards. Two thousand is too short to allow of all possible errors in range.

*   *   *

So far we have been dealing with systems of Radar which have this common characteristic, that they are used to ascertain the bearing and distance of an object; though it may be from air to air, air to ground, or ground to air. There is still a quite different type, perhaps the most difficult to grasp in principle, of which the best example is the famous 'Gee'. This, and similar systems, are not means of homing to one point, but provide the means of homing to *any* point within coverage of the system, as well as continuous and very accurate information on the position of the aircraft. The aircraft carries a receiver and indicator only, all the transmissions being from ground stations.

The CRT differs from others in having

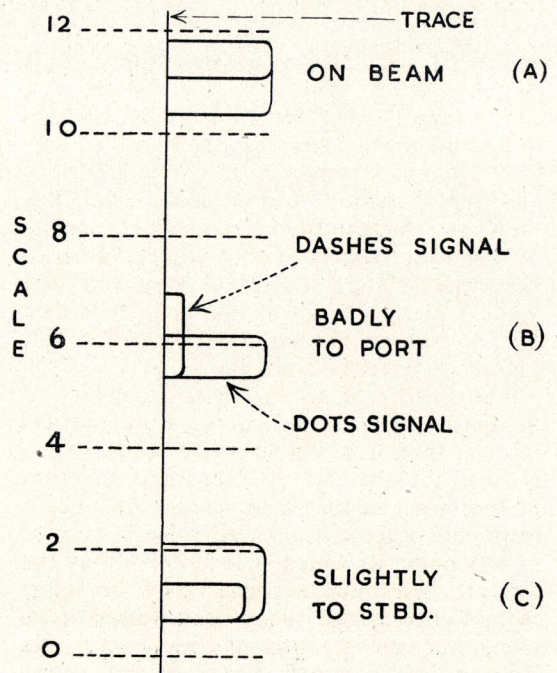

FIG. 9.—Appearance of Babs blips.

two horizontal traces (see Fig. 10). You can see how these are produced. The first time the spot crosses the screen a small but continuous potential attracts it up to the Y_1 plate; but next time the spot is pulled *down* towards Y_2; and so on alternately. As a result the observer sees two horizontal

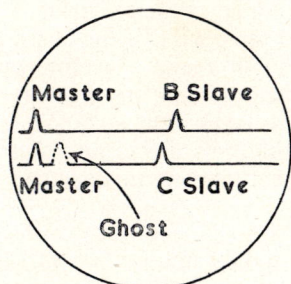

Fig. 10.—Appearance of Gee indicator with Master and two Slaves.

traces. The trace speed is 250 a second; that is, each *single* crossing lasts 1/500th of a second. On the ground a transmitter (the 'Master' or 'A') sends out pulses at the rate of 500 a second. So two blips will appear on the screen, one on each trace, and, as the intervals between them are even, these two blips will always appear exactly above and below each other.

A second ground station (known as the 'B' Slave), which is situated at some distance, say a hundred miles, from the Master, is triggered by the pulses from it, and transmits one of its own after every other one from the Master. So aircraft will now receive three blips in each cycle—two from the Master and one from the Slave. But the alternate Master pulses that do not trigger the B Slave are used to trigger a second, or 'C' Slave. The sequence of blips on the traces will now be Master—B Slave—Master—C Slave, or, more simply: A—B—A—C. The whole thing is so timed that wherever you are you cannot receive the blips in any other order but this.

Now it is easy enough to identify the two Master blips, as they are vertically in line; and if you now move the blips along the trace until the Masters are at the left-hand edge, there is bound to be one Slave, on each trace, on the right of the Master. But it is

still impossible to tell which Slave is which; so after the even Master pulses (the ones that trigger the C Slave), a faint 'Ghost' pulse is transmitted, so that the operator can now separate all four blips without ambiguity. The final arrangement is shown in Fig. 10, the order being: Master—B Slave (on the upper trace)—Master/Ghost—C Slave (lower trace).

The process of obtaining the position of the aircraft starts with measuring (by means of calibration pips) the two time intervals on the traces, Master—B Slave and Master—C Slave. Now the Slave signals left the Slave stations at the moment that the Master signal arrived there; so they can be regarded as indirect signals from the Master. That is to say, what we call a Master blip is made by a pulse that has come direct from the Master station, whereas a Slave blip may be taken as the *same* pulse having travelled via the Slave station, and therefore arriving later; unless the receiving aircraft lay in a straight line with the Master and Slave, beyond the latter, in which case the two would arrive simultaneously.

Now the time interval between Master and Slave can be converted into distance, and we will assume that we have measured an A—B interval as eighty miles. This does not mean that we are eighty miles from anywhere, but that the Slave signal has been eighty miles *further* than the Master. In Fig. 11 you can see that with an aircraft at any of the positions shown, the indirect signal has to go eighty miles further than the direct one to reach it. The same will be true anywhere on the dotted line joining these positions, which is a hyperbola. By plotting on a map the hyperbolæ for all the possible time intervals, a line of position can be obtained; the operator has only to take his reading, with the calibration pips, and then look on his map for the curve that corresponds with the reading he has obtained; and he knows that he is somewhere on that line on the map. The line is infinite in length, and becomes virtually straight at any distance from the ground stations.

But to obtain a fix you need two lines of position that intersect; hence the need for the second Slave.

Fig. 12 shows the pattern of intersecting

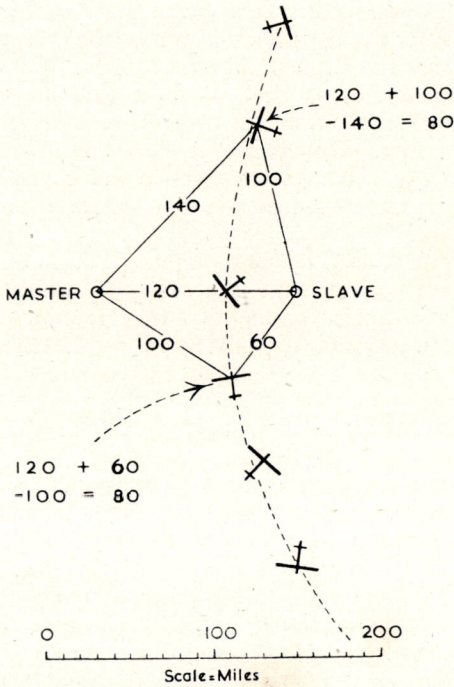

FIG. 11.—Hyperbola joining all points with a distance difference of 80 miles.

hyperbolæ that results from a two-slave 'Chain'. The values given in it are purely imaginary. In practice the curves on the map are given their values in the same units that the calibration pips measure. The dotted lines show what happens if you add a third Slave; how this is done there is no space to show, but you will see that the area with good intersections is very nearly doubled. The siting of the transmitters is a very tricky business. The best range is achieved by placing them on the tops of hills; but the best hills may not be conveniently situated to make a good pattern of hyperbolæ; and may be quite unsuitable for housing the people who have to look after the equipment.

There is a second way in which Gee can be used. If instead of arranging the blips as you have to for a fix, and then taking readings from the calibration pips, you reverse the process, and having ascertained from the map the values of the point to which you want to fly, set the calibration pips to these figures, and then manœuvre the air-

craft so as to bring the blips into alignment, you can home to any desired place within the coverage of the chain. It is not as easy as homing to a Beacon, but it is simple enough, and can with practice be brought to a very high degree of accuracy. In this connection, if the Master and Slave were placed very close to one another, the curves would become almost straight lines all pointing to the centre of the chain; and such a system might make a useful approach aid to an airfield if for any reason the better service that Babs, for instance, gives, were not available, or if homing were required from longer ranges than Babs can give.

*   *   *

These are only one or two of the varieties of Radar that exist, but they are typical ones, and between them they illustrate the principal ways in which Radar has developed, and also show what are the main possibilities for the future. It is easy to see how aviation can make use of the three principal types that I have described, which may be classified as Ground Control, Approach Beacons and Hyperbolic Navigation. But the reader must remember that Radar is not the only

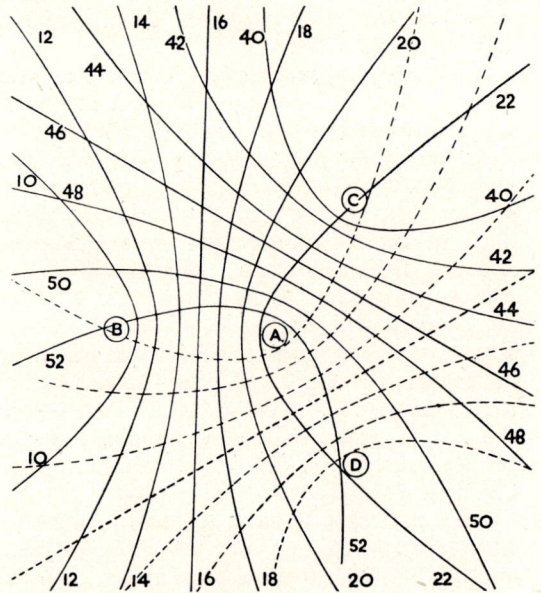

FIG. 12.—Pattern of hyperbolæ intersecting, with two Slaves. The dotted lines show the effect of adding a third Slave.

pebble on the beach, and that there are other branches of ordinary radio that may be more suitable for certain purposes. It is quite likely that the landing aid, for instance, that will be selected as standard will not be a Radar installation at all.

For there are certain drawbacks to Radar that will count for more in peace than they did in war. There is first of all the matter of cost. In war-time, it was worth putting a thousand pounds' worth of Radar into a bomber if it was going to make sure of doing many times that amount of damage to the enemy; and the loss of bomb-load was made up for in the same way; it is better to drop 2,000 lb. of bombs on the target than 2,500 off it. But a civil operator sees things differently; the payload is his constant care; and every 100 lb. of extra equipment means that much less paying cargo. The necessity, at present, to carry a separate operator, usually a navigator, for the Radar, involves the double expense of wages and the loss of a passenger.

Further, Radar is still in a state of development, and a civil operator can hardly be expected to install costly and heavy equipment in his aircraft when he knows that in a short time it may be obsolete, or produced in a lighter form; especially as the number of 'boxes' required is quite large, and any one of them may become out of date at any time. In any case it is no use to install any equipment at all unless you can be assured that the corresponding ground services will be laid on everywhere, and retained for an economic length of time. As far as long-range air traffic is concerned, this means a measure of international agreement that is not yet in being.

Lastly, from the pilot's point of view, Radar appliances suffer from one principal disadvantage; it is, at present, necessary for the indications of the CRT to be passed verbally from the operator to the pilot; not only does this call for a very high measure of mutual confidence, which is rare though attainable, but it also introduces a time-lag which cannot be avoided, and which becomes more serious as aircraft become faster. Both these snags will be partly overcome when the CRT can be made to animate dials on the pilot's dashboard;

[Photo : John Stroud

Airport approach radar aerials on the nose of a British Overseas Airways' Avro Tudor I.

and this development is on the way. After all, imagine yourself to be piloting an aircraft above 10/10ths cloud. The operator tells you that you are now in between the mountains that you know lie on either side of your destination, and that therefore you can come down through the clouds. His confidence is based on Radar alone. Would you feel comfortable in doing what *he* says is safe ? Wouldn't you rather see for yourself on a dial in front of you ? You may in the end obey him, but unless you trust him in a way that very few crews have reached, you will hesitate for a few seconds, and you are travelling between 100 and 200 yards in each of them.

In short, until this happy state of confidence in Radar becomes general among pilots, and the economic risks that must now deter the airline operator are removed, the future of Radar in civil aviation will rest on no healthy foundation.

*   *   *

But where there is a will there is a way, and we will suppose that all these difficulties are going to be overcome before very long, and proceed to consider in what ways Radar can contribute to the fulfilment of the prime needs of aviation, which are, presumably, safety, speed, regularity, punctuality and comfort.

Let us take safety first. A world-wide network of Radar stations on the ground, by keeping continuous watch on the movements of aircraft, will do much to prevent them from colliding with each other or with obstructions to flying. With the increase in air traffic that is going to come, collision will be a possibility, and a disturbing one, at all times. In the denser traffic that will occur around an airport, aircraft will be under close control by an officer who will have the traffic pattern, reported by Radar, always before him, and who will therefore be able to organise landings and take-offs so as to cause the least possible delay and vexation in the air. On the ground, the pilots of aircraft, who may have been brought down in complete fog, will need to be guided to their allotted place on the apron by another controller, again assisted by Radar. It is no use being able to land in blind conditions if you can't taxi in them too.

Before we leave the subject of safety, we should mention the possible use of Radar to assist meteorologists in their work. This service would be linked up with the network of aircraft plotting stations, which would have a third task in organising the rescue of aircraft forced down. A start has already been made in the organisation of this triple service in the North Atlantic area; its extension may proceed as fast as goodwill, equipment and skilled men become available; the first of these three will be the hardest to provide.

Meanwhile, in the air, the pilot will have means of keeping very accurately to his allotted track, without requiring to see the ground or to talk to anybody down there; he will also be able to receive warning of the proximity of other aircraft or of dangerous storms; and with the aid of beacons on the ground he will be enabled to make safe approaches and landings even in fog conditions.

By speed, which we gave as the second great need of air traffic, we mean not the speed of the aircraft alone, but the rapidity of the journey from door to door. The faster aircraft become, the more annoying will seem each minute lost in hanging about on the ground or in the air. This is one of the most difficult problems that faces the future organisers of air traffic, and one that Radar can help to solve in so far as its use will permit a more rapid handling of movements. This, of course, is closely bound up with the regularity of services, and with their punctuality. Both of these are very important, as no airline, at any rate none that depends on results to get customers, will ever build up goodwill without proving itself second to none in these two particulars.

Unfortunately, none of the essential preliminary steps towards establishing the basic services can be taken until agreement is reached between the nations on what form they are to take. This great task will be undertaken by the International Civil Avia-

The array of aerials on the nose of this German Messerschmidt Me 262 night fighter was used for night interception by Radar.

[*Photo: John Stroud*

FLIGHT REFUELLING

by

John Stroud

A MAJOR problem of aviation is that of getting an aeroplane into the air safely with a large payload and also with sufficient fuel for a long-distance non-stop flight.

The needs for long-distance flights without landing for fuel are numerous. In commercial air transport it is necessary to fly long non-stop trans-ocean flights such as those on the North Atlantic routes. Although very long stages on air routes are not desirable simply for their own sake, elimination of landings saves a lot of time, frequently as much as the entire flying time for the whole journey. The elimination of landings reduces fees payable for landing at airports and customs clearance, reduces the number of staff necessary along the routes, removes many immigration and customs formalities for the passengers and, as the few accidents to transport aircraft normally happen during take-off and landing, there is an increase in safety. For war, it is frequently necessary to fly great distances without landing in order to photograph or bomb enemy territory.

An aeroplane can carry a much greater load in the air than it can safely lift off the ground under normal take-off conditions. With increasing weights of aircraft, and the ensuing increase in wing loadings (the part of the total weight of an aeroplane in pounds supported by each square foot of wing), it has become necessary to consider seriously methods of assisted take-off.

Various methods of assisting aircraft into the air have been developed. The Wright brothers were the first to introduce assisted take-off in 1904 (following their original flight in 1903) when they found their first airfield at Dayton was too small.

One way of assisting an aeroplane into the air is by mounting it on top of a more powerful, but lightly loaded aircraft and then releasing it in the air. This was tried successfully in experimental transatlantic flights in 1938 in the form of the Short-Mayo Composite aircraft which consisted of a seaplane, the *Mercury*, which was assisted into the air on the back of a large flying-boat, the *Maia*. This method of assisted take-off is described elsewhere in this book. The idea of placing one aircraft on top of another in order to increase the range was not new at that time, for during the 1914–18 war a single-seat fighter aircraft capable of rapid climb but without a wide radius of action was mounted on the top wing of a reconnaissance flying-boat which had long range, but poor climbing qualities. The flying-boat used to take-off and patrol while carrying the fighter and, when an enemy Zeppelin was sighted, the fighter was released to climb rapidly and intercept the enemy. Although this early experiment and the Short-Mayo Composite were for very different purposes, the solution was related.

Assisted take-off by means of rockets has been used extensively. In this case rockets are fired during the take-off run and these have the effect of increasing the power of the aircraft and thereby the thrust, which in turn gives greater acceleration, a shorter take-off run and steeper climb—rockets do not help to reduce the wing loading. Rockets, rejoicing under the names RATOG (Rocket Assisted Take-Off Gear) in Britain, and JATO (Jet Assisted Take-Off) in the U.S.A., were used during the war to help naval aircraft to leave the decks of aircraft-carriers and were used on aircraft ranging from single-

seat fighters to large 4-motor bombers and flying-boats. In Central America the airline TACA has used rockets to assist Douglas D.C. 3 airliners into the air on taking off from small aerodromes at high altitude and American Airlines has used this method of assisted take-off on its Douglas D.C. 4 freighters in Mexico.

Catapult-assisted take-offs were a regular feature of the Royal Air Force Displays at Hendon between wars and this type of assistance has been used widely on ships.

So far the most practicable method of enabling an aeroplane to carry a greater load than it can lift from the ground safely is flight refuelling, in which method the aeroplane takes off from the ground or water with its full payload and sufficient petrol for flight until it has taken on its main petrol supply from another aircraft flying alongside on the initial stage of its journey.

The Beginning

Flight refuelling experiments were begun towards the end of World War I, and they have been carried on almost continuously ever since. During the late 1920-early-1930 period, flight refuelling was used largely in the United States by people attempting to set up endurance records, but although numbers of them succeeded it is doubtful whether they contributed much to the development of this important aspect of aviation.

In Britain it was Sir Alan Cobham who foresaw the great possibilities of refuelling in the air and in 1932 he began a series of experiments with de Havilland 9 and Handley Page W 10 aircraft, using very crude equipment. This work was continued throughout 1933 and in 1934 Sir Alan Cobham and Squadron Leader Helmore attempted to fly non-stop from England to India in an Airspeed Courier monoplane. After taking off from Portsmouth the Courier was successfully refuelled from a Handley Page W 10 and a second flight refuelling was made from another aircraft of the same type which took off from Malta. Shortly after the second refuelling had taken place a defect in the throttle linkage of the Courier caused a

STAGES IN FLIGHT REFUELLING.
1. The tanker approaches below and behind the receiver.
2. The receiver trails a line from its tail.
3. Contact has been made, the tanker now above as the hose is hauled into the receiver.
4. The hose has been made fast and petrol is now flowing into the receiver's tanks.
5. The breakaway commences, vapour can be seen flowing away from the junction.
6. The hose is released from the receiver but is still attached by the line.
7. Separation completed, the receiver continues on its way.

[*All photographs by John Stroud*

forced landing to be made and the aircraft just managed to stretch its glide to Malta. The Courier had a normal weight of 3,900 lb., but when flight refuelled could carry an increase of 1,600 lb. Although the non-stop flight had to be abandoned, flight refuelling had proved itself and Flight Refuelling Ltd. was formed to continue experiments and development.

An intensive series of experiments was undertaken in the winter of 1935, a large number of air to air refuellings being made.

Commercial Trials

In 1937 a series of seventeen experiments took place when the *Caledonia* long-range C-class flying-boat of Imperial Airways was refuelled in the air over Southampton Water, mostly during extremely bad weather. Following these tests Flight Refuelling Ltd. carried out further trials for thirty days with two of its aircraft. This series of tests was completed to a planned schedule.

During July 1939 further trials were undertaken with a modified C-class flying-boat when the *Cabot* was refuelled by a Handley Page Harrow tanker. Later a Harrow tanker was positioned at Rineanna (now Shannon Airport) and another was stationed in Newfoundland at Gander in preparation for the first series of scheduled transatlantic experiments using flight refuelling. On 5th August, the Imperial Airways flying-boat *Caribou* left Southampton for New York making calls at Foynes near Rineanna, at Botwood near Gander and at Montreal. The *Caribou* was refuelled in the air after taking-off from Foynes. This flight was the first of sixteen scheduled for the season and made by the *Caribou* and the *Cabot*. The flying-boats were successfully flight refuelled by the Harrows after leaving Foynes on the westbound flight and Botwood on the eastbound journey. The payload of the modified C-class flying-boat when flight refuelled could be increased by 7,000 lb.

War stopped further commercial experiments, but flight refuelling was not abandoned. The next phase came with a request for help from the United States Government. The project was to increase the range of the

[*Photo : John Stroud*

The receiver shown from above. The white line painted along the top of the aircraft was used as a guide line during early night refuelling tests.

Boeing B 17 Flying Fortress to 5,800 miles while carrying a full war load. This was achieved.

The company was later given a contract to equip one thousand Avro Lincoln and Lancaster bombers with the necessary apparatus for flight refuelling in order to enable them to fly with bomb loads over the great distances entailed in Pacific war operation. This project was never completed as the progress of the war against Japan made the whole scheme unnecessary.

The Present Day

In 1946 a series of scheduled tests was undertaken to the orders of the British Government. The use of flight refuelling

[*Photo: John Stroud*

View of the receiver from the nose of the tanker in the position maintained for initial contact.

can only be accepted by airline operators provided that the whole process is 100 per cent. reliable in all weathers, both by day and night. Throughout the summer and autumn of 1946 and continuing to the end of the year regular trials were conducted in all kinds of weather, by day and night and at varying heights and speeds. In order to ensure that these trials were carried out impartially the crews of the receiver aircraft were always supplied by the British South American Airways Corporation.

Equipment had by this time been highly developed, interception was made by radar and the contact and actual refuelling were both made by simple and foolproof methods.

[*Photo: John Stroud*

This view of the receiver taken from the nose of the tanker shows the position of the two aircraft maintained throughout the operation of passing fuel.

Equipment

The aircraft used for these tests were converted 4-motor Avro Lancaster bombers.

The equipment installed in the receiver aircraft weighs about 300 lb. and consists of (1) a windlass driven by the aircraft's hydraulic system; (2) a 250-foot length of 15-cwt. hauling line to the end of which is attached a sinker weight and pawl grapnel. This line is covered with hemp apart from a section seventy feet long, adjacent to the sinker weight, which section is bare. The hauling line terminates in a weak link composed of six inches of 3-cwt. cable, which is in turn attached to a weak link line—this is 250 feet of 5-cwt. cable; (3) tanks for containing the petrol taken on; (4) fuelpipes from the tail reception coupling to the tanks and (5) an operators' panel.

The tanker has to carry extra fuel tanks from which to supply the receiver, hose drum reel unit and operators' cabin, all of which are housed in the bomb bay of the Lancaster. The drum is driven by a hydraulic motor powered from the aircraft system. The tanker also carries line-throwing gun, projectile and line.

The Refuelling

Tests have shown that the tanker aircraft must be in position on the receiver's route and ahead of the receiver—if the heavily-laden tanker is behind the receiver before interception the time taken to regain position is excessive. The receiver 'homes' on the tanker by using radar. On interception the receiver trails its hauling line and sinker weight, the tanker takes up a position to starboard of the receiver and slightly behind and below, and on instructions from the tanker pilot the tanker's fuel operator fires the line-throwing gun which is aimed forward at an angle of $41\frac{1}{2}$ degrees to port. The receiver's hauling line forms an arc across which the tanker's projectile and line falls. Sliding down the hauling line the projectile engages the pawls of the grapnel and contact has been made. The initial contact is made by the bare line of the tanker and the bare section of the receiver's hauling line, thereby

[*Photo : S.B.A.C.*

Flight refuelling in being. The tanker is on the right.

neutralising any difference in electrical potential between the two aircraft and eliminating any danger from static.

Having made contact, the throwing line and hauling line are wound into the tanker where the throwing line, projectile and grapnel are removed and the hose attached. The hose is then run out and the receiver operator winds it in and makes it fast in the reception coupling where it is held under pressure. When the hose has been made fast the tanker is signalled and petrol is allowed to flow from the tanker, which has climbed above the receiver so that gravity may transfer the fuel from one aircraft to the other.

Should an emergency arise the hose can break free from the receiver's coupling as soon as the pressure exceeds 1,400 lb.; it can, of course, be released by the receiver operator.

The initial contact normally takes about five minutes, after which fuel passes at about 100 gallons a minute.

[*Photo : John Stroud*

The tanker pilot's view of the receiver while fuel is being passed.

[*Photo : Charles Brown*

A Flight Refuelling Handley Page Harrow refuelling the Imperial Airways Short C-class flying-boat *Cabot* over Southampton Water during tests prior to flight refuelled mail services across the North Atlantic in 1939.

The Breakaway

When refuelling is complete the hose is released from the receiver and paid out attached to the hauling line until the weak link line appears (this is painted in distinctive colours), then the tanker pilot breaks formation and the strain on the line breaks the weak link. The hauling line is wound in to the receiver which continues on its journey while the hose, which is steadied by a drogue, is wound into the tanker. The breakaway takes about ten seconds.

Before and after passing fuel the whole system is flushed with nitrogen to eliminate any danger of fire.

Speed, Height and Temperature

Refuelling in the air with Lancaster aircraft has been successfully undertaken at speeds varying from 150 m.p.h. to 190 m.p.h. indicated air speed.* The higher figure is equal to 260 m.p.h. true air speed at 20,000 feet or 311 m.p.h. at 30,000 feet. Lancasters have been used for experiments up to 23,000 feet and in temperatures as low as —20 degrees Centigrade. Later equipment makes the operation possible at greater speeds and altitudes and in temperatures down to —30 degrees Centigrade.

The Future

At the time of writing, a series of London–Bermuda tests with B.S.A.A.C. has recently been completed and North Atlantic tests with B.O.A.C. are about to begin.

* The indicated air speed is that shown on the air-speed indicator on the instrument panel. This figure is accurate at sea-level, but is inaccurate at any height above sea-level. The true air speed is equal to the indicated air speed divided by the air density at that height. To ascertain true air speed, add 8 per cent. at 5,000 feet; 16 per cent. at 10,000 feet; 37 per cent. at 20,000 feet and 64 per cent. at 30,000 feet.

A Pan American World Airways Constellation Clipper.

[*Copyright : Lockheed Aircraft Corporation*

Copyright : Consolidated Vultee Aircraft Corpor

The 6-motor United States Army Convair XB–36 long-range bomber.

THE LITERATURE OF FLIGHT

For I dipt into the future, far as human eye could see,
Saw the Vision of the world, and all the wonder that would be;
Saw the heavens fill with commerce, argosies of magic sails,
Pilots of the purple twilight, dropping down with costly bales;
Heard the heavens fill with shouting, and there rain'd a ghastly dew
From the nations' airy navies grappling in the central blue.

TENNYSON—Locksley Hall, 1886

yright : Vickers-Armstrongs Ltd.

The Vickers Viking provides British services to the European capitals.

THE LITERATURE OF FLIGHT

Wha kens perhaps yet but the warld shall see
Thae glorious days when folk shall learn to flee;
When, by the powers of Steam, to onywhere,
Ships will be biggit that can sail i' the air
Wi' as great ease as on the waters now
They sail, an' carry heavy burdens too,
What else are thae balloons, contriv'd of late,
But th' art o' fleeing in its infant state.

ANDREW DUNCAN, 1826

[Copyright: 'Flight']

Pioneers at Shorts, 4 May 1909. Left to right: The owner of Mussel Manor, then the home of Short Brothers and the Aero Club, Oswald Short, Horace Short, Eustace Short, Frank McClean, Griffith Brewer, Hedges Butler, Dr. Lockyer and Warwick Wright. Front Row: Moore-Brabazon, Wilbur Wright, Orville Wright and the Hon. C. S. Rolls.

PIONEERS WHOM I HAVE KNOWN

by

C. G. Grey

Founder and for many years Editor of 'The Aeroplane'. Editor of
Jane's 'Aircraft', 1916–41.

WRITING ABOUT pioneers suggests that two points must be settled at the start, (*a*) 'What *is* a pioneer?', as Mr. Handley's friend Naïve used to say, and (*b*) 'It all depends on what you mean by a pioneer', as Professor Joad would certainly say.

The answer, ordinarily, to the question is that a pioneer is a man who starts, or is in at the start of, a new movement, and generally loses in it all the money he ever had. The United States, until quite lately, were pervaded by old, old men who lived in shacks on hillsides overlooking prosperous cities,

and claimed that all that wealth belonged to them, because they were 'first over the divide'. They were the pioneers. But there were also the more able or more energetic, or less honest, men who followed them and bought or stole the land in the valleys and were the pioneers of new cities or new industries, and lived prosperously on their well- or ill-gotten gains—which thing, as the Bible says, is an allegory.

What is meant by pioneers for the purposes of this article is quite difficult to define. They might be the first men who flew,

99

A Pan American Airways D.C. 4 Clipper.

[Copyright: *Douglas Aircraft Co. Inc.*

certainly the pioneers of flying. They might be the first men who made flying-machines on which the pioneer pilots flew. They might be the first men who made flying-machines *and* flew them.

Then the first men who made aeroplanes and sold them were certainly the pioneers of the aircraft industry, which cabinet ministers have told us employed more workpeople than did any other industry in the war of 1939–45. Or, and probably more important in a way than all the rest, there are the pioneers of service flying, without whom we should have had no Royal Air Force, and consequently no victory, and logically no need for this book or this article.

The choice is wide, and I could write a book on each class, if those who were killed or maimed for life, or who just failed to stay the course or make the grade, were included. And here I think that we ought to acknowledge our debt to those who died or failed, for they also contributed to the success of flying. Some of them by dying enabled others to discover facts which led to making flying less dangerous. Frankly, I cannot understand why anybody who went up in an aeroplane before 1914 is alive to-day, so flimsy and unstable were the machines, and so ignorant were the designers and builders. And yet there are hundreds of us still alive and many of us still flying, and liking it.

So with those preliminary remarks let us get on to the individual pioneers who started in the earliest days.

The First of the Pioneers

Without doubt the pioneers of pioneers were the Wright brothers, Wilbur and Orville, of Dayton, Ohio, U.S.A. Although Dayton is Middle West, the Wrights always struck me as typical Yankees of the New England type from the North-Eastern States, who are the only true Yankees. Wilbur was long and thin and lantern-jawed, and silent. He died of fever in 1912. Orville (who died in February 1948) was short and round-faced and, though a quiet man, was not so much like an oyster. I cannot claim to have known them well, but I remember Wilbur, when they were both being entertained by our Aeronautical Society

(not yet Royal) after they had been flying here and on the Continent, excusing his silence by saying that the parrot was the bird which talked most and flew least. And certainly Wilbur flew most. Orville had a bad crash in 1910 or so, and flew very little afterwards.

The Wrights were brought over here in 1909 by Mr. Griffith Brewer, a well-established patent agent in London, who went to the States to see them about watching their patents in Europe, and, through that connection became one of our own pioneers, in that as a passenger with Wilbur Wright in 1908 in France he became the first Englishman to fly. I may add that Griffith Brewer himself became a pilot in 1914 in the United States, gave up flying, and started again in 1929 when he was about sixty years of age.

The sad thing about the Wrights was that the type of aircraft on which they made those first flights—sometimes called engine-assisted, catapulted hops—was so difficult to fly that by 1914 it had faded out of existence, because it was a 'dead-end' design which nobody could develop.

A more successful pioneer was Glenn Curtiss, also very much a New England type, who had the dryest and neatest type of humour. He had been a successful motor-cycle racer and built his own engines. That put him in touch with a syndicate started by Dr. Graham Bell (Edison-Bell telephones and phonographs) of Baddeck, Nova Scotia. With two young Canadians, McCurdy and Baldwin, and Lieutenant Selfridge of the United States Army, they started to build experimental aeroplanes in 1908 at Hammondsport, New York, where Curtiss had his works. The work must have been sheer joy, for they all regarded it as the most serious thing in the world and the greatest fun. Anyhow, 'Casey' Baldwin got off the ground on their first machine in 1909, the first to get off by its own power. It sat down hard and broke up, but it did get off.

'Casey' told me all about it thirty years later, when he had become an affluent business man and was over here to do trade. He still thought it was great fun. McCurdy also did well, and in the war of 1939–45 was a valuable asset to aircraft production in Canada. So there were two pioneers who

made good, although they practically dropped out of aviation after about 1914.

Glenn Curtiss was the most successful of all the first-grade pioneers. I met him at the world's first flying meeting at Rheims (France) in August 1909, when he won the Gordon-Bennett Cup for speed, and beat all the Frenchmen, who were supposed to be the only people who knew anything about flying at that time. I remember Glenn sitting in his tent-hangar with his machine, and a couple of very Yankee-type mechanics, being very polite to hordes of people who, like me, came around asking silly questions. Remember, none of us knew anything about aeroplanes in those days—even less than our great scientists do to-day. One journalist pushed in and asked, 'Mr. Curtiss, do you think anyone could fly up to 1,000 feet?'—which sounded a colossal height then. Glenn smiled his rather tired smile and drawled, 'Getting *up* to 1,000 feet is dead easy', leaving the questioner to answer himself about getting down. I let out a vulgar hoot of laughter, and from that day to his death Glenn and I were the best of friends.

In 1912 Curtiss designed and built the first flying-boat and brought it over here. Lieutenant John Porte, R.N., one of our naval pioneers, became interested in it, and, during the war of 1914–18, developed from the Curtiss America boats the Felixstowe 'F' boats, from which all our great flying-boats of to-day are the lineal descendants. A big book could be written about that too. I may add that the Curtiss boats and little J.N. trainers, called 'Jennies', were sold in large numbers to this country.

The Curtiss aircraft firm became fabulously wealthy, and Glenn with it. He retired to Florida and made more wealth out of real estate. He died there when under fifty

M. and Mme. Blériot.

years of age—a great loss. But the Curtiss-Wright firm became one of the greatest in the world.

Naturally the U.S.A. produced many pioneer pilots, a high percentage of whom were killed 'chucking stunts'. A stunt has been defined as something which is difficult to do, and not worth doing when done. But one of them whom I came to know later on, in 1924, has done very well for himself and is a millionaire, in either dollars or pounds, many times over. Glenn Martin (queer how the unusual name Glenn crops up) was a youngster in California and he had a mother who doted on him—and still does, I am glad to say, at the time of writing. He built himself a pusher-biplane, very much of the Curtiss type, and took it out barnstorming. That is a word that became general in the U.S.A. for exhibition flying and what we call joy-riding. It comes from the old travelling theatrical companies who played in village barns.

About 1916 he had built up a nice manufacturing business and in 1924, when I met him, he had a big factory at Cleveland, Ohio, on the Great Lake Erie. From there, a few years later, having landed some big Navy contracts, he moved to Baltimore, Maryland—near enough to the Navy Yard in Philadelphia to be in touch when he wanted, and far enough away not to be everlastingly bothered by inspectors out for an airing and a few free meals. There he built the big Martin Clipper flying-boats, and the Marauders and Baltimores and other very good landplanes for this war.

There are many more United States pioneers whom I know and on whom I should like to discourse. There was Charles Lawrence, a rich young man who spent a lot on making radial air-cooled engines, and got his money back—much to his surprise

—when the Wright company bought up his patents and designs, and from them developed the Wright Whirlwinds and Cyclones. Then there was Grover Loening, a member of New York's top social set—the 400 as it is called—who happened to be also a top-level engineer. He built amphibian flying-boats which were used for dangerous explorations on and around the otherwise unexplorable lakes in the Rocky Mountains. Grover always had the best of everything. He was over here about 1938, and on our way back from somewhere at night in a very fast 25 h.p. saloon car which I had at the time I was doing some rather fancy traffic driving, when Grover remarked, ' Yes ! These little cars are very handy in traffic.' I could have slapped him. Eventually he became Aeronautical Adviser to the U.S. Government.

The French Pioneers

Two men stand out among the French pioneers—Blériot and Farman. I will not claim either as a personal friend, but I knew them both slightly. Farman was English by descent. His father was the *Daily Telegraph* representative in Paris round about 1890–1900. Blériot was French of the French. Henry Farman, who looked very English with his brown beard, and his brothers Maurice and Dick were in the retail motor trade. Blériot made motor lamps and Klaxon horns in quite a big factory.

Farman learned to fly on a box-kite biplane made by the Voisin Brothers, who were pioneers even before him and did fairly well, but faded out after 1918. Farman started building biplanes in 1909 and became a good pilot and constructor. At the Rheims meeting of 1909 he covered huge distances, 100 miles or so, non-stop round a track about four miles to the lap. He had one peculiarity. Having been a cycle-racer as a youth, the rudder-bar of an aeroplane always seemed to him to be a handlebar, so he flew with his rudder-wires crossed. If anyone else had flown the machine he would have broken his neck and the machine as soon as he got off the ground.

Henry Farman's designs were shocking. Wings, tails, ailerons, elevators and rudders looked as if they had been built by the mile and sawn off to length. But they flew. Henry was nearly as silent as Wilbur Wright and never played for popularity. Brother Maurice was an artist and built biplanes on his own which, although they were just as much box-kites as Henry's, had nice round corners, and were polished and painted and looked good. Also I really believe they were better machines. Brother Dick was a salesman. He flew fairly well, but he sold things better. He was a cheery soul. Everybody liked him.

Eventually, after 1918, Maurice got out of the aircraft business, so did Dick, but Henry stopped in and made some of the ugliest aircraft ever built, the Goliath and the Jabiru, the latter a four-engined (two in tandem on each side) high-wing monoplane, as fantastic as its name. But they flew. Henry died in 1935, about.

By 1936 the Farman firm had 5,000 employees and could turn out ten big bombers or transports per day—so they said. In 1937 it was nationalised. After that I do not know what happened. I do know that in 1938, when war was looming ahead, the total output of the French Nationalised Aircraft Industry, under M. Pierre Cot, fell at one time to *twelve* machines in one month.

Louis Blériot, the apostle of the monoplane from 1908, was heavily-built and had a drooping black moustache and grey eyes, a nice face, but without a trace of humour. He was very much the flying fanatic. For example, when he flew the Channel, in July 1909, in his little monoplane, which hoped that it had 35 h.p. in its three-cylinder radial air-cooled Anzani engine, he flew with one foot in bandages because he had burned it a few days before. And he went through the receptions in London very much as a martyr, alleviated by the presentation of the *Daily Mail*'s £1,000 cheque.

From then on he became the great ' industriel ', but I believe that the flight saved him, for the experiments with his aeroplanes spent all the money he had made out of his lamps. He did grand work during the 1914–18 war. In fact, Blériot machines were about the best the French had—especially the Spads. His son was killed in an

accident somewhere between wars—which nearly broke his heart—and he himself died of heart failure about 1937.

Another of the great pioneers whom I knew slightly was Louis Bréguêt. He was not a pilot, he was a great industrialist. I forget what his job was, but he spent money lavishly on experiments. I met him at the world's first Aero Show in Paris, just after Christmas 1908. He was showing a huge apparatus built of steel tubes, which flailed round and round, with things like canvas paddles on the end. It was intended to lift vertically as a helicopter does. I think that he was optimistic rather than enthusiastic about it. Anyhow it never came to anything. But by 1910 he was building biplanes of steel tubes and fabric, which flew remarkably well for those days and were real engineering structures, not just sticks and wire.

In the war of 1914–18 he built the best of all the French bombers, which after the war were turned into quite good passenger craft— if one can look on single-engined machines as good. He was a dignified and kindly man who took a lively interest in his workpeople. But, like all the rest, when his works were nationalised the output disappeared, and Bréguêt drifted out of the business.

There is no room to talk about Robert Esnault-Pelterie and his ambitious patent claims or those charming Morane brothers, or the de Nieport (commonly called Nieuport) brothers, all of whom were pioneers, and pilots and successful constructors. But I must mention Paul Deperdussin, a silk merchant who was bitten by aviation, and paid for the building of fast aeroplanes designed by Bêchéreau and Koolhoven and got so deeply into debt that he defrauded the bank to finance his aeroplanes. He went to jail, and when one of his aeroplanes did 120 miles in an hour (the first time a human being had done two miles a minute for an hour on end) the designers, pilot and mechanics sent him a telegram to the prison congratulating ' le bon patron '—' the good boss '.

The English Pioneers

Hereabouts I think we had better start talking about the English pioneers—I use the word English advisedly for there were no Scots or Irish or Welsh among the earliest.

Leaving out Sir George Cayley of 1808, and Wenham and Stringfellow of 1848, whom I had not the honour of knowing, and who did not fly anyhow, the first of our pioneers who ultimately flew was J. W. Dunne (he of ' An Experiment with Time '), who started with a glider in 1906–07 and developed it by 1908 into an arrow-shaped or Vee-type

Blériot and his monoplane after landing at Dover, 25th July 1909.

tailless biplane, of the most modern appearance except that it was a biplane. He experimented with the glider at Blair-Atholl, guarded by the Atholl Highlanders against foreign spies. He built the engine-driven biplane on the Isle of Sheppey, at Leysdown, where the Aero Club had some flat marshes over which experimenters tried to fly, and later took it to Eastchurch, which Mr. Frank McClean bought and lent to the Club in 1910. Unfortunately Dunne's Vee-type experiments, though very interesting, got nowhere after 1914. But indirectly they had important results.

The outfit, camp, aerodrome, or what you like to call it, at Leysdown was dominated by Horace Short, to my mind the most remarkable of all our pioneers. His two younger brothers, Eustace and Oswald, had been making balloons for the Aero Club for some years, in the railway arches under Battersea Park station. Horace was the right-hand man of the Hon. Charles Parsons (later Sir Charles) and with him had developed the Parsons Turbine, which revolutionised steamships. He also invented an awful thing called an Auxetophone, which, by some turbine blower arrangement, could produce from a gramophone record about three times the volume of sound of a brass band.

Horace was a big man and he had an astonishing head, at least twice the size of any other human head I have ever seen. He was a terrifying sight to women and children, and men got a shock when they saw him for the first time. But when one got to know him he was a wonderful companion and a sterling friend. That great head of his was full of brains, and his sense of humour and his wit were devastating. Historically he was the inventor of the name 'Blimp' for small airships, and the originator of the 'thrush test'.

I have a vivid memory of sitting in a tin hut at Leysdown on a winter night (1909 I suppose) with the rain drumming on the roof, and watching that strange head and face in the light of a paraffin lamp, while Horace held forth, logically and impressively, on the explanation of the Lost Atlantis. He was one of the few men whom I have admired without reservations. His death in 1916 was a great loss to the aircraft industry.

In 1908, as I have said, Griffith Brewer took charge of the Wright patents in England. The Short brothers took on the Wright agency and Horace came down from Newcastle to manage the building of Wright biplanes. And they settled on Leysdown as flying ground and factory. They also designed an aeroplane of their own, on Wright lines but with more reasonable controls.

There they collected a whole gang of pioneers. Dunne, aforesaid, was one. There were also the Hon. Charles Rolls, of the Rolls-Royce car, who was killed flying at Bournemouth in 1910; the Hon. J. T. C. Moore-Brabazon, now Lord Brabazon of Tara; Cecil Grace, of the South American Grace Shipping Line, who was lost at sea when flying back from France; Frank McClean, now Sir Francis, who bought a Short biplane; Professor Huntingdon, who was building a Dunne-type machine; Jezzi, who built a little tractor biplane of his own; and perhaps one or two others whom I did not know so well. They were all enthusiasts and spent all their spare time in that wilderness.

The two great events at Leysdown were the first authenticated flights in Great Britain by Moore-Brabazon on a Voisin biplane which he had imported from France, where he had learned to fly (this won for him Pilot's Certificate No. 1), and the flying of the first mile in a closed circuit (not necessarily a circle) on an all-British aeroplane. Young Moore-Brabazon of those days was a logical humorist, as Lord Brabazon is to-day, so he took up a pig in a basket to prove that pigs might and could fly. If you see a small smart car around London bearing the number FLY 1, that is his.

In 1910 the whole of that crowd moved to Eastchurch, which in 1914 was commandeered as a Naval air station, and so became in due course an R.A.F. station.

Among the very earliest of the pioneers was that eccentric genius Noel Pemberton Billing, who after fighting in the South African war, and dealing in yachts, tried to make an aerodrome at Fambridge in Essex in 1908–09. Then he formed a company called the Supermarine Works, at Southampton. I could tell lots of funny stories about

The Wright brothers at Short's works in 1909. Orville Wright by rear of car, followed by Wilbur Wright. In shed Horace Short and Griffith Brewer.

[Copyright : ' Flight '

him. But he discovered two men who have played a big part in our air history, Hubert Scott Paine, who built up the Supermarine business after P.B. left, and later built up Power Boats Ltd., and Mitchell, the designer of the first Spitfires which helped the Hurricanes to win the Battle of Britain.

Another pioneer was old José Weiss, an Alsatian painter, who painted lovely pictures and sold them so that he could build bird-like tailless gliders. He launched young Gordon England (later a well-known pilot) off Amberley Mount, Sussex, in them and he covered a good mile for his best distance. Their engine-driven machine was not a success; aerodynamically it was sound, but structurally it was a menace.

Quite a different sort of pioneer was Claude Grahame-White, who holds Pilot's Certificate No. 6. He learned to fly on a Blériot, at Pau (South France), started a school there, came back home and teamed up with Richard Gates, bought the ground where

Hendon aerodrome now stands, and made it a regular show place. In 1912–13–14, regular week-end crowds to see the flying and air racing there ran to twenty thousand or twenty-five thousand, and on Aerial Derby days two hundred thousand or more crammed the enclosures and the surrounding landscape. There was no by-pass then. Only green fields. Claude and Richard and their press agent Bernard Isaac could have taught the U.S.A. something about publicity.

Hendon primarily owed its existence to George Holt Thomas, a rich newspaper owner, who brought a French pioneer pilot, Paulhan, over to give exhibition flights in 1909. He brought him back to compete against Grahame-White for the *Daily Mail* £10,000 prize for the first London–Manchester flight. He discovered a field at Hendon from which Paulhan started and won. But G.-W. bought the field and made far more out of Hendon than Paulhan did.

Here comes in Geoffrey de Havilland.

Claude Grahame-White flying a Farman biplane.

He designed and built for himself, with his friend Hearle, in 1909, a biplane at Newbury. Then he joined the Royal Aircraft Factory and there designed the famous B.E. biplane which won the Military Aeroplane Competition in 1912 and was developed into the infamous B.E. 2c of 1915. In 1912 Holt Thomas had established the Aircraft Mfg. Co. Ltd. and in 1913 he engaged Geoffrey de Havilland as chief designer. That was how the long series of famous D.H. types began, which has provided up to the end of 1947 the Vampire and the D.H. jet turbine. And D.H. himself is now Sir Geoffrey.

Now we must go back to another sort of pioneer. Frederick Handley Page, a very young engineer, started a workshop on the spoil-dumps from the tube railways at Barking in 1909 and built for other people quaint things which they thought would fly. Then he moved to Fairlop and built two bird-like monoplanes which did fly; he and his joyous crew decided to call them the Antiseptic and the Yellow Peril. He was nicely established at Cricklewood when war broke out and huge orders followed. Commodore Sueter of the R.N.A.S. (whom you will meet later) commissioned him to build a twin-engined bomber. A four-engined bomber followed. Then, after the war, came slots, and giant airliners. And in this war came Halifaxes—and Sir Frederick.

About contemporary with him was Bob Blackburn, the son of a Leeds engineer. He built his own machine in a bit of his father's works and tried to fly it off Filey Sands in 1909. Then he built a big monoplane which flew well, and from that he became a manufacturer in a big way. The firm's history in the 1914–18 and in the 1939–45 war is most interesting as an example of organising for quantity production in a sound hard-headed Yorkshire way. The firm's last war-time production, the Firebrand, is most impressive.

106

Commander Samson leaving his Short biplane at Lodmore, 1912.

Another contemporary was Richard Fairey, another trained engineer, and a young lecturer at the Finsbury College in 1909. He made a study of inherent stability and built elastic-driven models to test his ideas. And he won competitions with them, aided a bit by the fact that he stood six feet six inches, and they had a slight advantage in being launched from a height of about eight feet. His experiments brought him in touch with J. W. Dunne, who engaged him as works manager in building his Vee-type biplane at Eastchurch. Thence he became works manager of Shorts.

In 1915 he started the Fairey Aviation Co. Ltd.—one of the funniest stories of the foundation of a firm. And from then on he never looked back. At one time there were more Fairey machines in service in the R.A.F. than all other makes put together. He became Sir Richard in 1936, and in 1940 he became head of the British Commission in the U.S.A. for the procurement of air material.

Quite among the earliest pioneers was A. V. Roe. He was a seagoing engineer, but made a model aeroplane which won a prize in 1908 at a Crystal Palace show. His father, a doctor, financed him in building a tractor triplane on Lea Marshes. Then his brother Humphrey, an officer in the South African war, and in 1909 a successful manufacturer in Manchester, agreed to finance a bigger concern, and registered A. V. Roe and Co. Ltd., then, and ever since, known as Avros. They took a shed inside Brooklands motor-track where Major Lindsay Lloyd was making an aerodrome. With A. V. were Chadwick, Parrott, Dobson and Raynham, whose names are now famous. They were themselves pioneers of almost the first rank.

From that developed the famous Avro trainers of 1914–18, in which all the world's Air Forces learned to fly. From them are descended the Ansons, Lancasters, Yorks and Tudors of to-day. A. V. is now Sir Alliott Verdon Roe.

A pioneer of quite another sort was the great Sir George White of Bristol, the tramway king who electrified tramways all over the British Isles and in many foreign cities round about 1900. In 1909 he saw the value of air transport, so he registered the

The first aeroplane mail in England, 10th August 1910. Placing special cards into a mail bag before the start of the flight. The pilot, seen in the centre, was C. Grahame-White. This flight, which was to have been from Blackpool to Southport, was organised by the *Empire Illustrated*. Owing to bad weather the pilot landed after only seven miles and the cards were then posted.

British and Colonial Aeroplane Co., built sheds at Lark Hill on Salisbury Plain, where the Aeroplane Company, R.E., came later, and also at Brooklands in 1910. His nephew, Sydney Smith, and Lady White's nephew, Herbert Thomas, ran the business. Frank Barnwell was chief designer, and produced the historic Bristol Fighter of 1917, which did much towards winning that war. I have a vivid memory of Sir George standing in front of his fire and telling a few of us how he acquired tramways and why he decided to found an aeroplane firm. He was a very great man, and the great Bristol Aeroplane Co. Ltd. is a worthy monument to his memory.

Now we come to a pioneer who started a shade later than the rest, but has achieved much. Thomas Octavius Murdoch Sopwith was Octavius because he had seven sisters older than himself. He was the only son. When I first met him in 1910 he was a young man about town, who ran fast cars and fast motor-boats, and had a faithful engineer named Fred Sigrist who kept them in tip-top order. But he had studied engineering quite seriously and was a born mechanic with a wonderful eye for form. He came to Brooklands as a motorist and became an aviator.

He bought a monoplane called an Avis, built by Howard Wright and W. O. Manning under the railway arches at Battersea, next to Shorts' balloon works. Then he bought a tandem Blériot. Then in 1911 he and his sister May and Fred Sigrist, with a sportsman named Dudley Sturrock as impresario, went to the U.S.A. to do some exhibition flying. He won a lot of money, and when he came back, bringing a Wright biplane with him, he decided to build some aeroplanes himself. So with his eye and Fred Sigrist's 'know-how' they built sundry experimental things and then a tractor biplane which was approved by Commodore Sueter's engineers at the Admiralty.

A dozen was ordered, and on the strength of that the Sopwith Aviation Co. Ltd. started in business in a skating rink at Kingston-upon-Thames. And Fred Sigrist stood in on the deal as a partner. Thousands of Sopwith fighters were built during the war and the Sopwith Company was a 'good thing'.

After the war it was shut down, but the same partners, in essence, started the H. G. Hawker Engineering Co. Ltd. to make motor-cycles. Harry Hawker had been the firm's test pilot.

Some years later the Hawker Company started making aeroplanes, and Hawker aircraft won a high reputation. The designer was Sidney Camm, who was himself a pioneer as a young man working for Martin and Handasyde at Brooklands. The ultimate result was the Hurricane, of which, with its eight guns, there were five in the Battle of Britain to one of any other type.

I may add that, before the war began, Tommy Sopwith and his co-directors had put an order into the works to put 1,000 Hurricanes into production, while the Air Ministry was wondering whether to order a couple of dozen or a couple of hundred. Which was why, in spite of rumours, we were never short of fighters throughout the battle, even though at times all the reserves at the front-line aerodromes may have been in the air at once. We had Tommy Sopwith's pioneer spirit largely to thank for that.

I wish there had been more room in which to write of other less prominent pioneers and of people who became important but were not early enough to be quite first-line pioneers. One combination, Martin and Handasyde, officially Martinsyde Ltd. of Brooklands, must be mentioned, although the firm died soon after the 1914–18 war. 'Handy' was a first-class Clydeside engineer and their workmanship was beautiful. Then there was the Aviation Department of Vickers Ltd., also at Brooklands, started in 1911 by Captain Bertie Wood of the 12th Lancers and Captain Peter Acland, an Indian Cavalryman, who were not quite early enough to come into the first line. Yet when you think of the faithful Wimpey, the claim of Vickers Ltd. to be pioneers seems justified.

There were the early pilots, too: Benny Hucks, who learned to fly at Pau with Grahame-White; and Gustav Hamel, handsomest of all our pilots, a wonderful performer, but couldn't tell a sparking plug from a spanner; and Otto Astley, with his Blériot and wonderful hands; and Keith Davies, the first man to fly in Asia, now a prosperous owner of fleets of motor coaches; and dozens more about whom the old-timers still have stories to tell of their pluck and courage, or their crazy escapades or their quaint sayings. They were a joyous crowd. And the marvel is how many of them survive and have preserved their joyousness, in spite of the fact that aviation has become a great industry.

The Service Pioneers

Last, but most important of all, we come to the Services. Without them the work of the flying and constructing pioneers would have been wasted, or at any rate delayed for years before enough of the public became interested enough to spend money on aeroplanes.

An interesting point is that in all countries Army and Navy officers were the first genuine 'customers' of the aircraft firms. They took to flying as a sport or because they foresaw its use in war. But that is a long story in itself.

In England Army officers took to flying before the Navy did. J. W. Dunne, already mentioned, was an Army officer. Captain

J. B. Fulton, a gunner, and a good friend of mine, was given some money grants for improvements in guns, and spent them in buying a Blériot in 1910. A dozen or so regular officers were among the first fifty holders of flying certificates. Among them was Captain Bertram Dickson, another gunner, who flew his own Farman at various meetings at home and abroad. I had my first flight and crash with him at Lanark in 1910. In fact all the officers of the Aeroplane Company of the Air Battalion, R.E., of 1910–11 were pioneers, and I knew most of them.

But the two men who were the great pioneers were those officers who built the Royal Naval Air Service and the Royal Flying Corps, which were amalgamated in 1918 into the Royal Air Force.

Taking the Senior Service first, Captain Murray Sueter, R.N. (now Rear Admiral Sir Murray, ex-M.P.), was a pioneer of submarines before naval airships flew. Presumably because an airship is much the same shape as a submarine, he was appointed to superintend the building of a big rigid airship

Louis Paulhan winner of the £10,000 prize for a London–Manchester flight in 1910.

Mr. Frank McClean
flying his Short biplane
under Tower Bridge,
10th August 1912.

which was to be built for the Navy at Barrow-in-Furness. It was jestingly named the *Mayfly*, but it never did. Then he was turned on to organise an Air Department at the Admiralty. In that job he not only built a wonderful air service but he built up the British aircraft industry by ordering aircraft for the Navy when the Army was having aircraft of the wrong type built in the Royal Aircraft Factory at Farnborough and ordering 'Chinese copies' of them from a few favoured firms.

Murray Sueter, although a watch-keeping officer by rank, was a born engineer, and he collected round him a staff of first-class naval engineers, the finest of all engineers. They picked out all the best ideas among the young aircraft firms of 1910, 1911 and 1912, and ordered their types in numbers (as many as a dozen at a time, believe it or not) so that when in 1916 the Germans had nearly beaten the R.F.C. out of the sky, the R.N.A.S. came to the rescue with trained squadrons of fighter pilots and with spare machines with which to equip R.F.C. squadrons.

When eventually the R.N.A.S. was amalgamated in the R.A.F. it was sufficiently big and well established to be a most valuable asset.

After Murray Sueter, I think, one should put Captain Godfrey Paine, R.N., the first Commandant of the Central Flying School, which was set up in 1911 to teach Navy and Army and Civilian Reserve officers to fly. He was a typical Navy captain, bluff and terrifying, with a bark that was much worse than his bite, but a fine disciplinarian and a great trainer of men.

I have only room to mention here a few of the other pioneers of naval flying. Three naval officers, Lieutenants Samson, Gregory and Longmore, and a Marine, Lieutenant Gerrard, were allowed by Their Lordships to draw full pay while they were taught to fly, free of cost, by George Cockburn of the Aero Club, himself a pioneer pilot, on Short biplanes lent to the Navy by Frank McClean, who paid for their building. I used to spend days at Eastchurch with them in 1911. It was a cheery place. Samson did well in the war of 1914–18 and retired as an Air Commodore in the 1920's, and died of heart trouble. Longmore, at the time of writing, is Air Chief Marshal Sir Arthur, and was Air Officer Commanding, Middle East until 1941. Gerrard retired as an Air Commodore and did good work training the A.T.C. in 1939–45. Poor Gregory gave up flying and died as a Lieutenant Commander, commanding a destroyer in Chinese waters between wars.

The first naval officer to have his own aeroplane was Lieutenant Spencer Grey, who bought a Blackburn monoplane in 1911, just about when the other four were learning at Eastchurch. Then there was John Porte, already mentioned in connection

The first flight of a controllable heavier-than-air craft. The Wright brothers at Kittyhawk, 17 December 1903. (*From a drawing by James Gardner shown at the Shell exhibition 'See How They Fly'.*) The artist has inadvertently included in the background the derrick for assisted take-off which was not used until a year later. The first flight was unassisted, the aircraft only using a rail to reduce friction.

with the Curtiss flying-boats. And there were many more whom I knew well, but who must be left out here because they were just too late to make history.

On the Army side the great pioneer was Major Hugh Trenchard, now Marshal of the R.A.F., the Viscount Trenchard, who built up the R.A.F., which not only won the Battle of Britain but won the war by its bombing and by blasting the way along which the Army marched to victory.

Hugh Trenchard, already a middle-aged Major in the Royal Scots Fusiliers, with a D.S.O. from the South African War, had been sent home from Nigeria to die of fever. He refused to do so, and in 1913 was made Assistant Commandant of the Central Flying School, under Captain Godfrey Paine. There his deep voice and explosive way of speaking won him the nickname of 'Boom'. It has stuck to him ever since as a mark of the deepest affection and respect.

When war broke out in 1914 every aeroplane the Army owned went to France with the first three squadrons of the R.F.C. and 'Boom' was sent to Farnborough to build a second Flying Corps in a row of empty sheds out of a few wrecked aircraft and some human wrecks unfit for service. In 1916, after he had built up and sent out thirty or forty squadrons, he was sent to France to build up, for the third time, the strength of the R.F.C. after the 'Fokker scourge', and he commanded it till brought home at the end of 1917 to be Chief of the Air Staff of the new R.A.F.

In May 1918 he went to France again, to build a fourth air force, the Independent Air Force, for the bombing of Germany. When the war ended, the R.A.F. was severely axed. It was cut to 1/10th of its size, and in 1923 'Boom' started for the fifth time to build up an Air Force. When he left in 1930 we already had the biggest and best Air Force in the world. He said that he had laid the foundations of a castle and, if nobody wanted to build anything bigger than a cottage on it, they would at any rate have a jolly good cottage. Those foundations, and his organisation, have withstood the expansion of the R.A.F. to a strength of several millions of men and women who, beyond dispute, won the war. 'Boom' has been the greatest of all our pioneers.

THE LITERATURE OF FLIGHT

'Of Flyers Too I Spoke'

Of flyers too I spoke, their resilient way
Over a course of continents, their homing
Through wind and fog, against error and
  expectation.
High spirits they had: gravity they flouted.
Often have your ambitions, flown too steep
For the power that engined them, lost grip
  and stalled:
In clouds you have lost your bearings; and
  in the desert,
Repairing a broken air-screw, envied the
  sand
That has no need to travel.
'Those were free agents: we are tied——'
  Listen,
Freedom is knowledge of necessity:
It is using the currents of air to waft your
  wings
And adverse ranges for test of climbing
  speed;

It is learning from drift how aim should be
  corrected,
And from emergency the extreme course;
Here flight is trimmed to meet capricious
  weather
And shaped by all elements shall master them.
It is also love revealed as the stern landlord,
And common calamity waking each house in
  a street
With a birthday present. It is the will to
  prove
Your case, though that last word
And clinching argument should be your death.
  Yes, you too, even now, the unregarded
Who were called hands (but those hands
  have been always
The ground mechanics of our wide-wing pride,
Made vision fast and cast molten imaginings)
—Into your hands history commits her spirit.
  C. DAY LEWIS—*A Time to Dance*

The Spitfire Trainer provides dual instruction at $6\frac{1}{2}$ miles a minute.

[*Copyright*: *Vickers-Armstrongs Ltd.*

JET-PROPELLED AIRCRAFT.

Top left.—The first British jet-aeroplane, the Gloster E.28/39.

[*Crown Copyright Reserved*

Top Right.—The Gloster-Meteor, first R.A.F. jet-fighter.

[*Copyright: Barratt's Photo Press*

Centre.—The de Havilland Vampire.

[*Photo : Charles Brown*

Bottom.—The de Havilland 108 research monoplane.

THE BRITISH EMPIRE'S CONTRIBUTION TO AVIATION

by

E. Colston Shepherd

Secretary-General of The Air League ; Formerly Editor of ' The Aeoroplane'

IF SCEPTICISM, distrust, caution and lack of encouragement could have killed British prospects of leadership in the art of flying, and in the science of aerodynamics, our fate would have been sealed between 1903 and 1914. If niggardliness and parsimony could have destroyed a promising industry, we should have lost one of our finest assets between 1918 and 1935. By all the laws of probability, Britain should have made only spasmodic contributions to the cause of flying and should have shared little in its progress.

Individual Enthusiasts

Individual enthusiasts set British aeronautics going and kept it going on a fairly steady, unspectacular course which has been lit at intervals by flashes of achievement apparently out of all proportion to the plan and intention behind them or to the resources from which they proceeded. High hopes and unquenchable persistence drove on the Shorts, the Roes, the de Havillands and the Handley Pages in years which were bleak financially and empty of public appreciation.

In a later generation a corresponding tenacity kept aircraft firms not only alive, but active in the work of development and improvement during that period between the wars when the State was barely interested and the public was unconvinced. Faith grew out of those early hopes; and there were always enough acolytes willing to serve in the temple without much reward, and more than enough devotees of the art of flying ready to embrace adventure and accept risks for the joy of flying and the glory of accomplishing great things.

British individuals were continuously ahead of others in those early days. They leapt at the chance of flying the Atlantic in aircraft designed for much less ambitious purposes. They set out gaily on Channel flights with untried engines. They entered for the earliest Schneider Trophy races in seaplanes which were virtually experiments. They cheerfully flew their early bombers over long land routes where neither bases nor facilities were available and they repaired and patched and improvised as they went. At the earliest stage of all, pilots like Charles Rolls and Moore-Brabazon proved by their flying that the aeroplane could not be ignored and patrons like Francis McClean persuaded the authorities to consider the aeroplane without having to accept financial obligations.

The two streams of faith ran together in fertilising the movement out of which a great constructing and operating industry was to grow. Who shall decide how the credit for progress should be apportioned ? The challenge of things waiting to be done presented itself jointly to designers and record-breakers; and economic considerations could limit, but not determine, the efforts of both to succeed. Wars and the dangers of wars have played some part in making progress possible. Their influence has been to give rein and to diminish the time factor in certain directions. That influence has been much less marked in evoking developments and demanding new ideas. Conditions are perhaps being reversed to-day. The State has become responsible for most of the research. The State is seeking to prescribe the aircraft, both military and civil, of the future. Customer and manufacturer react less directly upon each other. Adventure is being taken out of flying. Enterprise is passed through the sieve of State control.

115

The New Power

One factor which should modify the deadening effect of State control is the emergence of new sources of power together with the immense opportunities arising from it. State and industry alike are faced with the fascinating chance to carry the aeroplane as such on through the critical phase around the speed of sound and to apply to practical purposes the range of supersonic speeds, which have hitherto been out of reach because of the lack of sufficient power in small packets. Zest, which has been the mainspring of British aeronautical progress for nearly forty years, is restored by the arrival of jet-propulsion just at the time when the cautious hand of bureaucracy might have held it in check and finally worn it down.

Specifications may be laid down by ministries, and developments may have to depend largely on research work done at State establishments, but individuals in State and in private employment are moved once again by a sense of standing on the threshold of great things. The old stimulus of having new wing sections, new shapes, new control systems, new structures to work out, and of getting the best output, the highest reliability and the best specific consumption out of engines, is operating to-day in Britain much as it did between 1908 and 1918, with the difference that the work is more centralised and better equipped and organised.

This time the goal is more clearly seen and the path is more surely plotted. The aeroplane is accepted and established whereas in 1908 it was regarded with suspicion. British pioneers had not only to find their own way through the unknown quantities of a new science, but to convince a sceptical world of the value of their work. However much they might believe in the practical applications of flying, they had to prove their case to the military and naval authorities, and persuade the travelling public that flying could serve the needs of transport.

A Slow Start

Great Britain came slowly to the business of flying. France had a far more liberal attitude towards the new idea. Not only did France give the first encouragement to the Wrights in 1908, but she claimed also in that year to have 100 pilots. The British had been plodding along towards full-scale flight. The Aeronautical Society had been going since 1866 and had stimulated a fair amount of research with models, gliders and kites. The Aero Club had come into existence in 1901 and some of its members like C. S. Rolls, Griffith Brewer and Hedges Butler were quick to make contact with the Wright brothers when they arrived in France in 1908.

Work indeed had been in progress in England for some time. A. V. Roe, Handley Page, Hiram Maxim and others had made a start, but these beginnings were difficult and relatively unproductive. The lack of a suitable engine was at the bottom of the trouble and yet there was something more to account for the lead which France had in 1908. It was the union between a desire to fly and a desire to make a flying machine. In Britain, the emphasis was rather on creating the machine. The Aero Club went on being devoted to the balloon after the aeroplane had appeared, and individual members had to import the aeroplane, learn to fly in France, and push the Club into providing an aerodrome.

The influence of France and of the Wrights was strong in England in those early days. The French aeroplanes by Farman, Santos Dumont, Blériot and Voisin were flying and, although J. W. Dunne was obtaining remarkable results in Scotland, and A. V. Roe had made promising trials at Brooklands in 1908, British products were not yet ready to give the pilot the opportunites he wanted. The people who wanted to fly had to take the means where they could find them — and they found them in France. While they were using what France could provide, they took steps to push forward the foundation of an aircraft industry in England.

Short Brothers, who had been making balloons, were persuaded to take up the building of aeroplanes. The British motor-car trade was induced to take an interest in engines for aeroplanes and out of that interest came the first British Aero Show at Olympia

Left.—The de Havilland D.H.4 2-seat fighter-bomber of World War I. This type was later converted for passenger carrying and became Britain's first civil transport aeroplane.

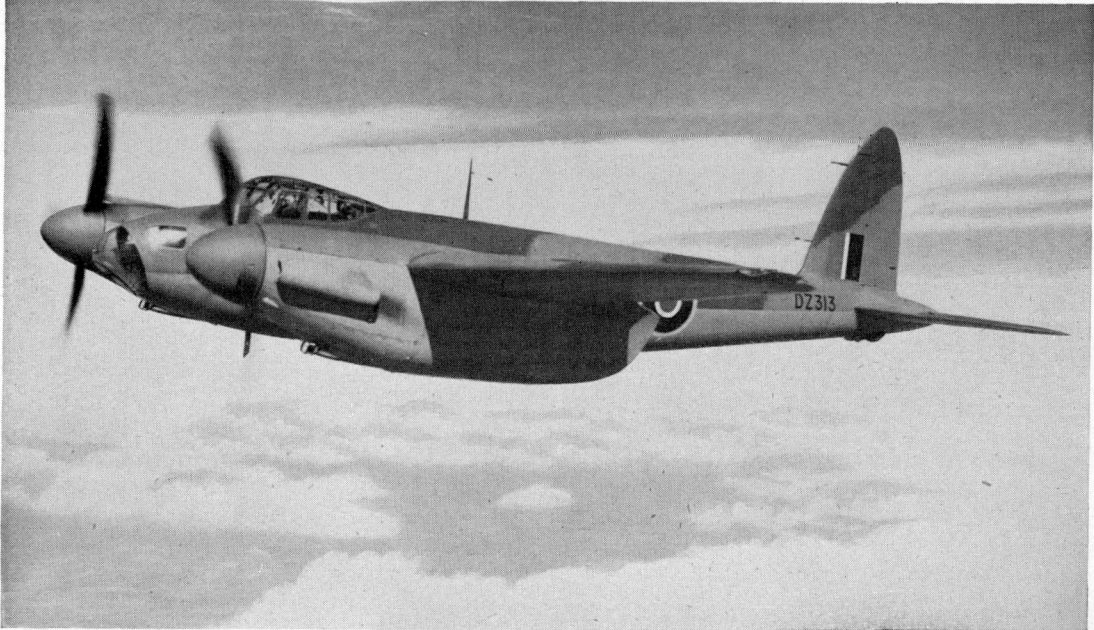

Above.—The de Havilland Mosquito, one of the most versatile aircraft used by the Royal Air Force during World War II. Fighter Bomber, Photographic, Torpedo, Trainer, and Civil Transport versions were all produced.

[*Photo :* ' *Flight* '

Right.—The 1916 Bristol Fighter.

117

LIGHT DE HAVILLAND
TRANSPORT AEROPLANES.

Right.—The 4-passenger Fox Moth.

Lower left.—The 2-motor Dragon
    Rapide.
        [*Photo : John Stroud*

Lower right.—The 4-motor D.H. 86
    Express.
        [*Photo : Imperial Airways*

Bottom.—The post-war Dove.
        [*Photo : Charles Brown*

in 1909. Meanwhile, there were the flying-meetings at Doncaster and Blackpool, the former frowned upon by the Aero Club. People like Moore-Brabazon and Grahame-White had had to go to France to learn to fly; Moore-Brabazon had to take the initiative in getting a flying ground on the Isle of Sheppey; Shorts had to draw on the experience of the Wrights in building their first aeroplanes for sale; an unofficial committee had to arrange the first flying-meeting at Doncaster; and the motor trade gave British designers the first chance to show their wares.

Britain Gets Under Way

True to tradition, we muddled our way into the flying movement and we abandoned our insularity to do it. We were to remain behind for three or four years. Then we were to begin to go our own way. A. V. Roe introduced the idea of the tractor airscrew instead of the pusher of the early days. Roe and de Havilland made a success of the biplane against the continental fashion of the monoplane. The great firm of Vickers by then had taken up the building of military aircraft. T. O. M. Sopwith had produced an aeroplane which looked like having military applications and other firms which have since become famous were taking form. The impetus to the movement had been given by the people who wanted to fly and their immediate needs had to be met with the help of experience already won in the United States and France.

From that time in 1912–13 when a certain agreement on the fundamentals of design was reached, British effort had a character of its own. This is not to say that it was unaffected by what happened abroad, although there were times when we resisted foreign influence too long—in the adoption of the monoplane and of the retractable undercarriage, for instance. Nor is it to say that we became at once independent of foreign help, for the French Gnôme rotary engine was an indispensable part of British equipment during the first world war. What is clear is that by 1912 we were launched on a course of independent design and development which was to be cautious and sometimes slow, and yet produced, with a steady direction, a continuous crop of results which have been of the utmost value.

The Military Influence

Two wars made their mark on those achievements and have tended to encourage the development of military aircraft at the expense of the commercial types. The belief grew out of the first world war that profits in the aircraft industry could only be made out of military aircraft; and that hampering conviction is only now, in 1948, being broken down. After two wars, this country has tried to adapt certain military aircraft to civil needs and has twice proved the futility of the attempt. Yet almost paradoxically this country had shown the world between the two wars the wisdom of designing big for commercial purposes. The airliner with four engines, roomy, comfortable, safe and withal a little slow, was demonstrated as a public vehicle and established as the best type of commercial aeroplane by Great Britain.

After each war, British aeronautical progress has had to shake itself free of the military influence and work out afresh its utilitarian salvation. Between the wars, this result was realised in the face of public parsimony. Private money and a great fund of personal enthusiasm and devotion were sunk in the effort and the nature of the result revealed some of the limitations. For example, we built capacious and reliable airliners, but we did not build for speed. They were supposed to enable British air transport to 'fly by itself', that is to say, without subsidy.

After the second world war, parsimony was replaced by State control and we have still to see how enterprise and personal endeavour will fare under a system of prescription from above. Aircraft and engine design for military purposes was subject to similar specification from above between the wars, and still private effort yielded some of the most brilliant designs and improvements. Much in the future will depend on the readiness of Government departments to trust designers and engineers to make the best use of the fruits of Government research. Henceforth most of the research must be done in Government establishments, but most of the development work must still be done by the practical men in private industry. The bulk of the aeronautical triumphs of Great Britain in the past was derived from private research.

What an immense fund of ingenuity and skill has been at the service of the nation in the last thirty years would perhaps be best expressed by a catalogue of the aircraft and engines which have followed each other with varying success. If that catalogue were dissected, one would have some difficulty in establishing a conscious aim, a deliberate sense of direction, a well-defined policy of progress, but one would be impressed with the remarkable solidity of each response to a new demand and with the avoidance of improvisation. When we decided that we must have two-seat fighters towards the end of the first world war, having made a real success of our single-seaters with aircraft like the Camel, we later turned out types like the Bristol Fighter.

Having had relatively little success with our engines, apart from the Rolls-Royce Eagle, during that war, we stuck to our purpose until we did produce an engine of high merit after that war was over and the Napier Lion went on as a success for another ten years. Even before then, our needs had forced us to aim far beyond the approved ideas of the time and had driven us to the big bomber. The Handley Page multi-engined bombers of 1918, which were never used against Germany because the war ended too soon, and the Vickers Vimy which belonged to the same school, were a long way ahead of the products of the rest of the world.

Beginnings of Long-Distance Flight

In fact they ushered in the idea of long-distance flying while the other nations were still thinking of the aeroplane as a weapon limited in range to flights of 300 or 400 miles. Those aircraft, which were to have been flown from England to Berlin and on to Hungary in 1918, remained after the war to incite adventurous airmen to take on the Atlantic in a single hop and to contemplate flying between England and Australia and

between England and the Cape. Because the aircraft were in existence and the pilots were falling over each other to fly them, there were far-seeing officers in the R.A.F. led in particular by Geoffrey Salmond, who began the preparation of air routes through Arabia towards India and through Africa towards the Cape.

Visions had been awakened by imaginative designing and sound construction. Those visions have not yet exhausted themselves or ceased in their turn to inspire designers. The designs themselves were to persist in general outline for many years in bombers and liners. They were destined to lead by a process of conservative development to the first of the really big, comfortable airliners. The great Handley Page biplane liners of 1931—true spiritual descendants of the bombers of 1918—introduced the four-engined type. They cruised at 90 m.p.h. while some of their smaller competitors cruised at 150 m.p.h., but they were setting a standard in safety, capacity and comfort for long journeys which the rest of the world was to acknowledge unreservedly ten years later.

This prophetic insistence on the importance of the big long-distance aeroplane was to have its counterpart in the development of the big flying-boat. In this department, commercial flying showed the way to military flying. The Short Empire flying-boat of 1936, with its high-wing monoplane design and its four engines, was a revelation. Its influence on flying-boat design in various countries was flattering evidence of its quality. But in this respect also, the country which had the right idea and worked it out and proved it in service, was not the one to press it immediately to its logical conclusion and add high performance to those other qualities of reliability and capacity.

Speed

Speed, the chief commodity which air transport has to sell, has always been at a discount in the utilitarian products of the British aircraft movement, not because this country was incapable of designing for speed but rather because we have grudged the cost of speed and mistrusted the craze for speed except where sporting distinction or

AIRLINER DEVELOPMENT.

Left (*above*).—Converted de Havilland 4A bomber of 1919.

Right (*above*).—20-seat Armstrong Whitworth Argosy of 1926.

Left. — 38 - seat Handley Page Heracles of 1931.

Right.—The 1936 200 m.p.h. Short Empire flying-boat.

[*Photo : Imperial Airways*

Lower left.—The high-speed de Havilland Albatross of 1938.

[*Photo : ' Flight '*

Lower right.—The Handley Page Hermes of 1947.

The Handley Page 0/400 heavy bomber of World War I.

national defence insisted that we should apply it. In many senses we were right to be suspicious of high speed. Power was limited. We had no engine of more than 800 h.p. in general use until 1930. Landing speeds worried us and, in view of the circumstances even as late as 1930, we had good reasons for worry.

Grass aerodromes were the rule up to that time and there were no wheel brakes and no trailing-edge flaps. The reversible airscrew had not been thought of. High landing speeds therefore would have meant using enormous aerodromes. Even so, there would have been other matters to consider, for we were still using narrow wheels and tyres with a small tread, and we were merely at the beginning of undercarriage shock absorbers. Landing at high speed in such conditions would have been hazardous, apart altogether from the variable state of a grass surface in the European climate.

All these factors had their part in delaying the advance towards high speeds for general purposes. They were of much less account in seaplanes, and the development of fast seaplanes was encouraged from 1913 onwards by the offer of the Schneider Trophy for international competition. Great Britain won the trophy in 1914 with a Sopwith biplane fitted with a 100 h.p. engine. The speed was 86.8 m.p.h. After the trophy had changed hands several times, Great Britain won it outright in 1931 at a speed of 340 m.p.h. with the Supermarine S.6B float seaplane fitted with a 2,300 h.p. Rolls-Royce engine. The world's speed record made in

the same aeroplane that year was 407.5 m.p.h. In that summary of seventeen years progress from the 100 h.p. engine and the speed of 87 m.p.h. to the 2,300 h.p. and a speed of 340 m.p.h. is to be found a marvel of aeronautical and mechanical developments. High alighting speeds could be accepted on the water. The S.6B in 1931 alighted at an air speed of 120 m.p.h. Full-scale research could thus be undertaken at high speeds and the influence of this on control, on wing forms and structures, on power output and engine reliability, on fuels and even on pilot selection and training was of the greatest value. Writers have often claimed that the Spitfire came out of the Schneider Trophy contests; and that is true, but there was more gain than that.

The Spitfire began its career with a top speed of 330 m.p.h. and was improved during the war until there came a Spitfire with a top speed of 425 m.p.h. Most of the knowledge we needed of how to overcome flutter in ailerons, how to prevent the twisting of wing-tips, how to avoid tail buffeting, how to increase engine output, how to design airscrews for high efficiency and how to give adequate strength to a structure without adding too much weight, was at our disposal in 1931, or soon afterwards, as the result of work devoted to the winning of the Schneider Trophy. Indeed, the work done in that cause can be said to have provided us with the means of advancing safely to the limit of the airscrew period.

We could probably have gone forward from the airscrew to the jet at speeds beginning

The Avro Lincoln heavy bomber of World War II.
[*Copyright : Barratt's Photo Press*

at 400 m.p.h. In fact we did nothing of the kind. We tried our first jet in the Gloster E.28/39 at speeds well below 400 m.p.h. and so felt our way forward again cautiously to the Meteor with its modest 450 m.p.h. From that, over a period of four years, we have gradually pushed the Meteor to its limit as more power became available, and we are now embarked on the next stage in high-speed development—the investigation of the swept-back wing which should carry us on to a speed equal to 95 per cent. of the speed of sound, or 720 m.p.h. in a temperature of 30 degrees C. (86 degrees F.).

Private and Official Encouragement

Given the necessary endowment, results of this kind were perhaps to be expected, but they could not have been certain. Endowment in the aircraft industry is rarely direct and precise. For example, the British entry in the Schneider Trophy contest of 1931 depended on the contribution of £200,000 for the purpose by Lady Houston. That sum undoubtedly paid for the aircraft and engines required and for the training of the team, but there were other reasons why those aircraft and engines were ready to be bought. One reason was that the R.A.F. was interested, no matter how firmly wedded to the idea of disarmament the Labour Government of the day might be.

This meant that the Royal Aircraft Establishment at Farnborough was interested and was ready to help designers work out their problems in the wind tunnel and the seaplane

tank and by various research methods. It also meant that aircraft and engine firms were interested for business reasons. Rolls-Royce, for instance, had only a few years before entered the aircraft field. Prejudice against the 'plumbing' troubles associated with liquid-cooled engines had begun to set in with the rise of the Bristol types of radial engines; there was no obvious successor to the Napier Lion; and Rolls-Royce were ready to seize the opportunity to produce a liquid-cooled engine of high power and small frontal area as a demonstration of what might be expected from their Kestrel 500 h.p. engine, then beginning a distinguished period of service in aircraft like the Hawker Fury and Hart.

Biplane versus Monoplane

On the aircraft side there was the powerful incentive of the knowledge that the biplane would soon have to give way to the monoplane. The Fairey long-range monoplane and several civil monoplane designs were beginning to show the way. The firm of Vickers-Armstrongs was thinking in terms of monoplane fighters and radial engines. There were good grounds for its associated firm of Supermarine to press on with a combination of the monoplane with a liquid-cooled engine. On all points, including that of acquiring additional prestige for the British aircraft industry, there was a real enthusiasm for the business of building fast aeroplanes. The atmosphere at the time of that last Schneider Trophy contest was one of encouragement rather than endowment. The progress was

Right.—The S.E. 5A of World War I.

Left.—No. 1 (Fighter) Squadron, R.A.F. Hawker Fury fighters, early 1930's.

[*Photo :* '*Flight*'

Lower left. — Vickers - Armstrongs Supermarine Spiteful.

[*Photo : Charles Brown*

Right. — Jet-propelled Vickers - Armstrongs Supermarine Attacker of to-day.

not the result of commissions. It was partly speculative and partly competitive. Without the sporting element introduced by the contest we should probably have marched more slowly towards the goal of high speeds.

Speed records could not have evoked the same response and they could not have demanded the same admixture of reliability. The Schneider Trophy aircraft had to be seaworthy as well as airworthy; they had to be flown not over a three-kilometre course (as in the speed record) but over a course of 350 kilometres with fairly sharp turns. After the end of the Schneider contests, Italy took the speed record from Great Britain. The quality of Italian fighters when war came was a surprising sign of how little relation a world's speed record by itself might bear to the application of speed to practical ends.

In this respect, as in making a start with her aviation, Britain owed something to France. When Jacques Schneider gave the trophy for competition, he started something which was to become the greatest international flying event and he set on foot a contest capable of producing something of permanent value. By linking the sporting element with the useful and practical he gave the British people a chance they might never have created for themselves. The lure of a sporting event, the British would be unable to resist; the Frenchman's idea was to use the sporting event to evoke not freak racing aircraft, but aircraft sufficiently developed to contribute to flying progress.

Now that the Schneider contest is finished, we can see how the process of achievement in high-speed flying has been reversed. We no longer design for a fantastic speed and so, with a special effort for a special great event, chart out the course by which the everyday aeroplane can strive during the succeeding five or six years to match that achievement. Our jet aircraft have started modestly and gradually worked up to a performance at which they could expect to make a new world's record. That was the way with the Meteor. It will be the way with the de Havilland 108 and with other aircraft which use swept-back wings. It will be the way with supersonic aircraft.

We are no longer faced with a challenge every two years, requiring us to defend our title or to take back the title from a competitor who had wrested it from us. We are not impelled to intensive work either by the menace of a date or by the threat of war. We are not moved too violently now by a sense of foreign competition, for the Government of the day is vowed to the internationalisation of commercial air transport and is attracted by the idea of international police forces. The one factor that promises still to exert some pressure is that of overseas sales. We can still sell speed for military purposes, as witness the orders for D.H. Vampires from Sweden and Switzerland. A few years hence, we may be able to sell speed in the field of commercial aircraft.

Personal Achievements

We are passing out of the phase in which sporting effort was productive. That phase had its results not only in speed, but also in the growth of aircraft for private and business flying. There were some among us in the years before the war who were doubtful of the value of certain of the record-breaking flights. When a Kingsford-Smith was lost or a Bert Hinkler crashed into a mountain side, we were unable to make the accounts balance and when the next aspirant set out to try human and mechanical endurance to the utmost, we wondered how much in human progress might justly be set against those risks to life. The truth is that some of the spectacular flights proved nothing but the courage of a pilot and yielded nothing but personal publicity. There were others which set certain standards and put up signposts for designers, engineers, instrument makers and public servants to follow.

Bert Hinkler was one of the best examples of this kind. He took a successful light aeroplane, the Avro Avian, improved it according to his own ideas and then proved that it could be flown and maintained on a fast journey of 11,000 miles by a single individual. That was in 1928. The descendants of the Avian were still giving splendid service when the war began. Before Hinkler made his great flight to Australia in sixteen days, there had been a less sensational flight from England to South Africa by R. R.

Bentley in a Moth. Other Moths are still flying after twenty-three years; and people like Bentley, Amy Johnson and James Mollison contributed a great deal of experience which was built into later models.

The Importance of Instruments

Engine reliability in varying climates and in all sorts of weather owed something to the hard tests to which engines were put by the pioneers and the record-breakers. The need for instruments of control more precise and accurate than those which served in the first world war was demonstrated by some of the earliest record flights. Ross and Keith Smith, who made the first flight from England to Australia in 1919 in a Vimy, found that blind flying could not be safely undertaken with the help only of such instruments as they had. These consisted of an air-speed indicator to warn the pilot of involuntary diving or climbing, an inclinometer for lateral stability, a compass for direction, and an altimeter. In combination these could reveal a sideslip, but they could not prescribe the amount of correction necessary to counteract it ; and the Vimy nearly sideslipped into the mountains of Siam during cloud-flying on its nineteenth day out from England.

The development of navigational instruments received a similar stimulus from the demands of pilots who were determined to make the aeroplane do difficult things. The gyroscopic compass was one result. The device for automatic observation and recording of celestial bodies was another.

The degree of accuracy obtainable from frequent shots at the sun was shown when Francis Chichester set out in a Moth from Auckland to fly 500 miles over the sea to Bull Island, a tiny piece of land about a mile and a half long. His success rested on frequent sextant shots and the subsequent plotting of position lines on his chart.

He had practised for this event by running along the beach at Auckland and taking shots with the sextant over his shoulder as he ran. When he came to take similar observations while he flew his Moth, he knew he could trust the angles of elevation; and his location of Bull Island proved it. Long-distance flying to-day is invariably associated with celestial navigation. Chichester's lone flights from Auckland were made by a specialist in navigation and now observation and the recording of observation is done in the bigger aircraft by means of a somewhat bulky instrument.

Meanwhile, the private pilot was beginning to test the claims made for directional wireless. John Grierson in 1930 made a plan to fly a Moth seaplane to America by way of Iceland and Greenland with the help of a homing loop. Having failed at the first attempt because of a mishap at Reykjavik, he repeated his attempt with a Fox Moth on floats. In the course of these two attempts he acquired a fair knowledge of the possibilities and the limitations of directional wireless—sufficient to encourage further work on this subject.

Slow Adoption

No-one would pretend that Britain exploited all the ideas that were thrown up by the adventurous souls who went blazing new trails and creating new records. Our genius for discovering things and failing to make full use of them has been as fully demonstrated in aeronautics as in other fields. Short Brothers, for instance, were the first aircraft manufacturers to make use of

The first de Havilland Moth 2-seat light aeroplane.

[Photo: ' Flight '

stressed-skin construction, but as a nation we were extremely slow in making full use of their discovery and others forged ahead of us for a time. A still more startling piece of waste was the neglect of the swept-back wing as a means of reducing drag, from the time of Dunne's flying wing of 1911 until the appearance of the Pterodactyl in 1930 and then again until the Germans showed us its value near the sonic speed barrier towards the end of 1944.

During the years between the wars there was a real community of the air. Knowledge gained by British airmen was generally at the disposal of the airmen of other nations. Exchange of information was free and almost unrestricted. The Cierva Autogiro, which had its beginnings in England, was developed simultaneously in the United States. Radio aids to navigation were improved, partly in one country and partly in another. Proposals for variable-pitch airscrews were put forward by two British scientists, Hele-Shaw and Beecham, and were so tardily taken up in Britain that the first airscrews of this kind to be used on a British aeroplane came from France, for the D.H. Comet which won the MacRobertson race to Australia in 1934.

Direction-finding grew up in one form in Britain and Europe; in another form in the United States. Turn and bank indicators in Britain were matched by artificial horizons in America. The gyroscope was made to serve the needs of the aeroplane through one form of compass, automatic pilot and blind-flying instrument in Britain and other forms elsewhere. Progress along these lines was to be attributed to the requirements chiefly of civil flying and to the enterprise which sprang from the pioneering of British pilots, yet behind all this there ran also a current of military needs, small in volume and velocity until the clouds began to gather again and pre- cautions against war had to be taken. From that point in 1935

when Britain resolved on rearmament, the R.A.F. became interested in other matters besides speed; and out of that concern for air defence came the greatest advance in the art of direction-finding and the provision of aids to navigation.

Radar

Radiolocation, or radar to adopt the more convenient American term, was a wholly British product. The principle of reflecting radio impulses back from distant objects had been examined and tried as a means of determining the height of an aeroplane above the earth or the depth of water beneath a ship. Radar stepped beyond the range of frequencies which had hitherto been available to radio and applied the principle of the radio echo to purposes of detection and location for which radio had never been considered. It was investigated in secrecy and its apparatus was manufactured in Britain under the strictest safeguards.

Before the war began, it had been tested while air exercises were in progress. Soon after the war began it was given the most stringent test with the help of a civilian pilot. Philip Wills, who held most of the British gliding records, was towed in a glider across to the French coast and, having been released at a sufficient height, flew his sailplane back across the Channel to England, so that the radar stations

The Supermarine S.6B seaplane, winner of the Schneider Trophy for Britain in 1931.

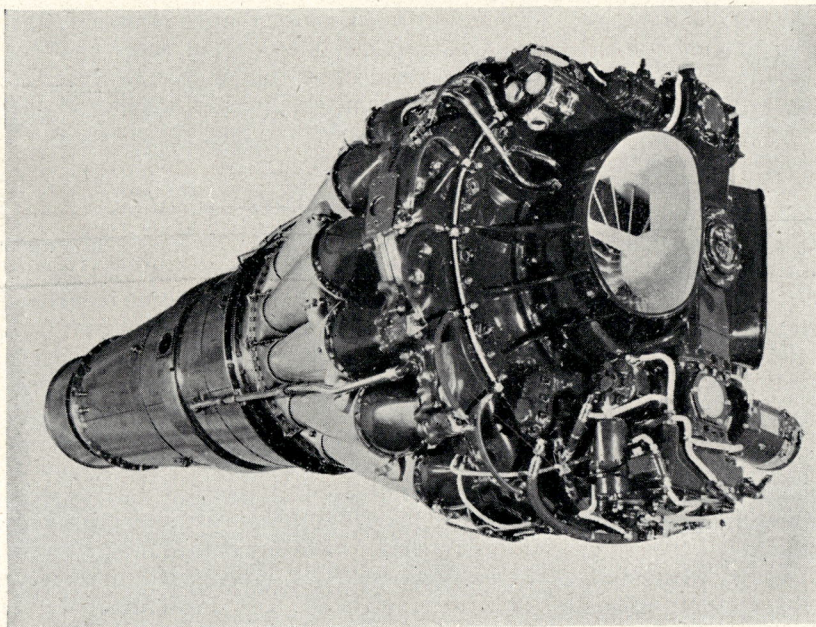

De Havilland Goblin
gas turbine.

might be tested for the detection of wooden aircraft. We knew then that with radar in our service, we could not be surprised, except by enemy aircraft flying at sea-level or near it.

The system was later adapted for use as an aid to navigation. The radar system known as Gee was of great value to British bombers and there were other variations which allowed targets in enemy territory to be exactly located and then marked by flares for bombing, often through cloud, by the main force. Gee is now being accepted as a standard navigational aid on commercial air routes. If necessary, a radar aid to landing in poor visibility can also be provided. Britain was alone in devising, testing and using radar for these purposes during the early years of the war. At a later stage, the resources of the United States were employed to help in putting the airborne apparatus into compact form and in manufacturing apparatus on a big scale.

Jet-Propulsion

There is no exact parallel between the exploitation of radar and the equally successful leadership of Britain in the gas-turbine field. Work on gas turbines and on jet-propulsion was being done before the war in Switzerland, Italy and Germany as well as by Frank Whittle in England. Whereas Britain had no competitors in her radar work, she had several in her efforts to make the gas turbine serve the theory of reaction-propulsion. Not only were there competitors but there was a lack of official interest and encouragement in the early days of the work which would have taken the heart out of any less stubborn genius than Frank Whittle.

Again the threat of war came to the rescue. A revolution in aircraft engines and consequently in aircraft design was at hand and

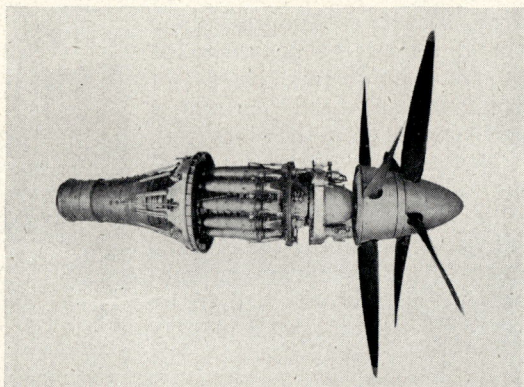

Armstrong Siddeley Python gas turbine driving
airscrews.

the State waited until the last minute before acknowledging it and helping to bring it to pass. Having decided to foster it, the State took a course which made the inventor furious and yet yielded enormous dividends. It took over his company and allotted to it the duty of research and development. At the same time, it called in a private aero-engine manufacturer to make the gas turbines which were to be used in aircraft. It also wisely called on the metallurgical industry to undertake the production of metals capable of heavy duty at high temperatures and capable of being moulded only at somewhat higher temperatures.

Between the work of Frank Whittle and his colleagues in Power Jets Ltd. of the engine firms, of Rolls-Royce Ltd., Metropolitan-Vickers Ltd. and of the Mond Nickel Co., Britain succeeded in marching ahead of the rest of the world in gas turbines. Through the skill of the designing and test flying teams of the Gloster Aircraft Co. the products of this co-operation were put into the air and jet-propulsion had arrived for Britain.

Notwithstanding her late start, Britain had from the outset a better gas turbine than any of her competitors. She was a little behind Germany in applying the jet to high speeds, but she paid less heavily in human life for every step forward she took; and now, with Germany out of the race, Britain stands pre-eminent as a producer of gas turbines and as a user of them in fast fighter aircraft.

A more efficient and more durable product was provided by British industry than was available in any other land. That distinction still rests with Britain. The most promising start has also been made by this country in turning to account in terms of flying, the peculiar properties of jet-propulsion. With the gas turbine, plentiful power from small, light units became available and the aeroplane designer could contemplate speeds which had been beyond his reach. By using jet-propulsion, he could escape from the limitations of airscrew tip speeds. Difficulties arising out of local velocities near the speed of sound were transferred from the agent of

thrust to the airframe. In consequence a revolution in airframe design is now in progress.

Britain stands a fair chance of leading that revolution, partly because she has already

The de Havilland Comet, winner of the England–Australia race in 1934.

accumulated so large a fund of experience in high-speed flying. She may lead the world, too, in applying her discoveries to commercial as well as military ends. But that is by no means so certain. Britain is still more cautious than some of her contemporaries. That is not perhaps a serious fault, especially as there are no signs of her losing the zest or declining the risks in finding solutions to new problems. This method of discovery, followed by careful development, may have an appearance of indolence and may lack the flash and sparkle of more spectacular ways; and yet it has paid Britain quite handsomely.

The modern fighter, the flying-boat, the gas turbine, the big four-engine aeroplane, high-speed and high-flying aeroplanes, jet-propulsion, radar, the light aeroplane and a host of lesser products stand as a record of what Britain has done by her system of adventure allied with plodding and thorough development. Much diffused effort is now coming together in the processes of centralisation which complication and expansion compel. So long as the tradition and spirit of British aeronautics persist, the triumphs of the future should match those of the past.

Above.—The Avro Tudor II designed for Britain's Empire air routes. *Below.*—A British Overseas Airways' Avro York developed from the Lancaster bomber.

BRITISH AIR TRANSPORT

by

John Stroud

Formerly member of the publicity staff of Imperial Airways. Author of 'Japanese Aircraft', 'Red Air Force', etc. Mr. Stroud will also be remembered for his drawings and descriptions of war-time aircraft in service which appeared in 'The Aeroplane'.

THE OPERATION of British scheduled air transport has been made the responsibility of three State-owned corporations. These corporations are the British European Airways Corporation, British Overseas Airways Corporation and British South American Airways Corporation, normally known by their initials.

B.E.A.C. is responsible for all scheduled air routes between the United Kingdom and European destinations and within the British Isles except those between the United Kingdom and Eire; B.O.A.C. is responsible for all overseas services from Britain with the exception of those to Europe, Central and South America; B.S.A.A.C. has the job of connecting Britain with the Central and South Americas.

In order to understand the present operation of British air services it is well to look back over our air transport history. On 5th October 1916, in the midst of World War I, and the first large-scale use of aircraft for military purposes, Aircraft Transport and Travel Limited was formed to carry air traffic. George Holt Thomas was the Managing Director. Eighteen months later, in April 1918, two Handley Page 0/400 bombers of the R.A.F. began the first cross-Channel air services for the carriage of ferry pilots engaged in delivering aeroplanes to France. In November of the same year, Aircraft Transport and Travel Limited announced that arrangements were being made for a London–Paris service. During that year the first flights were made between England and Egypt, Egypt and 'Iraq and Egypt and India, while between December 1918 and January 1919 the first England–India flight was accomplished.

No. 1 (Communications) Squadron Royal Air Force was formed in December 1918 to provide transport between London and Paris for members of the Government attending the Peace Conference. For some time this and other communications squadrons maintained regular services between Britain and France, Belgium and Germany, for the carriage of personnel and air mail.

In June 1919, Captain John Alcock, D.S.C. and Lieutenant A. Whitten Brown made the first direct flight across the North Atlantic. Starting at Harbour Grace, Newfoundland, in a Vickers Vimy 2-motor biplane, this flight ended 15 hours 57 minutes later on a bog at Clifden in Ireland.

The First Commercial Flights

The 14th of that June saw the incorporation of Handley Page Transport Limited. On 13th July the first commercial flights took place between London and Paris when Captain H. G. Shaw flew the Aircraft Transport and Travel Limited Airco 9 biplane G—EAAC from Hendon to Le Bourget. On the same day Handley Page Transport Limited flew an 0/400 converted bomber from the company's aerodrome at Cricklewood to Le Bourget by way of Hounslow (then the London Airport). One week later Lieutenant-Colonel W. Sholto Douglas, then chief pilot of Handley Page Transport and now Marshal of the Royal Air Force Sir William Sholto Douglas, G.C.B., K.C.B., M.C., D.F.C., flew an 0/400 on the first

A de Havilland 4A converted for passenger carrying and used by the Royal Air Force Communications Squadrons on the first cross-Channel air services in 1918 and 1919.

commercial flight between London and Brussels.

Twenty-fifth August 1919 was a notable day in the history of British air transport, for on that day Aircraft Transport and Travel Limited and Handley Page Transport Limited both flew services between London and Paris, the former starting from Hounslow, the latter from Cricklewood, both using Le Bourget as the Paris terminal. Major E. L. Foot, M.C., flying a Handley Page biplane with eleven passengers was first away and he was followed by Lieutenant E. H. (Bill) Lawford flying the Airco 4 G EAJC. Major Cyril Patterson flying an A.T. & T. Airco 16 also operated a service that day. The A.T. & T. service began regular operations on this date, whereas the H.P. service began regular working on 31st August followed on 21st September by a London–Brussels service.

The single fare between London and Paris was £15 15s. 0d.; to-day the return fare is £14. 8s. 0d. It was actually much cheaper in 1939.

In October 1919 the first British internal air services were flown by the Royal Air Force. These services linked London with Bristol, Birmingham, Newcastle, Manchester and Glasgow and were for the carriage of mails only. Introduced during the Railway Strike, these services were short-lived, lasting but six days.

The shipowners S. Instone and Company Limited began a private air service between Cardiff and Paris via London on 13th October 1919. Using a converted de Havilland 9A flown by Captain S. L. Barnard

this service was for the transport of company's staff and documents. From this service grew a considerable organisation for the carriage of passengers between England and the Continent.

Before the end of 1919 the first flight between England and Australia had taken place. The flight was made in a Vickers Vimy flown by Captain Ross M. Smith, D.F.C., A.F.C., and Lieutenant R. M. Keith Smith from Hounslow to Port Darwin.

Without Government assistance and in face of heavily subsidised foreign competition the British companies could not survive and on 30th October 1920 Handley Page Transport Limited ceased to operate its London–Amsterdam service. Less than three weeks later the company withdrew its London–Paris service and one month later Aircraft Transport and Travel Limited ceased to operate all its services.

Instone Air Line continued to operate after this date and Daimler Hire Limited (successor to Aircraft Transport and Travel Ltd.) and the British Marine Air Navigation Company Limited came into the picture, the latter with a flying-boat service between Southampton and Guernsey begun in 1923.

The Formation of Imperial Airways

The first attempt to put British air transport on a sound footing came on 1st April 1924 with the incorporation of Imperial Airways Limited as the ' chosen instrument ' of the

[Photo : ' Flight '

An Airco 16 used by Aircraft Transport and Travel on the first commercial air services between England and France in 1919.

British Government with the mission of developing British Commercial Air Transport on an economic basis. Imperial Airways was formed out of Handley Page Transport Limited, Instone Air Line Limited, Daimler Hire Limited and the British Marine Air Navigation Company Limited.

The company's fleet was made up of the 2-motor 10-passenger Vickers Vimy Commercial *City of London* and four single-motor 8-passenger de Havilland 34s taken over from Instone Air Line; the three 2-motor 14-passenger Handley Page W8b biplanes *Princess Mary*, *Prince Henry* and *Prince George* from Handley Page Transport; three further de Havilland 34s from Daimler Hire and three single-motor 6-passenger Supermarine Sea Eagle amphibian flying-boats from British Marine Air Navigation.

The land-plane operations of Imperial Airways were based on Croydon Airport which had been opened on 25th March 1920.

Imperial Airways had the job of getting British European air routes reopened and also of developing air communications between Britain and the Empire, the latter requiring a vast amount of planning, surveying and negotiating. In addition suitable aircraft had to be designed with which to operate both European and Empire routes, the latter entailing flying in greatly varying extremes of climate in much of which little regular flying had been undertaken.

The company quickly got down to the European services, opening daily services to Paris on 26th April, between Southampton and Guernsey on 1st May, London to Brussels, Ostend and Cologne on 3rd May and a summer service from London to Basle and Zürich via Paris. On 3rd November the first new airliner was commissioned by Imperial Airways—this was the 3-motor 12-passenger Handley Page W8f *City of Washington*.

In the first year of operation the company flew 853,042 miles; 391,032 traffic ton-miles; carried 11,395 passengers and 212,380 letters. 'Traffic ton-mile' is the unit used in transport comparison and is obtained by multiplying the weight of paid traffic in tons by the distance the tons are flown. This includes passengers, mail, baggage and freight.

The Start of the Empire Routes

By 1st October 1925 operational and technical surveys of the Cairo–Karachi air route had been completed by the Air Ministry and Imperial Airways.

1926 brought a large increase in the company's fleet.

[Photo: 'Flight'

A Handley Page 0/400 of Handley Page Transport about to leave Hounslow for Paris on 25th August 1919.

The 3-motor 14-passenger Handley Page W9 *City of New York*, and the 2-motor 14-passenger Handley Page W10s *City of Melbourne*, *City of Pretoria*, *City of London* and *City of Ottawa* were all christened at a ceremony at Croydon on 31st March; the new 18–20-seat 3-motor Armstrong Whitworth Argosy class began service on the London–Paris route on 16th July and the first of the 3-motor de Havilland *Hercules* airliners designed for the Egypt–India service left England for Egypt on 20th December. Seven days later a fortnightly service was begun between Egypt and 'Iraq. This was the first stage in the building up of the large network of British Empire air routes.

The first flying-boats designed for Imperial Airways were the Short Calcutta 3-motor metal-hulled boats built in 1928. These

A de Havilland 18 of Aircraft Transport and Travel. This was the forerunner of the de Havilland 34 of 1922.

boats were of similar design to the 2-motor Short Singapore in which Sir Alan Cobham had made his valuable 20,000 miles' flying-boat survey of Africa from November 1927 to June 1928. The Calcuttas went into service on the Mediterranean section of the weekly London–Karachi service which began on 30th March 1929. Later the same year the route was extended to Jodhpur and Delhi.

In 1930 Imperial Airways began a thrice-weekly internal air service linking London, Birmingham, Manchester and Liverpool. These services connected with European services at Croydon and worked from 16th June until 20th September when they were closed through lack of support.

In April the operational technical and commercial survey of the Cairo–Cape Town route was completed and on 28th February 1931 the first part of this route was opened when a weekly service began between London and M'wanza in Tanganyika. Calcutta flying-boats were used on the trans-Mediterranean section and south along the Nile from Cairo.

The Australian route was also developing in 1931 and on 1st April the first experimental London–Australia air mail flight left London. At Koepang in the Netherlands East Indies the mail was transferred to an Australian aircraft and it arrived in Sydney on 29th April. A second trial took place between 25th April and 14th May.

The First 4-Motor Airliners

The year 1931 was an historic one for fleet introductions when two types of 4-motor airliners came into service.

On 27th April the *Scipio*, first of three 16-passenger Short flying-boats left England for work in the Mediterranean, while the *Hannibal*, first of the world famous Handley Page 42s, operated on the London–Paris route for the first time on 11th June. Two classes of these airliners were built, the 24-seat *Hannibal* class for work on the Egypt–India and Egypt–Central Africa routes and the 38-seat *Heracles* class for European routes. Powered by four 490–555 h.p. Bristol Jupiter motors and carrying stewards serving full course meals in the air, these aircraft set a new standard in air travel. Eight of these airliners were built and each flew well over a million miles.

The England–Central Africa service was extended to the Cape on 20th January 1932 for the carriage of mails. Passengers first left London by air for South Africa on 27th April.

At the beginning of 1933 Imperial Airways introduced its first 4-motor monoplanes. These were the Armstrong Whitworth

[*Photo: 'Flight'*]

Instone Air Line's famous Vickers Vimy Commercial *City of London* taking-off from Croydon Airport.

Imperial Airways' Handley Page W10 *City of Melbourne* over the Rhine at Basle.

Atalantas which operated from Central Africa to Cape Town and east of Karachi, as the service was extended to Calcutta on 6th July, Rangoon on 23rd September and Singapore on 9th December. These aircraft had a cruising speed of 125 m.p.h. and a top speed of 155 m.p.h.

It was also in 1933 that Imperial Airways completed its first 10,000,000 miles of flying.

To Australia

The year 1934 brought with it the beginning of further great steps in the development of British Empire air routes, the first coming on the eighteenth day of the year with the formation of Qantas Empire Airways Limited. Combining the interests of Imperial Airways and Qantas (Queensland and Northern Territory Aerial Services Limited), the Australian company was formed in November 1920 and under the leadership of Mr. Hudson Fysh developed air routes in Queensland and Northern Territory. The shares in the new company were held 50 per cent. by each concern, and its object was to operate in association with Imperial Airways the Trans-Australian route. On 8th December, the London–Singapore route was extended to Brisbane for the carriage of mail, the Singapore–Brisbane section being operated by Qantas Empire Airways. Passengers were carried over the entire England–Australia route from April 1935.

In March 1934 a network of services was begun in Nyasaland and Rhodesia with the opening of a weekly service between Blantyre (Nyasaland) and Salisbury (Southern Rhodesia). These services were operated by Rhodesia and Nyasaland Airways (R.A.N.A.), a company in association with Imperial Airways.

The operation of the Singapore–Brisbane section of the Australia route had entailed the production of a new type of airliner suitable for the service. It was the de Havilland 86, a 4-motor 10-passenger biplane having a top speed of 175 m.p.h. An order for this type was placed by Imperial Airways for service on certain of its continental and Empire routes in addition to those built for Qantas Empire Airways. Imperial Airways commissioned the first of these new airliners on 25th May 1934 under the class name *Diana*. The Qantas aircraft worked under the class name *Commonwealth*, individual aircraft being named *Adelaide*, *Brisbane*, *Canberra*, *Melbourne* and *Sydney*.

The introduction of a 'flat' rate for air mails to certain destinations on the Empire air routes was made on 17th November, with rates of 3d. per ½ oz. to the Near East and 6d. to East and South Africa, India and Malaya. Before 1934 drew to its end, the British Government announced that 'beginning in 1937, as a matter of principle, letter mails dispatched from the United Kingdom for delivery within the British Empire will,

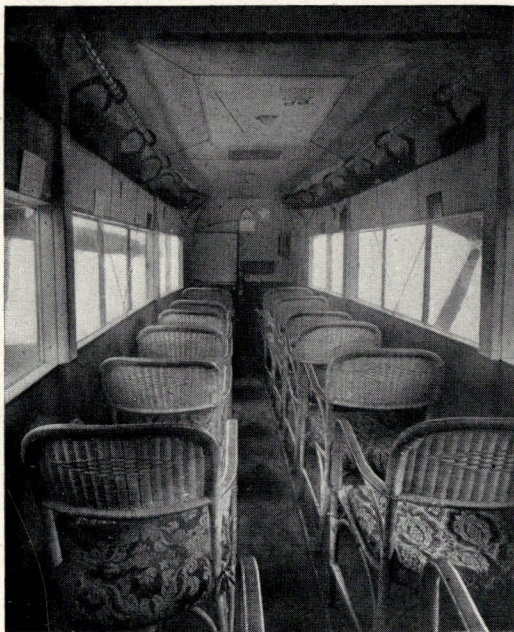

The cabin of an Imperial Airways' Handley Page W 8b of 1924.

so far as is practicable, be carried by air without surcharge'.

Imperial Airways' improved fleet position due to delivery of the *Diana* class made new European routes possible and so on 1st April 1935 the company opened a new daily service between London and Budapest via Brussels–Cologne–Prague and Vienna, operated with the new class of airliner. During that year the frequency of both the London–Singapore and London–Johannesburg services was doubled.

Further work for *Diana* class airliners was found in 1936 with the opening on 19th February of a weekly mail service between Kano in Nigeria and London. The *Diana* class worked between Kano and Khartoum where this West African service joined the main Africa trunk route. This service later carried passengers and the route terminal was extended on 15th October to Lagos and on 13th October 1937 to Accra on the Gold Coast. The pioneer work done by Imperial Airways on this West Africa route was invaluable during the war, when this route became a main air supply artery to the Middle East. Starting on 14th March 1935, another

Diana operated service was introduced, this time between Penang and Hong Kong. Linking with the main Australia route at Penang, this gave for the first time a weekly service between London and Hong Kong. Later on this connection was made at Bangkok.

It was in 1936 that South African Airways came into the scheme of British Empire trunk air services when it took over on 24th March the operation of the England–South Africa route between Johannesburg and Cape Town. South African Airways is now working in collaboration with British Overseas Airways on the present *Springbok* service between London and South Africa.

A Great Year

Looking back over a decade, 1936 was a truly outstanding year, for it was on 30th October of that year that the *Canopus*, first of the great fleet of Short Empire flying-boats, made its first service flight on a trans-Mediterranean service. Taking a very bold step, Imperial Airways ordered twenty-eight of these advanced 4-motor monoplanes straight off the drawing-board without awaiting trials of the first aircraft. This class of flying-boat was a great success and subsequently further orders for this type brought up the number to forty-two.

These flying-boats were built to put into operation the Empire Air Mail Programme and they probably did more for British air transport than any other type of aircraft built. The last of these boats are only now being withdrawn from service as this history is being written. Two of the first batch of Empire flying-boats built were long-range aircraft and the first of these, the *Caledonia*, on 21st to 22nd December flew 1,700 miles from Alexandria to Southampton via Marseilles in fifteen and a half hours.

In the first twelve years of operation, Imperial Airways' operating figures had risen for the year 1935–36 to 68,372 passengers carried, 30,997,575 letters carried, 4,560,718 miles flown and 4,803,427 traffic ton-miles. The totals for the twelve years were 446,455 passengers carried, 90,159,363 letters carried, 20,591,230 miles flown and 19,100,395 traffic ton-miles.

For some time it had been necessary for Imperial Airways to carry passengers by train between Paris and the Mediterranean on the Empire routes. With the introduction of the Empire flying-boats an all-air route commenced on 16th January 1937 operating from Southampton by way of Marseilles–Rome–Brindisi–Athens and Alexandria. Following this improvement all Empire services were operated from Southampton on and after 5th March, Croydon being the base for European services only.

During May 1937 Imperial Airways completed its 40,000th service across the English Channel and also its 1,000th service from England to the Empire. In the same month, actually on the 15th, land aircraft were withdrawn from the England–South Africa route as far south as Kisumu in Kenya Colony. Empire flying-boats operated these services, using once again the Nile bases employed earlier by the Calcutta boats. On 2nd June the flying-boats took over the entire route which was switched to fly down the East coast of Africa from Mombasa with the terminal transferred to Durban.

The first British Atlantic air service began on 16th June when Imperial Airways and Pan American Airways began a joint service between Bermuda and New York. The British service was flown by the Empire flying-boat the *Cavalier*.

The 'All-Up' Mails

The Empire Air Mail Programme was inaugurated on 29th June 1937 when the Empire flying-boat the *Centurion* left Southampton with 3,500 lb. of non-surcharged mail for South and East Africa. All mail was carried at 1½d. per ½ oz. and this made it possible to post airborne letters in ordinary

[*Copyright: Charles Brown*

Imperial Airways' Armstrong Whitworth Argosy *City of Glasgow* flying over the Thames on one of the Imperial Airways' 'Tea Flights' which used to be flown over London.

137

The *City of Karachi*, one of Imperial Airways' de Havilland *Hercules* airliners, the first type designed for use on the Empire routes.

red letter boxes and without air mail labels.

The C-class Empire flying-boats were very much in the news during 1937. The *Caledonia* and *Cavalier* made a series of survey flights across the North Atlantic. On 27th to 28th September the *Cambria* made the fastest flight across the ocean and set up a record with a time of ten hours thirty-six minutes for the journey between Botwood (Newfoundland) and Foynes (Eire). The first of these survey flights was made by the *Caledonia* on 5th to 6th July.

Other Empire flying-boat surveys made in 1937 were Southampton–Lisbon on 6th July by the *Cambria*, the first Alexandria–Karachi Empire flying-boat survey 6th to 9th September by the *Ceres*, the second Alexandria–Karachi survey 18th to 20th September by the *Centaurus*, Southampton–Azores 6th to 7th October by the *Caledonia*, Karachi–Singapore 15th to 21st November by the *Cordelia*, and Southampton–Sydney–Auckland 3rd to 27th December by the *Centaurus*.

Following the surveys to Karachi, Empire flying-boats went into service between England and India on 3rd October. The *Clio* operated the first service as far as Alexandria from where the *Calypso* continued the service.

Summing up 1937, Imperial Airways had commissioned the world's largest fleet of commercial flying-boats, changed from 100 m.p.h. land aircraft to 165 m.p.h. flying-boats on both the Africa and India routes, inaugurated the Empire Air Mail Programme, made ten crossings of the North Atlantic to schedule, taken the first step in opening the longest air route in the world—15,000 miles from England to New Zealand—carried over 70,000 passengers and flown over

Imperial Airways' Short Calcutta flying-boat *City of Stonehaven* refuelling on the Nile at Kareima.

[*Photograph:*
B. C. H. Cross

6,000,000 miles—a fine achievement for British air transport.

In 1938 the schedules on the Empire routes were accelerated, and the following services and times were in force from April. England–Egypt 7 services a week—30 hours, England–India 4 services a week—3 days, England–East Africa 3 services a week —3 days, England–South Africa 2 services a week — 5 days, England – Australia 2 services a week—9 days, England–Hong Kong 2 services a week—6 days, and England–Gold Coast 1 service a week —4½ days.

The air mail figures for the first quarter of 1938 gave some idea of how the Empire Air Mail Programme was working. The scheme had already taken in India and in three months over 100 tons of mail had been flown on the Africa route and nearly 100 tons on the India route. This facility had given a great service and loud praise for our performance was forthcoming from the United States from which country only two tons of air mail were carried every week in 1937. Australia, New Zealand, Tasmania, Papua, Fiji, Norfolk Island, Lord Howe Island, Nauru, The Mandated Territory of Western Samoa and the Territories under the Jurisdiction of the High Commissioner for the Western Pacific were brought into the Programme on 28th July.

[Photo : John Stroud

The *Horatius*, one of the famous Imperial Airways' Handley Page *Heracles* class of airliner.

More New Airliners

Two new classes of airliner were commissioned by Imperial Airways during 1938. They were the 20-ton 4-motor Armstrong Whitworth *Ensigns* produced in two versions, a 27-passenger Eastern type for use on Empire routes and a 40-passenger Western type for Europe. The Empire type saw some service on European routes, carried heavy mail loads during the Christmas period in 1938 and did some valuable work between the United Kingdom and France in 1939 and 1940. Although the *Ensigns* were used by B.O.A.C. in the Empire the war prevented the *Ensign* airliners from carrying out the duties for which they were designed. Contributing to their failure was the fact that the aircraft were about two years late in being delivered to Imperial Airways, largely due to rearmament and trouble with the Tiger motors originally installed.

The second class of Imperial airliner introduced in 1938 was the de Havilland *Albatross*, known as the *Frobisher* class. An all-wood design, the *Albatross* was a beautiful 4-motor monoplane with accommodation for twenty-one passengers and a high top speed of 234 m.p.h. Designed for European routes, this type set up a number of records for flights between European capitals

[Copyright : Fox Photos

Imperial Airways' flying-boat *Satyrus* flying the Greek flag and being refuelled at Crete. The *Satyrus* was one of the Short *Scipio* class.

The *Astraea*, one of Imperial Airways' Armstrong Whitworth *Atalanta* class airliners, seen landing at Kuala Lumpur.

including London–Brussels 200 miles in forty-eight minutes by the *Falcon*.

Flying the North Atlantic

One major problem of air transport has always been to get heavily-loaded aircraft into the air safely with a reasonably short take-off run. Imperial Airways experimented with two methods, assisted take-off and flight refuelling. The assisted take-off experiments were undertaken with the Short-Mayo composite aircraft. This aircraft consisted of the small low-powered float seaplane *Mercury* mounted on top of the large 4-motor flying-boat *Maia*, which was similar in design to the Empire flying-boats.

The *Mercury* was the aircraft designed to carry mail over long distances, but it did not

The Qantas Empire Airways' de Havilland 86 *Commonwealth* class airliner *Melbourne*.

have sufficient power to take-off from the water unassisted when carrying a full load of mail and fuel. For operation this aircraft was mounted on the back of the *Maia* (Mother of Mercury in mythology), and the aircraft took off using the power of all eight motors and the wing surface of both aircraft. After climbing to a suitable height the aircraft separated, *Mercury* to set course on its journey, *Maia* to return to base.

Commanded by D. C. T. Bennett, late of Pathfinder fame and Managing Director of the British South American Airways Corporation, the *Mercury* was first used in a successful North Atlantic trial when at 20.00 hours (BST) on 21st July 1938 it left the parent aircraft near Foynes (Eire)

Loading air mail on to a Qantas de Havilland Giant Moth at Archerfield Aerodrome, Brisbane, on 10th December 1934. This was the first Australia–England regular air mail.

and flew non-stop to Montreal, 2,930 miles in twenty hours twenty minutes. After off-loading cargo at Montreal, the *Mercury* flew on to New York with newspapers and news photographs, having flown from Foynes in twenty-five hours eight minutes. On these flights the *Mercury* had set up three new records, the first commercial flight across the North Atlantic by a 'heavier than air' machine, the first east to west crossing from the British Isles to Montreal and the fastest east to west crossing of the North Atlantic. The time taken from Foynes to the New-foundland coast was thirteen hours twenty-nine minutes. The *Mercury* played its part later in carrying Christmas mail between Southampton and Alexandria when, during the first three weeks of December 1938,

Building the *Canopus* in Short Brothers' works at Rochester in 1936. This was the first of the Empire flying-boats built for Imperial Airways.

Imperial Airways' fleet flew 420,000 miles in addition to regular services in order to carry Christmas mails.

The *Mercury* achieved further fame when in the autumn of 1938 this aircraft separated from the *Maia* near Dundee after taking-off from the Tay and flew 6,045 miles non-stop to Walvis Bay just short of Cape Town. This was the longest non-stop flight by a seaplane and the speed of 144 m.p.h. was the highest maintained on a long-distance test.

In the summer of 1939 the last type of aircraft designed for Imperial Airways was launched from Short Brothers' works at Rochester. This was the 33-ton flying-boat *Golden Hind* first of three in the class. War stopped this class of boat going into commercial service as planned, although it did war service on Atlantic patrols. One of these boats, the *Golden Fleece*, was lost on military service, the other two, *Golden Hind* and *Golden Horn*, being handed over to British Overseas Airways in 1941.

Flight Refuelling

Fifth to sixth August 1939 brought yet another stage in Imperial Airways' trans-atlantic experiments, for on these dates the modified C-class flying-boat, the *Caribou*, commanded by Captain J. C. Kelly Rogers, flew from Southampton to New York via Foynes, Botwood and Montreal. Carrying air mail on a scheduled flight this was the first of a series of flights by the *Caribou* and the *Cabot* in which the aircraft were refuelled in the air after leaving their bases.

Handley Page Harrow tanker aircraft of Flight Refuelling Limited were based in Eire and Newfoundland and the air refuelling took place after the flying-boats had taken off and set course for the ocean sector of the route.

War came during the 1939 programme of Atlantic flights, but the experiments were continued until the end of September as planned, the *Cabot* actually arriving in New York on the morning after war was declared.

Internal and Continental Airlines

Having reached the end of the story of Imperial Airways, which has had to be told far too briefly, it is necessary to go back in time in order to study, unfortunately even more briefly, the growth of British internal airlines as well as the airlines to the Continent operated by companies other than Imperial Airways.

The production of the de Havilland Dragon 8–10-seat biplane, powered by two 130 h.p. Gipsy Major motors, made the economical operation of short distance airlines a practical possibility. Hillmans Airways Limited, operating services between Romford and Clacton from 1932 with 2-passenger Puss Moths and 4-passenger Fox Moths, was the first company to operate the new Dragons. Five of these aircraft were put into service in 1933 and they were followed by the more powerful and still widely used Dragon Rapides in 1934. Using the Rapides, Hillmans were in 1934 operating services to Paris, Liverpool, Isle of Man and Belfast. The summer timetable of 1935 showed the company operating services from Essex airport at Abridge to Paris, Thanet, Ostend, Brussels, Liverpool, Manchester, Hull, Belfast and Glasgow, while in addition four services a day were operated in each direction between Thanet and Ostend. In 1935 Hillmans added five more Rapides to

its fleet and also commissioned three de Havilland 86 4-motor biplanes similar to the Imperial Airways *Diana* class.

Spartan Air Lines Limited, in the summer of 1933, began services between London and the Isle of Wight, using 3-motor Spartan Cruiser monoplanes. When the route re-opened in the summer of 1934 the services were announced as being operated in association with the Southern Railway.

In 1935 United Airways Limited came on the scene and flew services between London–Blackpool–Isle of Man, Carlisle–Isle of Man, and in conjunction with Northern and Scottish Airways Limited between Glasgow and Isle of Man. Blackpool–Liverpool, Blackpool–Leeds and Morecambe–Blackpool services were later added. These services were operated with Dragons, Dragon Rapides and Spartan Cruisers. In addition United Airways acquired the *City of Manchester*, one of Imperial Airways' *Argosy* airliners.

[*Copyright : Keystone*

The Empire flying-boat *Caledonia* flying over New York after completing the first of the North Atlantic flights in 1937.

Scottish Services

In Scotland, Midland and Scottish Air Ferries Limited had been working on services from Glasgow and in November 1934 a new company, Northern and Scottish Airways Limited was formed by Mr. George Nicholson. Northern and Scottish Airways, using Dragons and Spartan Cruisers, began services radiating from the Glasgow airport at Renfrew to Campbeltown and Islay in December 1934, Skye, Barra, South Uist, Benbecula and North Uist opened in stages in 1935 and 1936.

The history of air transport in the North of Scotland goes back to 1931, when after making joy-riding tours in the North and in Orkney, Captain E. E. Fresson, having discovered a demand for air transport across the Pentland Firth, began making survey flights northward from Inverness. In 1933 Highland Airways Limited was formed with Captain Fresson as Managing Director. Using a Monospar S.T.4 and Dragons, services from Inverness were opened to Kirkwall in Orkney on 8th May 1933, and to Shetland on 3rd June 1936. Orkney inter-island services were begun on 6th August 1934.

Captain Fresson carried the first regular British internal air mail, when Highland Airways received the first air mail pennant and left Inverness on 29th May 1934, with air mail for Kirkwall.

British Airways

A new company, Allied British Airways Limited, was incorporated in the autumn of 1935 to amalgamate Hillmans Airways, United Airways and Spartan Air Lines. Prior to this another company, British Continental Airways, had been operating services from Croydon to Holland and Germany. This company was taken into the new concern and Northern and Scottish Airways and Highland Airways were also controlled by it. Shortly after, the new company became British Airways Limited.

On taking over from the previous operators British Airways had a large fleet of aircraft which was made up of nine Spartan Cruisers, eight Dragons, thirteen Dragon Rapides, six de Havilland 86As, one Argosy, two Fox Moths, one Puss Moth, three Moths and a Spartan 3-seat biplane.

Northern and Scottish Airways and Highland Airways were not absorbed as were the other companies and so retained their individual identities and maintained their own fleets of aircraft. However, on 12th August 1937, the two companies came together and were incorporated as Scottish Airways Limited. The spheres of operation were as before, the N. and S.A. section being known as the Southern Area and the Highland section as the Northern Area. In May 1938 a new service from Renfrew to Inverness via Perth joined the routes operated by each area.

In addition to its internal interests, British Airways extended continental services to include the following routes: London–Paris, the Viking Royal Mail Express serving Hamburg, Copenhagen and Malmö or

The ceremony at Southampton shortly before the Empire flying-boat *Calypso* left with the first 'all up' mail for Australia in 1938.

[*Copyright: Topical Press*

The Routes of
BRITISH EUROPEAN AIRWAYS
1948

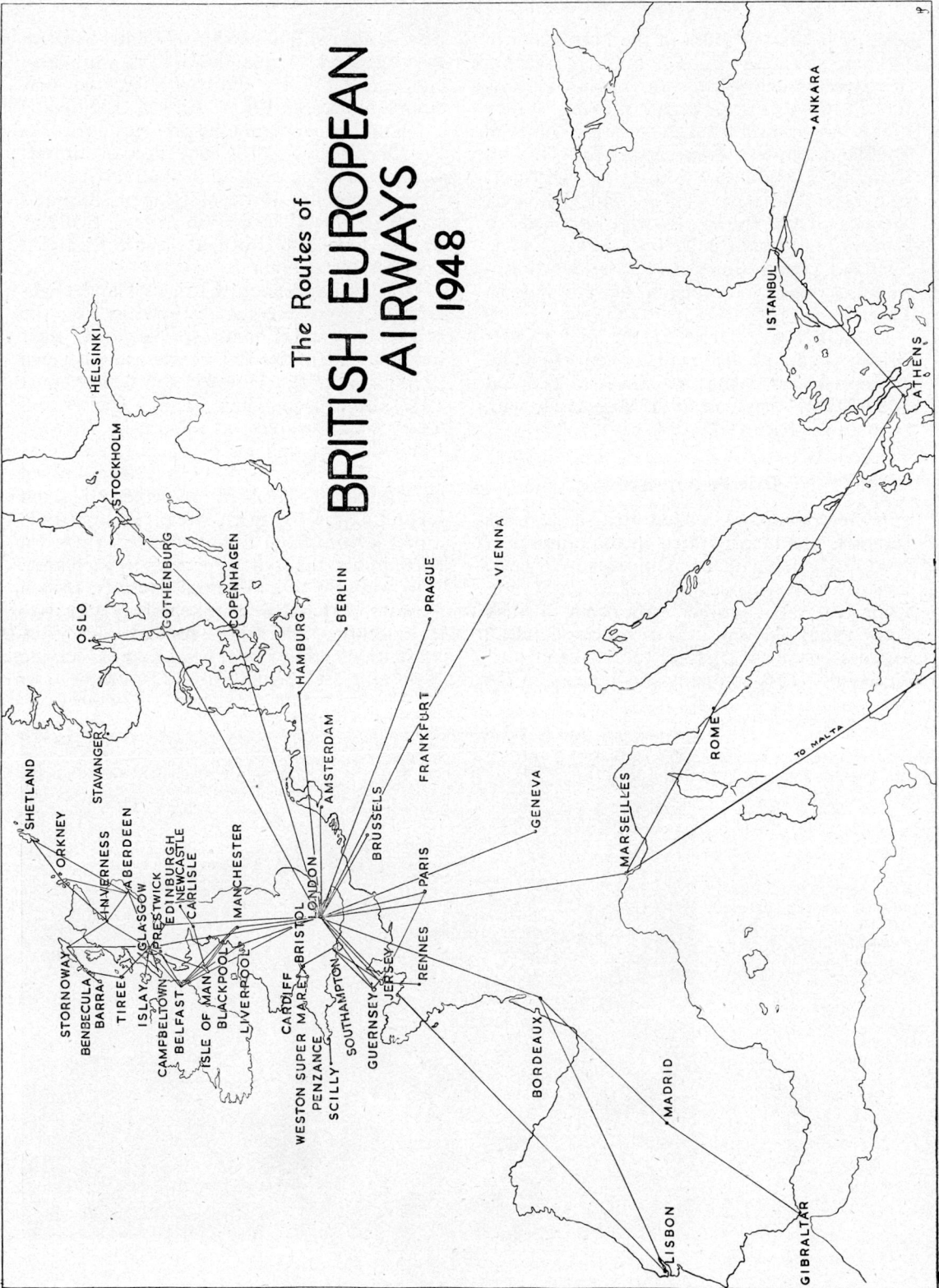

HELSINKI

STOCKHOLM

OSLO

ANKARA

ISTANBUL

ATHENS

GOTHENBURG

COPENHAGEN

HAMBURG

BERLIN

VIENNA

PRAGUE

FRANKFURT

AMSTERDAM

BRUSSELS

GENEVA

ROME

TO MALTA

MARSEILLES

SHETLAND

ORKNEY

STAVANGER

ABERDEEN

INVERNESS

EDINBURGH

NEWCASTLE

PRESTWICK

CARLISLE

GLASGOW

MANCHESTER

PARIS

STORNOWAY

BENBECULA

BARRA

TIREE

ISLAY

CAMPBELTOWN

BELFAST

ISLE OF MAN

BLACKPOOL

LIVERPOOL

CARDIFF

WESTON SUPER MARE

BRISTOL

LONDON

PENZANCE

SCILLY

SOUTHAMPTON

GUERNSEY

JERSEY

RENNES

BORDEAUX

MADRID

LISBON

GIBRALTAR

OTHER BRITISH AIR ROUTES

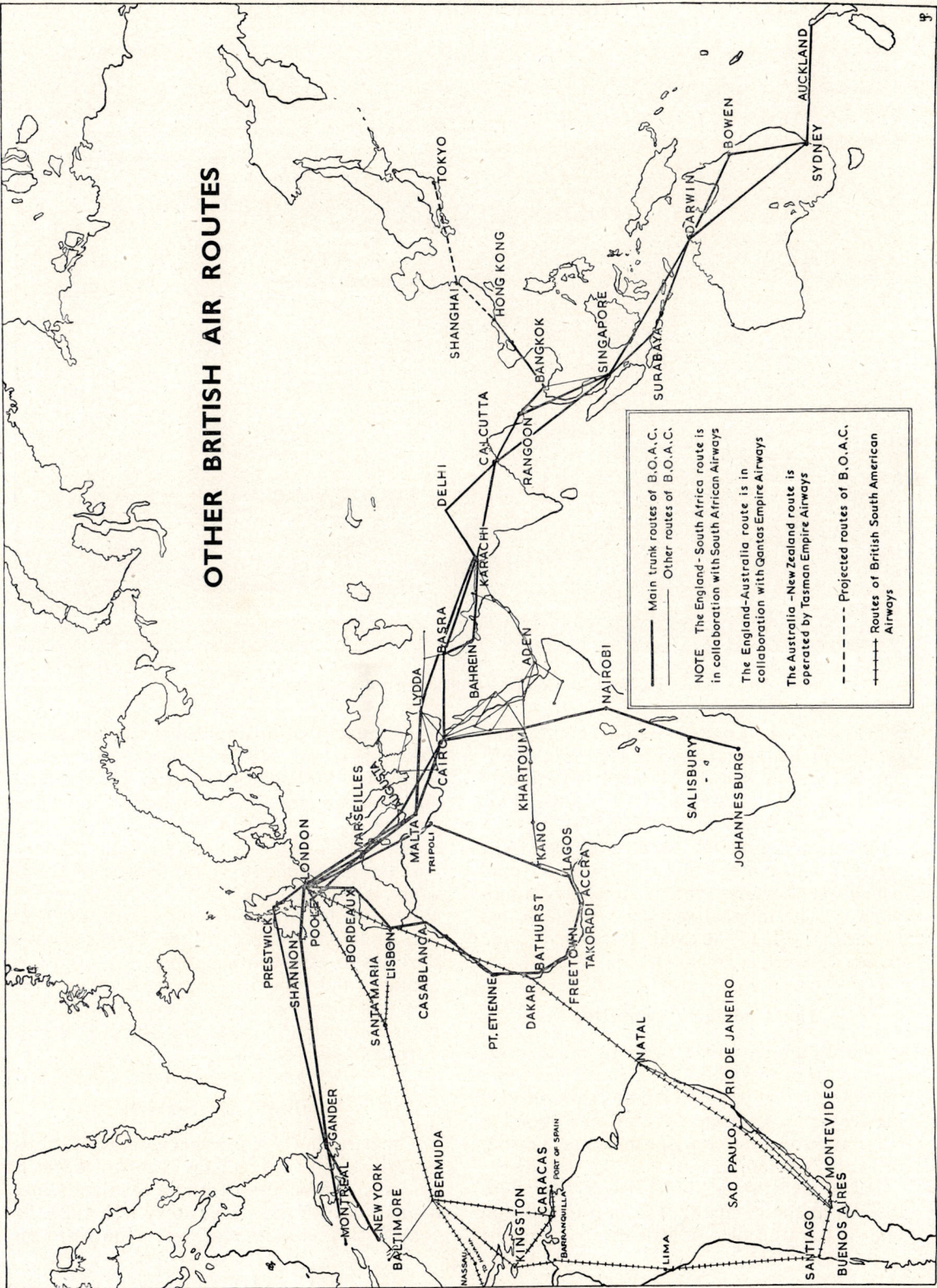

Main trunk routes of B.O.A.C.
Other routes of B.O.A.C.

NOTE The England-South Africa route is
in collaboration with South African Airways

The England-Australia route is in
collaboration with Qantas Empire Airways

The Australia-New Zealand route is
operated by Tasman Empire Airways

– – – – Projected routes of B.O.A.C.

++++++ Routes of British South American
Airways

AUCKLAND
BOWEN
SYDNEY
DARWIN
TOKYO
SHANGHAI
HONG KONG
BANGKOK
SINGAPORE
SURABAYA
RANGOON
CALCUTTA
DELHI
KARACHI
BASRA
BAHREIN
ADEN
NAIROBI
LYDDA
CAIRO
MARSEILLES
KHARTOUM
SALISBURY
JOHANNESBURG
LONDON
MALTA
TRIPOLI
KANO
LAGOS
TAKORADI
ACCRA
PRESTWICK
SHANNON
POOLE
BORDEAUX
LISBON
SANTA MARIA
CASABLANCA
PT. ETIENNE
DAKAR
BATHURST
FREETOWN
GANDER
MONTREAL
NEW YORK
BALTIMORE
BERMUDA
NASSAU
KINGSTON
CARACAS
PORT OF SPAIN
BARRANQUILLA
LIMA
NATAL
SAO PAULO
RIO DE JANEIRO
MONTEVIDEO
SANTIAGO
BUENOS AIRES

K

145

[Copyright : Topical Press

The *Maia* and *Mercury* immediately after separation.

Stockholm, a London–Berlin night mail service in conjunction with Deutsche Lufthansa, London–Brussels, London–Frankfurt–Budapest and London–Berlin–Warsaw. Fast Lockheed Electra and Lockheed 14 2-motor all-metal monoplanes were used on these services with the exception of the night mail which was flown by Junkers Ju 52/3m monoplanes. The internal services were operated by de Havilland 86 and Dragon Rapide types.

The Cadman Committee

The autumn of 1938 brought much criticism in the press and in Parliament concerning the operation of Imperial Airways and this led the Secretary of State for Air to appoint a committee of enquiry under the chairmanship of Lord Cadman.

Faults were found, but a lot of the abuse thrown at the company was unfounded and one of the tragedies of British air transport was the fact that this upheaval brought about the resignation of Mr. Woods Humphery, long the Managing Director of Imperial Airways and one of the men most responsible for the development of British airlines.

One of the results of the Cadman findings was the introduction to the House of Commons on 12th June 1939 by Sir Kingsley Wood of the British Overseas Airways Bill. This Bill gave effect to the Government's decision to establish a public corporation to acquire and operate the undertakings of Imperial Airways Limited and British Airways Limited. So came the British Overseas Airways Corporation.

Railway Air Services

The part played in internal communications by British Airways and the companies which preceded it was, apart from in Scotland, only a small part of the whole story. In 1929 the four British main line railways acquired from

146

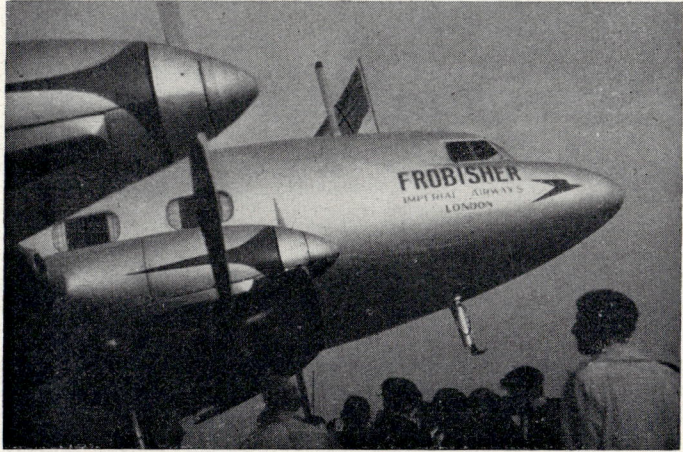

The Imperial Airways' de Havilland Albatross airliner *Frobisher* at Brussels.

The Imperial Airways' Armstrong Whitworth airliner *Ensign*.

Launching the flying-boat *Golden Hind* from Short Brothers' works at Rochester in 1939.

Jersey Airways' de Havilland Dragon *Rozel Bay*.

[*Photo*: '*Flight*'

Parliament powers enabling them to operate air services and in April 1933 the Great Western Railway introduced a service between Cardiff and Plymouth with a call at Haldon to serve Torquay and Teignmouth. The aircraft used was a Westland Wessex from Imperial Airways charter fleet. On 22nd May the route was extended from Cardiff to Birmingham and operated until 30th September when the service was withdrawn for the winter.

Railway Air Services Limited was registered on 21st March 1934 as a company composed of the four main line railways and Imperial Airways. By 7th May the company had reopened the Great Western service operated during the previous summer and had extended it to Liverpool. Another route began on 30th July with the inauguration of a service from Cowes to Birmingham by way of Southampton and Bristol. The company's main trunk route from London to Glasgow via Birmingham, Manchester and Belfast began on 20th August and was operated by two de Havilland 86s, the *Mercury* and the *Jupiter*.

The Railway Air Services' network was built up until in the summer of 1939 the following services were being operated—by a fleet of de Havilland 86s, Dragons and Dragon Rapides — London – Birmingham –

Manchester–Liverpool–Isle of Man–Belfast; London – Birmingham – Manchester – Liverpool–Glasgow; Glasgow–Belfast. Great Western and Southern Air Lines had also come into being and in that summer were operating Liverpool–Manchester–Birmingham–Bristol–Southampton–Isle of Wight–Brighton, Hove and Worthing; Scilly–Penzance–Plymouth–Exeter–Bristol.

Isle of Man Air Services Limited was at this time operating services linking the Isle of Man with Manchester, Liverpool, Blackpool, Glasgow and Carlisle.

War

The 3rd September 1939 brought war and stopped all internal airline operation, the companies placed their aircraft and crews at the service of the Air Ministry. These aircraft and crews did a lot of work on communications in the United Kingdom and between the United Kingdom and France. After a short delay, the companies were allowed to operate certain services—these were the most important ones, all of which involved over-water flying. Scottish Airways continued its services to the Hebrides, Orkneys and Shetlands; Great Western and Southern Air Lines flew between Land's End and the Scilly Isles; Railway Air Services maintained services from Liverpool and Glasgow to Belfast; Isle of Man Air Services continued operating from Liverpool to the Isle of Man; and West Coast Air Services maintained air communications between Liverpool and Dublin.

Jersey Airways and Guernsey Airways had built up efficient services between England and the Channel Islands and were busily engaged in evacuating people from the islands until the actual German occupation in 1940. Several of the internal services' aircraft were lost in France when services were interrupted so that aircraft and crews could assist in the great evacuation.

From that time Jersey and Guernsey Airways naturally ceased operations. The other companies already mentioned formed the Associated Airways Joint Committee, and it did magnificent work maintaining essential services with unarmed aircraft and frequently without radio aids. A Great Western and Southern Air Lines Dragon was shot down by a German aircraft while on its way between the Scilly Isles and the mainland and a number of other aircraft engaged on services encountered hostile aircraft. The only operator not within A.A.J.C. was Allied Airways (Gandar Dower) Limited operating services from Aberdeen to Orkney and Shetland.

B.O.A.C. in War

The story of British Overseas Airways' activities during the war cannot be told in detail here. It is only possible to give a very

[Photo: John Stroud

The Railway Air Services' de Havilland 86 Mercury.

short outline and to pick out certain of the outstanding achievements. Much of the valuable work undertaken by the Corporation was only made possible by the pioneer work of Imperial Airways in the fifteen years before. The work of British air transport during the war has been well told in the official publication Merchant Airmen produced by H.M. Stationery Office. This book of over 200 pages is well worth reading by those interested in a fuller account of the war-time air transport history, but even Merchant Airmen is unable to tell the full story in such small space.

The principal job of British Overseas Airways was to keep open Empire air communications with as few interruptions as possible, not an easy task as more and more sections of its routes came within enemy control. First sectors to be cut were the trans-European and trans-Mediterranean sections of the route which, of course, meant a serious interference with all routes to and from the British Isles. To meet this foreseen threat, a plan had been made for what was called the Horseshoe Route, that was a flying-boat service over the established route from Durban to Cairo, at which point it would be switched to follow the again established route to Sydney, thereby maintaining the original Australia and Africa routes from Egypt, but this meant the severance of these services from their main base in England, consequently depriving them of spares. This Horseshoe Route was put into operation.

By June 1940 the only air routes linking

[Photo: 'Flight'

Hillmans Airways' first de Havilland Fox Moth.

149

A Scottish Airways' de Havilland Dragon on the sands at **Barra in the** Outer Hebrides in 1939.

[*Photo : John Stroud*

British Airways' Lockheed 14 G–AFGN leaving Heston on 22nd September 1938 with the then British Prime Minister, The Rt. Hon. Neville Chamberlain, en route to Bad Godesberg for talks with Adolf Hitler.

[*Copyright : L.N.A.*

A British Overseas Airways' de Havilland Mosquito lines up on the runway at Leuchars in Fife, preparatory to taking-off for the night journey across enemy-occupied Norway to Stockholm.

[*British Official Photograph*

150

A British Overseas Airways' Avro Lancastrian used on the *Kangaroo* service to Australia.

[*Photo : Avro*

Britain with the outside world were between Poole and Lisbon, Liverpool and Dublin and Scotland and Sweden. Later in the summer the Empire flying-boats the *Clyde* and the *Clare* resumed the transatlantic flights.

On 6th August the *Clyde* left Poole and made a magnificent flight to West Africa and the Belgian Congo. This flight proved that it was possible to operate flying-boats between England and West Africa, and so by the winter of 1940–41 a link with the Empire routes had again been established, C-class

[*Photo : John Stroud*

In war camouflage a Scottish Airways' de Havilland Dragon Rapide arrives at Renfrew, the airport for Glasgow.

flying-boats flying between Poole and Lagos and land aircraft across the old trans-Africa route to link up with the Horseshoe Route. Later the flying-boats continued south from Lagos and then flew inland across the Belgian Congo, so giving two trans-Africa routes.

The Corporation's aircraft frequently performed duties in the various war theatres, which cannot be accepted as part of normal airline duties. Two of the Empire flying-boats were lost in Norway and others were used to assist in the Crete evacuation. B.O.A.C. worked closely with Air Marshal Tedder in the Middle East, and a great deal of transport flying was undertaken and many new services started throughout the area.

More major cuts in the Empire air routes came with the Japanese entry into the war, and the invasion of Siam, Malaya and the Dutch East Indies. Empire flying-boats of both B.O.A.C. and Qantas Empire Airways did wonderful work in evacuating these areas and also in supplying military forces. A large number of the flying-boats were lost through Japanese attacks, both while in the air and while the boats were at anchor on the water. The work of Qantas Empire Airways during this difficult time is told by E. Bennett Bremner in his book *Front Line Airline*, the war story of Qantas Empire Airways.

This break in the Australia route was closed in 1943 when B.O.A.C. and Q.E.A. opened the new service from Western Australia to Ceylon with Consolidated Catalina flying-boats. This route entailed a non-stop ocean crossing of over 3,000 miles.

Finally mention must be made of the night supply flights undertaken by B.O.A.C., between Britain and besieged Malta, the flights over enemy-occupied Norway between Scotland and Sweden (which were not operated without losses through enemy action), the special flights to the U.S.S.R. and, of course, the North Atlantic Return Ferry Service. Each of these subjects deserves much space, but here it cannot be given, though a few words must be said about the Atlantic service. In September 1941 this service was begun by B.O.A.C. to provide return transport across the North Atlantic for the pilots engaged in ferrying bombers across the ocean to Britain. This service was the first all the year round air service to be established over this ocean, and it created a wonderful record. It continued for some time after the war and completed five winters of operation. Finally operating daily, this service during the year ended April 1946 maintained a regularity of 99.7 per cent. Over 2,000 crossings were made in five years, over 20,000 passengers carried and nearly 4,000,000 lb. of mail and freight.

Return to Peace

With the return to peace, British Overseas Airways got back as quickly as possible to peace-time operation and now maintains the extensive network of world air routes, which is shown on the map on page 145. At the time of writing the fleet of B.O.A.C. consists of a total of 174 aircraft for operational and training purposes, while a further 110 are on order.

Avro Yorks are used on the *Springbok* service to South Africa, and between England and India; Avro Lancastrians operate the *Kangaroo* service to Australia (a journey of 12,000 miles accomplished in sixty-three hours); Lockheed Constellations are used between Britain and Canada and the United States; Short *Hythe* flying-boats operate to Australia and on the *Dragon* service to Hong Kong, and Lockheed Lodestars and Douglas Dakotas are responsible for maintaining many of the Middle East services.

The fleet on order includes twenty-four flying-boats developed from the *Hythe* class (these are the *Solent* and *Plymouth* flying-

The British Overseas Airways' Avro York *Mersey* at Nairobi on the *Springbok* service to South Africa.

Launching the British Overseas Airways' Short *Hythe* flying-boat *Harlequin* at the Corporation's base at Hythe on Southampton Water.

North Atlantic routes. In addition the large Saunders-Roe SR 45 flying-boat and the Bristol 167 will be operated by the Corporation.

British European Airways

The post-war European commercial air routes were opened up by the British European Airways Division of B.O.A.C. until the new British European Airways Corporation came into being on 1st August 1946.

Using mainly 24-seat Vickers-Armstrongs Viking airliners, B.E.A.C. is operating fast services between England and France, Belgium,

boats); sixteen Avro Tudor I pressurised airliners for the England–Canada services; twenty-six Avro Tudor II for the Empire services; twenty-five Handley Page Hermes and six Boeing Stratocruisers to replace the Lockheed Constellations now on the

British Overseas Airways' Lockheed Constellation *Balmoral* arriving at London Airport after a transatlantic flight in 1946.

Spain, Portugal, Holland, Germany, Austria, Czechoslovakia, Denmark, Norway, Sweden, Switzerland, Italy, Greece and Turkey.

On 1st February 1947 British European Airways took over the aircraft and routes of A.A.J.C., and is now responsible for the operation of internal airlines. These internal airlines, which are shown on the map on page 144, are operated with Douglas Dakota, and de Havilland Dragon Rapide aircraft while Vikings are being introduced on some routes. Fast new Miles Marathon liners are on order for internal services and Vikings may also be used. During April Channel Islands Airways which included Jersey Airways and Guernsey Airways came within B.E.A.C., as did Allied Airways.

The internal airlines have a reputation for safety and high regularity, many routes having been operated for ten years with 98 per cent. regularity of service.

British South American Airways

The third British airline operator made its first service flight on 1st January 1946,

[*Photo : John Stroud*

One of the Scottish Airways' de Havilland Dragon Rapides under the Civil Air Ensign at Renfrew. About forty of this type of aircraft were taken over by B.E.A.C. on 1st February 1947. They are used on the internal air routes.

when the Avro Lancastrian *Star Light* left Heathrow, the new London airport, for South America. Nationalisation least affected the operation of British South American Airways Limited and this Corporation retains its same personnel, aircraft and spheres of operation. Its present operational fleet consists of ten Avro Yorks, six Avro Lancastrians and four Avro Lancaster Freighters. Three Avro Tudor IVs are on order. Each aeroplane bears a name prefixed by the word 'Star' and collectively they are known as the *Starliners*.

The future of British air transport rests with these three corporations and they have, together with their predecessors, an unrivalled operating experience.

Above.—British South American Airways' Avro Lancastrian *Star Land* at London Airport.

Right.—British European Airways' Vickers-Armstrongs Viking *Valerie* leaving Northolt Airport for Copenhagen on 1st September 1946. This was the first *Viking* service.

154

[Copyright : de Havilland Aircraft Co. Ltd.

The de Havilland Dove feeder-line aeroplane is in world-wide service.

THE LITERATURE OF FLIGHT

The Pilot's United Nations

SUPPORT FOR world government may soon appear from a new quarter—we mean our Air Forces men, who are generally believed to be aloof from politics. It is just this breezy unconcern of theirs that may make them strong supporters of a cosmopolis. For several years now our fliers, particularly those in ferry or transport work, have been rattling around the world without much regard for political boundaries or foreign trade regulations. They have bought the best each land has had to offer and have flown off, without bothering with import or export controls. In a real sense they have been citizens of the world, stalking their native sky. Their accumulations provide a quick view of the dishes, customs, and institutions of to-morrow's world state.

When these fliers were asked, by a sober bystander at Casablanca, how many countries they had visited, most of them didn't know. From an elevation of ten thousand feet, a national boundary is a sometime thing, all jungles look green, all bigwigs are smallwigs, no matter who collects the taxes. It is just possible that these airmen, who are the men of the future in an age we are just beginning to glimpse, look on the world with different eyes from the eyes of the foreign ministers, whose traditional props are crumbling fast. Pilots distinguish between geographical stops more in terms of crosswinds, runway lengths, food, women, and liquor than in terms of mandate, colony, protectorate, republic, principality and empire. The invasion dollar and pidgin English have been accepted generally wherever these men have gone. It seems unlikely that airmen, in the age of flight, will have much patience with a post-war world of self-important states, called big, called little, each with its border police, its custom declarations, its visa fees and duties and exchange regulations and other petty nuisances of nationalist society. High in the cirrus above the council table where national integrity is at stake roam the younger men who know that, given a tail-wind, the whole issue can be completely left behind in an hour and forty-five minutes.

From *The New Yorker*,
20th October 1945

[*The New Yorker*. Copyright 1945
The F.R. Publishing Corporation

Cargo being loaded into the hold of a Fairchild Packet.

[*Photograph: Lockheed Aircraft Corporation*

Trans-World Airline Constellations maintain an air link across the North Atlantic.

THE LITERATURE OF FLIGHT

Take-Off

'THE landing-lights struck out brilliantly against the snow. It was exactly five minutes past midnight. Willie Moon pushed the four throttles forward slowly to thirty inches. At the same time he stood on the brakes. The *Gremlins' Castle* growled and shuddered and lowered her head like a bull about to charge. Then suddenly, Moon released the brakes and the ship lunged forward down the runway. He continued to push the throttles forward. Forty-eight inches. Twenty-seven hundred revolutions per minute. Full power.

Four angry snarling engines. From a standstill to forty miles in a few short yards—60,000 lb. From forty to sixty miles in another hundred feet. Acceleration. Power on power—the same old thrill that Willie Moon had never failed to know in all his thousands of take-offs. Seventy miles per hour. The runway a blur. Eighty—but this was hardly a beginning. The formula had barely been set in motion. Two thousand feet of the runway behind, 3,000 left to go. Ninety miles per hour on the airspeed.

Handley Page's Hastings military transport, precursor of the civil Hermes.

Take-Off—(contd.)

Willie Moon tugged gently at the control wheel and raised the long nose ever so slightly. Now in a second, the crux, the problem, the one point where Moon would be helpless. A hundred miles per hour—110. Now, just now, an engine must not fail, for it was too late to stop and a shade too early to begin. Moon gave the control wheel a gentle tug—not yet, not quite, but soon. He could feel it in his hands, in his mind, and in the seat of his pants, feel it coming—flight. The end of the runway rushed towards them. The landing-lights sucked up the precious yards. Speed. The formula was working. One hundred and twenty-five miles per hour. Now. Willie Moon pulled back on the control wheel. The runway sank. The sense of speed diminished. The *Gremlins' Castle* was airborne.'

E. K. GANN—*Island in the Sky*, 1945

CAREERS IN THE R.A.F.

by

Ross Wilson
Air Ministry

As a highly technical modern fighting service the R.A.F. can offer a career open to talent to almost every type of man and on such diverse duties as flying, engineering, electrical or clerical work, with remuneration and conditions related as nearly as possible to civil life.

For the next twenty years the R.A.F. will be busy applying the developments and discoveries in strategy, tactics and weapons of the war years. Marshal of the Royal Air Force Lord Tedder replied to the popular belief that the atomic bomb will make air forces obsolete by pointing out that somebody has to carry the bomb. At the moment there is no evidence that the atomic bomb can be delivered by rocket. In any case, the atomic bomb is not the sole weapon of war, nor the only strength to help maintain the peace and assure that Britain's voice is heard in the councils of the world. The outlawing of the atomic weapon is the objective of all the statesmen of the world.

Precise definition of the peace-time work of the R.A.F. is hard to set forth, but the broad outlines of its development can be foreseen quite clearly. It is at the beginning of the jet-propulsion era. It is approaching the swept-back wing which should bring it up to the sonic barrier and the flying wing which should reduce drag by half and so give a great improvement in range and pay-load. Take, for instance, one calculation of what might be done with a flying wing driven by four gas turbines of 5,000 lb. static thrust each. It could give a speed of 650 m.p.h., a bomb load of 25,000 lb. and a range of 3,000 miles. When aircraft of these characteristics come to be built in this country the R.A.F. will have them first. There are no signs that the R.A.F. will need huge aircraft of 200,000 to 300,000 lb. loaded weight, except for use by Transport Command. High performance and long range without bulk will be the aim. Until we are through the sonic barrier (see page 226) there may be a stage at which the bomber will be as fast as the fighter.

While this epoch of sub-sonic flying is in progress, work on the next stage will be in hand. Experiments with pilotless aircraft rocket-driven and capable of a speed of 800 m.p.h. (or 40 m.p.h. faster than the speed of sound in the most favourable circumstances) are about to begin. These will lead on to human flight at sonic and supersonic speeds. Again the R.A.F. will be the first to inherit the results. Only those who are serving in the R.A.F. can be sure of a part in this kind of flying. Not all the ' regulars ' in the Service will be able to do the flying. Not all may want to fly at supersonic speeds. No one pretends that every recruit has an equal chance of becoming aircrew, or of becoming an officer. But with few specialist exceptions, everyone, whatever the grading on his recruit's papers, starts on the same level as an A.C.2. In a mechanical world and age, a great many young men must long to see these exciting developments at close quarters and have a hand in conquering yet another of Nature's prohibitions.

Parallel with this development in the aircraft themselves must go similar advances in their ancillary equipment and air defence methods: in radar and radio aids to navigation, in armament, including bombs, rockets, cannon and the like, in aviation medicine and in the development of air tactics and strategy.

[*Air Ministry Photograph*

Airmen sight-seeing in Schwebo, Burma.

The field is immense and the R.A.F. must maintain a world lead over the whole of it, for to stand still is to fall behind.

All this can only be done by men—and women—who will make the Air Force their career, and by a necessary division of labour between officer branches and men's trades. To this end there are fourteen different officer branches and over eighty trades for airmen.

Officer Branches

The officer branches are: General Duties, Technical, Equipment, Secretarial, R.A.F. Regiment, Aircraft Control, Physical Fitness, Catering, Provost and the professional branches—Medical, Dental, Legal, Education, Chaplains. The functions of most of them are described by their titles, but each covers a variety of duties and offers a diversity of occupations. Moreover, the responsibilities of an officer extend far beyond his technical duties. The primary purpose for which he is granted the King's commission is his leadership and handling of men, summed up in the phrase 'man-management'. In peace, even more than in war, the efficiency and happiness of the Service as a whole demands that each and every officer is not only a fighting man but is also an administrator and commander; and the first duty of a commander in peace or in war is to look after his men. In practice it is a life-long process of education which begins when a man is first being trained as an officer, when he is given a course in administration, organisation and his responsibilities to his men in addition to his technical training. As he proceeds in his service career his education in these matters is continued, in part by filling posts in which these responsibilities are particularly pronounced and varied, and in part by the guidance and example of his senior officers.

The post-war policy of the Service is to draw most of its officers from the ranks, and the initial entry to commissioned rank as known before the war has practically disappeared. Nevertheless, there are many different avenues of approach to a commission. In detail they are: through an officer training establishment, such as the R.A.F. College, Cranwell; from one of the eleven University Air Squadrons; by reason of holding a university degree or technical diploma; from the ranks of the Aircraft and Administrative Apprentices and from enlisted aircrew and tradesmen in certain ground trades for the appropriate officer branch.

Duties of Branches

As its name implies, the R.A.F. is a flying and fighting Service. Its first requirements are aircraft and men to fly them and to keep them flying. The General Duties, the flying, branch is probably the best known branch and provides primarily the commissioned flying personnel of the Service. Officers of this branch, who will all have qualified on aircrew duties, will fill flying posts, command and administrative appointments which need flying experience, and a sufficient number of other staff and administrative posts to ensure that G.D. officers will possess the wide knowledge and experience necessary for their promotion to the highest ranks.

Behind those who will fly the aircraft and direct their strategical use must be a body of technical specialists, profoundly versed in all the weapons and aids the G.D. branch will be employing. In 1939 it was decided to form a Technical branch consisting of these highly qualified specialist officers who would be employed permanently on technical duties, to supersede the earlier system by which G.D. branch officers who had specialised in Armament, Signals and Engineering were employed intermittently on technical and non-technical posts. The war-time Technical branch has now been reconstituted and a new Air Council post created—the Air Member for Technical Services, who is responsible for the branch. The branch contains three sections: armament, engineering and signals, closely integrated to achieve efficiency and to provide appropriate careers. In order that the Technical branch may be able to keep in touch with the operational implications of its work as many Technical officers as possible, apart from those who already have pilot and aircrew experience, will be given flying training.

From an early date staffs at Command and lower formations will be re-organised into three branches of equal status, Air Staff, Administrative Staff and Technical Staff. At Command level the Technical Staff Head will be known as the Senior Technical Staff Officer—a title and post comparable to Senior Air Staff Officer—and will be the A.O.C.-in-C.'s policy adviser on the technical aspects of armament, engineering and signals. Such staff posts, together with others of a technical rather than a specialist connotation, will be open to officers of all three sections of the Technical branch. Officers must, therefore, be ready for posts of broader technical responsibility.

The work of the Aircraft Control branch is suggested by its title. Its responsibilities embrace the fighter control and raid reporting organisations and air traffic control work. It is a newly created branch, set up because these functions are daily becoming more highly skilled and specialised and so cannot

be conveniently or economically combined with those of any of the main branches. At the same time war experience has shown that the 'operational' and 'control' sides cannot be entirely divorced. A high proportion of the posts will consequently be filled by G.D. officers and from selected long-service pilot and navigator aircrew who will be commissioned at the average age of thirty-four. Those selected will have about a year's training in both the Air Traffic and Fighter Control sections, followed by an O.C.T.U. course. This will provide alternative employment for those no longer fit for operational flying duties, thus improving their careers and value to the Service.

Behind the flying and technical officers must be an organisation supplying the equipment they need. This is the role of the

R.A.F. Apprentice School. The drum-major and the school's mascot, Lewis the goat (now retired), on parade.
[*Air Ministry Photograph*

Equipment branch, whose duties include the demanding, receipt, identification and care of all Air Force equipment from aircraft and aero engines to uniforms and the movement of all freight and personnel by land, sea and air. The branch will also take over a number of administrative posts associated with equipment functions for which flying experience is not essential and which have been previously filled by G.D. officers.

The need for a Secretarial branch is obvious. It has taken over the duties of the former Accountant branch and deals with organisation, personnel administration and similar duties. Secretarial officers will fill a considerable number of administrative posts which do not require flying experience and which were previously filled by G.D. officers.

The R.A.F. Regiment fits into the pattern with two main responsibilities—first, the local defence of airfields and R.A.F. establishments against ground and low-level air attack, and secondly, maintaining a high standard of ground fighting efficiency throughout the Service. For its first task it maintains a nucleus force of regular squadrons—Armoured, Light A.A. and Rifle. For its second task, the Regiment provides staff officers and instructors at Commands and Groups, and instructors at recruit and other training centres. It also has two training depots at home, mainly for training officer and N.C.O. instructors. As far as possible a fair division between regimental duty in Squadrons and staff and instructional duties is maintained. Regiment officers will also have the chance to serve with native Levies overseas and to take over certain administrative posts held until now by G.D. officers. Like the Royal Marines, the Regiment has a Commandant General, a post at present held by an officer on loan from the Army and which it is planned should ultimately be open to an R.A.F. Regiment officer.

Three branches formally set up only in January 1947 deserve notice for their contribution to the efficiency and well-being of the Service. They are the Catering, Physical Fitness and Provost branches. In each case the decision to establish these branches reflects the need, proved during the war, for these specialist branches. Their functions are self-evident; the Catering branch will maintain and, if possible, improve the standard of messing achieved during the war with the introduction of specialist officers; the Physical Fitness branch can make an important contribution to positive health in an Air Force superbly equipped for exercise and sport; the Provost branch is the police force of the R.A.F., in the widest sense of the term. Every kind of task connected with the enforcement of security, traffic control and discipline, and with special investigation comes within the scope of the R.A.F. police.

There remain the five 'professional' branches, each with its own distinct contribution to the life of the Service. The routine work of the Medical and Dental branches springs at once to mind—Station M.O.'s and the like. Beyond this though are R.A.F. hospitals, greatly helped in their task by the Princess Mary's R.A.F. Nursing Service, and beyond those again, such establishments as the School of Aviation Medicine at Farnborough which is of paramount and growing importance, as the human body is subjected to increasing stresses and strains with high-speed and high-altitude flight.

The Education branch, replacing the former civilian Education Service, has a two-fold task: to impart the theory relative to an R.A.F. job at training establishments, and to encourage education in the wider sense throughout the Service. The Education officer has a magnificent opportunity for carrying out schemes for adult education. It will be his lot to assist men in their personal studies in whatever subjects they choose, to encourage cultural and practical hobby interests, and the study and discussion of current affairs and citizenship. Station societies for music, drama, art and the like will all owe much to his inspiration and be part of his responsibility.

The Chaplains branch, representing the major religious denominations, is the body of the R.A.F. clergy. To them falls the responsibility for the moral and spiritual welfare of the members of the Service, and in practice, for helping them in many of their personal problems.

Officers of the Legal branch are responsible, *inter alia*, for the legal aspects of discipline and administration in the R.A.F. They

De Havilland Vampires of No. 247 Squadron.
[Air Ministry Photograph

assist in the preparation and conduct of courts martial, and, equally important, lecture in the Service on Air Force Law, a subject in which all officers, as commanders of men, must have a good working knowledge if they are to fulfil the primary purpose for which they are commissioned—the leadership and handling of men.

Entry to Branches

The methods of entry to these branches vary and are set out in detail in an Air Ministry pamphlet entitled 'Commissioned Service in the Royal Air Force' obtainable free of charge on request from the Air Ministry Information Bureau, Kingsway, London, or on writing to Air Ministry (A.R.1), London, W.C.2. In the cases of the General Duties, Equipment and Secretarial branches and the R.A.F. Regiment, young men in civil life between the ages of seventeen and a half and nineteen may apply for cadetships leading to permanent commissions. Candidates are expected normally to hold the School Certificate or its equivalent and must be unmarried British subjects. After due advertisement in the press, the Civil Service Commission hold examinations in June and December each year, with some compulsory subjects and a choice of others. Those who hold a Higher School Certificate may be

exempted from part or all of this examination. This is followed by a medical examination and selection tests which aim at assessing certain personal qualities such as leadership. Applicants for G.D. branch cadetships also undergo flying aptitude tests. Men already serving in the R.A.F. are eligible to apply for these cadetships. In their case the upper age limit is raised to nineteen and a half, and they are not required to sit the Civil Service examination. Cadets are enlisted and paid as airmen, and, if successful, are commissioned at the end of their courses. A certain number of General Duties branch cadetships are reserved for specially selected aircraft apprentices, and some cadetships for the Equipment and Secretarial branches are similarly reserved for specially chosen administrative apprentices.

General Duties branch cadets are trained at the R.A.F. College, Cranwell, which was inaugurated in 1920 under the inspiration of Lord Trenchard, on the site of a former Royal Naval Air Service training centre. Until the autumn of 1933 cadets were housed in old war-time huts, but in that year moved into the New College, consisting of a central block containing the cadets' mess, lecture hall, lecture rooms, library, recreation rooms and laboratories, flanked on east and west sides by the Squadron's quarters with accommodation for cadets in separate rooms. The architecture externally and internally conforms to English tradition adapted to modern requirements. Externally the walls are faced with rustic and moulded brick work with the more important features in Portland stone. The façade of the central block is designed on classic lines with a central portico of six columns surmounted by a pediment and a 130-foot high tower.

Flying training forms part, and an important part, of the College syllabus, but the mere ability to fly by no means qualifies an individual to become an officer in the R.A.F. The College exists to prepare young men to become regular R.A.F. officers and is, consequently, an educational establishment ranking in importance with any other such establishment in the country. During their stay, cadets have to pass from the control and direction of school life to the freer adult, and largely self-disciplined, life they will live in the Service proper. This is essentially an educational problem. Each subject in the two and a half years' course is regarded as a means by which the cadet can be given an education in the widest and best sense of the word. The one purpose of the College and of every member of the staff is to provide that education, whether in the air, in the laboratory, in the lecture room and workshop or on the parade ground. The work should present no difficulty to a cadet, but his training does involve a great change in outlook, new responsibilities, subjects and

[*Air Ministry Photograph*

Spitfire credited with fourteen kills against the Luftwaffe.

ideas. As there is a limit to how much can be absorbed the first aim is to provide a syllabus which leads the cadet step by step from civil life to the duties and responsibilities of a regular officer and the captaincy of operational types of aircraft. At the end of his course the cadet should be a qualified pilot with a knowledge of all other aircrew duties, have reached the standard of the second year's work for a University Pass Degree, and be prepared to assume his responsibilities as a regular officer.

In detail, the course includes aeronautical science and engineering subjects, humanistic studies and general service subjects as well as flying training, all imparted by sound modern educational methods.

To train cadets for the Equipment and Secretarial branches, a special wing of the College has been set up at R.A.F. Station, Digby, near by. The courses for these cadets naturally vary greatly from that for the General Duties branch cadets, but the same object is kept in view of educating them in the widest sense of the term and fitting them for their role as regular officers, rather than providing them with a purely narrow technical training. Cadets for the R.A.F. Regiment do their cadet training at the Royal Military Academy, Sandhurst, where the same broad objective is kept in view as at the R.A.F. College, throughout the training in their specialist duties.

Membership of one of the eleven University Air Squadrons also provides a method of entry to a commission in the General Duties and Technical branches. Membership of a Squadron is restricted to men reading an approved course at one of these universities. They are required to complete at least twenty hours' flying training a year in term time, and fifteen days' continuous training during vacation at an R.A.F. Station. Ground training is also provided as necessary.

The Squadrons are located at Aberdeen, Belfast (Queen's), Birmingham, Cambridge, Edinburgh, Glasgow, London, Manchester, Nottingham, Oxford and Southampton Universities.

Selections for permanent commissions will be made at the end of the candidate's second year at the university, which allows rejected candidates time to consider an alternative career. Those selected complete their university course and are normally required to possess an Honours Degree; candidates for the Technical branch being accepted if they hold equivalent qualifications such as the diploma of a recognised institution. The age limits for this type of entrant will be twenty-one to twenty-four.

A limited number of aircraft apprentices are selected each year at the end of their apprentice training for a three years' university course during which they will be members of the U.A.S. and have all their university expenses paid. On completing their course successfully they will be commissioned in the Technical branch. This is a really magnificent opportunity for the right type of lad.

In the Equipment, Secretarial and Technical branches, and the R.A.F. Regiment, airmen in the appropriate trades, particularly former apprentices, will be selected for permanent commissions at a relatively early age.

There is no provision for short service commissions in the Technical branch, and the pre-war system of direct entry to short service commissions in the General Duties branch has been abolished. All short service commissions in this latter branch will be filled from enlisted aircrew and a proportion of these officers subsequently chosen for permanent commissions. In the case of the Equipment and Secretarial branches and the Regiment, men doing their National Service or serving as volunteers will be selected for short service commissions, and a limited number of these officers chosen for permanent commissions.

For the Catering branch it is hoped to recruit a proportion of officers on short service commissions from expert caterers in civil life. Similarly, for the Physical Fitness branch, officers will be mainly recruited directly from civil life on short service commissions, some being later chosen for permanent commissions. The main source of Provost officers will be from airmen R.A.F. police, and airmen cooks will form an important source for permanent Catering officers. A limited number of physical training N.C.O.'s will also be chosen for permanent commissions in the Physical Fitness branch.

We have already remarked that in the future Aircraft Control branch officers will normally be selected from long service aircrew in the pilot and navigator categories after fifteen years' service.

Officering the professional branches is a rather different problem. In the Legal branch, all appointments will be to permanent commissions. With the other four professional branches—Medical, Dental, Chaplains and Education branches—the normal procedure will be, first, appointments to short service commissions, during which officers may be selected for permanent commissions. Even should an officer return to civil life after his short service commission expires, he will have gained valuable and widened experience during his time with the R.A.F., and every assistance is given him to find suitable and congenial employment when he leaves the Service. He also receives a substantial gratuity on returning to civil life.

Aircrew

One outstanding feature of the post-war Air Force is the introduction of an entirely new aircrew scheme * for non-commissioned members of the Service, with their own badges, titles of rank and five categories of employment. The advent during the war of the big multi-engined aircraft with a large crew, and the increasing complexity of aircrew duty generally, has meant a large

* The term ' aircrew ' is confined to those members of the Air Force who are not commissioned and are engaged on one of the five categories of flying employment.

increase in the non-pilot categories as well as in their responsibilities and the standard required on entry and under training. During the war, to provide the number of crews required in the shortest possible time it was necessary to introduce somewhat narrow specialisation and the range of aircrew categories was extended until at the end of the war there were no fewer than eleven. It has since been decided to reduce the number of categories to five, and that aircrew shall be trained to a very high standard and fully qualified in all aspects of their job.

The five categories are known as: pilot, navigator/bomb-aimer, radio operator (air), flight engineer and air-gunner/armourer. For brevity's sake they are known as pilot, navigator, signaller, engineer and gunner. Although the titles suggest the nature of each man's duties they hardly give a fair picture of the range and complexity of his work. Pilots must, of course, be trained basically in flying and, in addition, to a high standard in navigation. They must have also a good working knowledge of other aircrew duties according to the type of aircraft on which they are employed. The navigator is trained basically in navigation and bomb-aiming, in the operation of radar equipment and in air gunnery. Some navigators will be trained in meteorological air observer duties and some in navigator (radio) duties for two-seater aircraft. Signallers will be trained in the operation of airborne radar, wireless telegraphy and radio telegraphy equipment, procedure and codes. The senior signaller in a large crew will be responsible to the captain for the training and efficiency of others. Engineers will be trained in engine management and range flying; they will maintain the flight log, and be capable of carrying out emergency repairs in the air. Gunners will be trained in air firing and defensive tactics, in special methods of sighting, manipulation of turrets, loading and fusing bombs, calibration of gun and bomb sights. The senior gunner in a large crew will be responsible to the captain for the training and efficiency of others. Signallers and engineers will also be trained in air gunnery as fighting members of the crew.

In the main, it is intended to recruit pilots and navigators direct from civil life, normally at the age of eighteen or nineteen, for a five-year engagement, with a reserve liability and a gratuity of £200. They will provide the sole field for appointment to short service commissions in the G.D. branch. Those not selected will be eligible for re-engagement as aircrew to complete twenty-two years' service for aircrew pension. Among these long service aircrew, some will be chosen for commissions in the Aircraft Control branch. Every assistance by way of study, advice and the like will be given aircrew on short engagements to fit themselves for a civil occupation on transferring to the Reserve. Former apprentices and others may be chosen during their first three years' service as tradesmen to become pilots or navigators. This is a result of war experience which showed the value of the apprentice-trained man as an operational pilot.

Signallers, engineers and gunners will be drawn from the ranks of certain highly skilled ground trades for a tour of five years' duty as aircrew, after which they will revert to their basic trade. A limited number of them will be chosen for pilot or navigator training, and some for a further period of aircrew service, mainly to provide the necessary instructional staff for training establishments. Signallers, engineers and gunners will be expected not only to carry out their duties in the air, but also to take part in the servicing, maintenance and inspection of their equipment on the ground.

The system of normal warrant and non-commissioned rank is not appropriate for aircrew and a new system of ranks solely applicable to aircrew has been introduced. These ranks, in ascending order, are: cadet pilot, navigator, etc., for those under training; pilot, etc. IV, III, II, and I, and master pilot, navigator, etc. Aircrew will then be known individually by the title of their rank and category, for example, master pilot, gunner III, and so on. In relation to ground ranks, master aircrew corresponds to warrant officer, aircrew I to flight sergeant, aircrew II to sergeant, and aircrew III and IV to corporal. Rates of pay for aircrew are different from those for ground tradesmen, and pilots and navigators are paid slightly more than signallers, engineers and gunners of the same rank.

Airmen's Trades

Just as the number of aircrew categories increased during the war and has now been reduced to five, so the number of ground trades grew from 50 to 235 and is now being reduced to about eighty. The war-time growth was due not only to the introduction of entirely new duties, but also to the need to reduce training periods to a minimum. At the same time the very high peace-time standard of technical proficiency is returning after the relaxation of war time, when promotion and educational examinations were suspended.

With a choice of over eighty different peace-time trades, and about 100 during the present interim period, to choose from, it is clear that there is a niche for almost every type of man. The various fitter trades, for example, illustrate the wide choice open to skilled craftsmen. There are air radio fitters, airframe fitters, armament fitters, electrical fitters, engine fitters, ground radio fitters, instrument fitters, jig and tool fitters, marine fitters, mechanical transport fitters and medical equipment fitters. The standard of skill reached in every one of these trades is at least equal to that for a similar job in civil life, the training is provided free, and a man is himself paid while under training. If an apprenticeship is preferred, then the R.A.F. can offer a well-proved and widely recognised top-notch apprentice training in the most highly skilled technical trades. At the other end of the scale from the fitter trades can be placed the clerical trades—clerks accounting, pay accounting, equipment accounting—for the man whose bent lies in the office and administration rather than in the hangar or the workshop. In these trades, as with the highly skilled fitter trades, a man may either learn his trade on coming in as an airman, or become an administrative apprentice. In either case he gets a sound training, and should he leave the Service before completing time for pension, he possesses a sure foundation and wide experience on which to base a civilian career. And for the man who can prove himself, there are opportunities to achieve commissioned rank as briefly outlined above.

To appreciate the complexity and range of the R.A.F. trade structure it is necessary to bear in mind that the Service attempts to meet most of its requirements from within its own ranks. The R.A.F. police provide a force undertaking the entire range of police duties wherever the R.A.F. may be serving; the Regiment provides the men for the local defence of its airfields and other establishments and the training of other members of the Service in ground combat. As the R.A.F. possesses its own Medical and Dental branches, so it has a range of dental, medical and nursing trades for men. Motor-boat crew, M.T. drivers, draughtsmen, fabric workers, metal workers, telegraphists, musicians, all these and others go to make up the trained personnel of the Air Force, to maintain it and meet its needs in peace and war.

For purposes of pay and administration the trades are divided into four groups—known as Trade Groups A, B, C and D,

[*Air Ministry Photograph*

Fitters and riggers and electricians working on a Gloster Meteor III jet-propelled fighter.

A being the most highly skilled and highly paid. Sergeants and above in B, C and D receive the same rate of pay.

But in whatever group a trade may fall, care has been taken that overall remuneration, including pay, is comparable to what is offered in civil life. Any comparison between civil and service pay must be very broad, but a starting-point was obtained for building up the new pay code by taking a semi-skilled worker in a Government industrial establishment whose pay is based on normal trade union rates and relating him to an aircraftman first class (A.C.1) in Group C who might be, for instance, an Equipment Assistant. Actually it is extremely difficult to compare pay in a fighting service and wages in civil life for two main reasons. In civil life single and married men are paid the same, whereas the marriage allowance system needs to be retained in the Service where conditions of life, frequent change of station, overseas service and so on, hit the married man much harder than the bachelor. Moreover, the Serviceman gets a good deal in kind—accommodation, clothing, food, for example—and also avoids certain expenses such as higher National Insurance contribution, cost of travel to and from work and the like, which the civilian has to pay.

This 'home saving' factor is estimated for the married man as worth not less than an extra 20s. a week to his pay. The actual cost to the State is much higher than 20s. and an unmarried civilian living in lodgings would certainly need to spend more than 20s. a week on the 'home saving' items.

It would not be possible to give here all the details of pay rates for different ranks in the different trades. The more highly skilled a man is, the higher his rank (and both these advancements are open to an airman to improve by his own efforts), then the higher the rate of pay. A recruit gets 28s. a week on entry. Normally he soon becomes aircraftman first class paid from 38s. 6d. a week in an unskilled trade to 49s. a week in a higher type of work. A Flight Sergeant gets from 84s. to 115s. a week, and a Warrant Officer from 105s. to 140s. a week. There are, also, other sources of increase—marriage allowance, beginning at 35s. a week, good conduct pay and an additional payment for length of service. Airmen, of course, are eligible for benefits under the nation-wide Family Allowance Scheme.

It is true there is something to be said on the other side: there are some disadvantages in Service life which the civilian does not encounter. On the other hand the opportunities for advancement in trade and rank are better than corresponding opportunities in many civilian jobs; the Service gives a much more generous allowance of paid holidays than most civil employment; the provision made for the Serviceman and his family in the case of accident or illness is more generous in many ways than normally made for the civilian in industry; a man discharged without a pension, but with not less than ten years' service is eligible for a gratuity on terms very much more favourable than those normally offered in industry; and above all, the Serviceman who completes a long engagement gets what practically no civilian in industry ever gets—a pension on a non-contributory basis when he is still capable of years of further work, and has several well-known bodies to help him find further employment.

Other benefits, less tangible perhaps, but no less real, are also the prerogative of the serving airman. As against the frequent loneliness of city life, the Service offers real comradeship born of a common life with its shared traditions, excitements and labours. It is no small thing to many men to belong to a body which the world holds in respect and regards with gratitude as it does the Royal Air Force. Membership of such a body provides a life which is consciously useful, creates a pride in one's vocation, and inspires a self-respect rarely found elsewhere. The work itself is interesting and in touch with the most modern aeronautical developments; it is directed to a national and international end of value to the community and mankind as a whole and offers security of job.

The Service sets great store by its members' health and not only provides an excellent medical and dental service, but takes positive steps to ensure health by the provision of plenty of free sport, exercise, a scientifically balanced diet, planned accommodation, and

[Air Ministry Photograph]

R.A.F. aircrews at Sarawak, Borneo.

generous paid leave (with free travel warrants) and frequent long week-ends. The Education officer is on the spot to help a man in any further studies he wishes to undertake; he gets many articles at reduced prices, including cinema shows; he can join station clubs and societies for literature, drama, music and the like, and there is a regular social life by way of dances and station socials.

While the most pressing need of the R.A.F. in the immediate post-war period is for men with war-time skill and experience, men are also wanted direct from civil life who are willing to make the Service their career. Men between seventeen and a half and thirty-three may volunteer to join for initial engagements of varying periods depending partly on their choice and partly on the trade they select. Five years is the period for less skilled trades, and combinations of active and reserve service making a total of twelve years, are the usual periods for

the more skilled trades. These combinations are eight years' active and four years' reserve service, or nine and three, ten and two, or twelve years' active service and no reserve service.

Provided that his trade is one to which the twelve years' period applies, it is entirely a matter for a man's own choice which combination he selects. There are, of course, chances to sign on again after this initial engagement to complete time for pension, the minimum period normally being a total of twenty-two years' service. In addition a long service scheme providing careers for airmen up to the age of fifty-five is being worked out.

General Conditions

Life in the war-time R.A.F. is no sure guide to the peace-time Service. Those years called for and witnessed unequalled heroism,

169

overwork and frequent boredom under, as a rule, emergency living conditions. The demands of total war saw to that. Stations had to be rushed up, quarters improvised, discomfort endured, for the overriding purpose of defeating the enemy. That purpose accomplished, the Service contracted rapidly, often with an increase in discomfort and inconvenience.

The introduction of the Newpaycode for officers and men heralded the return to peace-time conditions and established an important principle, relating Service remuneration to civil rates of pay for similar jobs. Accommodation plans followed adopting the same principle—that it is the aim of the Service to see that there are available to its members living conditions comparable to what they could reasonably expect in civil life. The proposals to be implemented entirely by the State or by some authorised corporation cover a wide field and include provision of single cubicles for airmen complete with bed, chair, table, wardrobe, etc., to replace the old barrack block; fully furnished semi-detached houses for married men and their families, airmen's clubs (with bars, recreation, visitors', reading and other rooms), modern dining-halls on the cafeteria system with absolutely up-to-date equipment in the kitchens and dining-rooms, handicraft and recreation centres taking in a cinema, a hall for social purposes, a gymnasium and shopping centres. The Station as a whole would be laid out on the lines of a well-planned rural housing development estate, so that men would not live right on top of their job, yet would have within easy reach in the best form available all that is necessary to live a full life.

These proposals were followed by Air Council instructions to Air Officers Commanding-in-Chief towards the end of 1946 restoring and extending peace-time off-duty privileges for members of the Service. The aim here again is to allow them roughly the same liberties as are enjoyed by their fellow citizens in civil life. Two innovations deserve notice; the setting up of fully representative Station committees under the chairmanship of the Station C.O., and the introduction of request hours, when members of the Station can interview their Officer Commanding in private on Service or personal matters. These fit in with the practice of the Service which is, increasingly, to take its members into its confidence on important matters, an aim which is also accomplished by such measures as Newpayforms, and Demobforms which explain the background to, and nature of, various decisions taken. In short, the R.A.F. regards its members as responsible adults, members of a fighting service which must also be an efficient and happy one, and members of a democratic community.

Various changes in uniforms are now proposed, the principle being that as the Air Force worked and fought as a team during the war, so this team spirit can be fostered by clothing all members of the force more nearly alike. It includes comfortable and appropriate working dress, and a smart No. 1 uniform for formal and ceremonial occasions. Here again, the Service is offering its members clothing and certain accessories more nearly the equivalent of what they could reasonably expect in civil life.

All these measures, Marshal of the Royal Air Force Lord Tedder was careful to emphasise, are not bribes—they are part of the square deal the Air Force is giving its members. Many of the proposals will take years to bring to fruition, just as in civil life it takes years to overcome the results of war. For the R.A.F. is not distinct and separate from the nation, it is but a part of it, and no man, it is considered, should be penalised for serving his country in one of the armed forces rather than in civil life.

Apprentice Scheme

The real backbone of the R.A.F.'s technical tradesmen, which made possible, for example, the rapid expansion of war-time, are those the Air Force has trained itself originally as apprentices. The aircraft apprentice scheme was begun by ' the father of the Air Force ', Marshal of the Royal Air Force Lord Trenchard, after the 1914–18 war, and has supplied the Service with thousands of its best tradesmen, who have been given the very best technical training for their jobs, together with a good all-round education, plenty of sport and all that goes to character building. In fact the R.A.F.

CAREERS IN THE R.A.F.

apprentice, when he passes out, is educated in the best sense of the word. The quality of the training is shown, for example, by the large number of former apprentices who have risen to air rank and the much greater number who have gained other high honours. Further, the appropriate trade unions recognise the R.A.F. aircraft apprentice training, so that an ex-apprentice who returns to civil life has his skill acknowledged. There is also an administrative apprentice scheme for those lads whose bent lies in a clerical direction.

The principal apprentices' school is set in a large wooded estate at Halton, near Wendover, in Buckinghamshire, and gives the soundest instruction in the finest conditions. As with training cadets, the problem is an educational one. The training has been worked out by experience gained over more than a quarter of a century. Theory is taught in the classrooms by some of the best R.A.F. Education officers and put into practice at once in near-by laboratories and workshops. Here engineering apprentices work on the most modern engines, a future airframe fitter on the latest aircraft types, future armourers on different types of gun turrets and with every kind of bomb from the humble 250 pounder to the armour-piercing type which sank the *Tirpitz*, radio apprentices on up-to-date radar and radio aids as used in R.A.F. operations.

The aircraft apprenticeship normally lasts three years, followed by a year's continuation training at a selected unit. General education is included in the syllabus, and all the sport possible—with pitches, grounds, gear, swimming pool, gymnasium, all available. Indoors, there are recreation rooms and a first-class library, and a camp cinema. The dormitories are light and airy, food liberal, diet scientifically balanced and the medical service the finest possible. So far from any charge being made for all this, apprentices are themselves paid.

As mentioned earlier, suitable aircraft apprentices are chosen each year to go on to the R.A.F. College, Cranwell, for training as G.D. officers, others for a free university course in preparation for a commission in the Technical branch. Others again, are chosen to become pilots or navigators. Whatever the

role the ex-apprentice may fill, it will always be one of responsibility.

There are three entries a year, for which candidates, who must be between fifteen and a half and seventeen, must be nominated. The simplest methods of obtaining nomination are through Headmasters, Juvenile Employment Officers or C.O.'s of A.T.C. Squadrons.

A candidate should have a good general education such as is acquired at a secondary school up to the age of fifteen and a half to sixteen. All candidates must pass an intelligence test, aptitude tests and be physically fit. There is an educational examination for those who do not hold an approved School Certificate. A Selection Board makes the final choice after an interview. Boys whose families have certain Service connections, and specially recommended A.T.C. cadets, have slightly preferential treatment.

All apprentices sign for twelve years' service from the age of eighteen, and may apply to complete time for pension.

The trades for which apprentices are trained are among the most highly skilled and highly paid Air Force ground trades, such as engine fitter, electrical fitter, instrument fitter, airframe fitter, armament fitter and air and ground radio fitters.

The age limits for administrative apprentices are from sixteen to seventeen and a half, on the first day of the month of entry. They do not undergo a written examination, but need a good general education, physical fitness, aptitude and intelligence. Their training, which lasts for sixteen months with a further eight months' continuation training, while directed to different professional ends, also includes character, health and general education training as given to the aircraft apprentices. The trades for which they are prepared are Clerk (general duties), Clerk (accounting) and Equipment Assistant. Ex-administrative apprentices may be chosen for cadetships for the Secretarial and Equipment branches, or to become pilots and navigators.

There is also a 'Boy Entrant' Scheme open to lads between fifteen and a half and seventeen and a half on the first day of the month of entry—February, June or October. The trades for which these lads are trained are: airframe, armament, electrical, engine and instrument mechanics, aircraft finisher and telegraphist. They need a good general education, intelligence, good health and aptitude, but do not undergo an entrance examination. They require, like the aircraft apprentices, to be nominated, the simplest methods being through their Headmaster, the C.O. of their A.T.C. Squadron, or through the Local Juvenile Employment Officer. They sign on for eight, nine, ten or twelve years' regular service from the age of eighteen, with four, three, two or nil years on reserve respectively, plus service up to the age of eighteen. Their prospects of re-engaging or gaining a commission are the same as for other airmen who are not apprentice trained.

Non-Regular Forces

Reserve Command was formed in May 1946 to command and administer all the non-regular air forces, the Royal Auxiliary Air Force, the Volunteer Reserve, the Air Training Corps and the University Air Squadrons. It comprises six groups in Great Britain and functions in Northern Ireland through R.A.F. Northern Ireland.

Towards the end of 1946 the twenty Royal Auxiliary Air Force Squadrons—thirteen day fighter, three night fighter and four light bomber squadrons—began to re-form. These are part of the first line post-war Air Force. These units are equipped with operational aircraft, the day fighters for the present having Spitfires, and the night fighters and light bombers Mosquitos. At present only officers and men who have served with the R.A.F. during the war are eligible for membership. An Auxiliary Squadron is a complete unit in itself ready for action at a moment's notice. It comprises officers, aircrew and ground airmen. Officers are commissioned for five years, and airmen enlisted for four years, with possibilities of extensions beyond those initial periods.

Early in 1947 was announced the formation of a number of Auxiliary Air Defence Units for the raid reporting and fighter control system. This first series is located from Hull to Bournemouth as far inland as Northampton and Nottingham. Membership of

these units is restricted to war-time ex-members, officers and other ranks, of the R.A.F. and W.A.A.F.

Further plans include the formation of a number of Royal Auxiliary Air Force Regiment Squadrons for the close defence of R.A.F. airfields. All Royal Auxiliary Air Force units are raised by Territorial and Auxiliary Forces Associations, which have a part in the administration of those they raise.

The R.A.F. Volunteer Reserve will concentrate at first in recruiting ex-pilots and navigators who will be given their flying training at civil schools. Town centres are being formed in populous districts for training which will include theoretical and synthetic training of aircrews. A new departure within the Volunteer Reserve will be the formation of such ancillary units as mechanical transport companies, air stores parks, ammunition parks and embarkation units.

University Air Squadrons have been formed at eleven universities, giving first priority to undergraduates who have not previously served in the Forces and second priority to ex-R.A.F. pilots. The Squadrons give basic flying training, with ground training as necessary. They assist young men to gain a commission in the R.A.F., or to prepare for their National Service, or to discharge their reserve training liability.

A Supplementary List of R.A.F. and W.A.A.F. officers has been instituted. It is open to ex-officers who wish to maintain their connection with the Air Force and are ready to volunteer for service if they should be needed in the event of an emergency. No peace-time training obligation is involved and those enrolled may transfer to the Volunteer Reserve or the Royal Auxiliary Air Force.

The Air Training Corps is administered by Reserve Command and is a pre-Service voluntary training corps open to young men between the ages of fifteen and eighteen. It is organised on a Squadron basis; some attached to schools, others, local free Squadrons. Training covers instruction in technical subjects and also aims at developing the spirit of teamwork alongside individual initiative. Apart from its functions as a pre-Service training body it is also a happy and useful youth organisation. The syllabus has been broadened since the war, gliding is available to cadets, sports figure prominently, and there is an annual camp. Air experience flights in Service aircraft are given, and everything possible is done to link the Corps to the Service. Those cadets who gain the Proficiency Certificate are guaranteed entry to the R.A.F. while vacancies exist, and also receive several privileges on joining the R.A.F., in recognition of the value of their training.

During the war the Corps did magnificent work in preparing young men for their service in the Royal Air Force. In peace the task may be less exciting and the occasion less urgent. It remains none the less vital to the Service, and the Corps is relied upon to provide a reliable and steady source for manning the Air Force of the future.

Detailed literature on any of the above careers is available on request from the Air Ministry, Information Bureau, Kingsway, London, from R.A.F. Recruiting Centres, or by writing to the Air Ministry, London.

Since the above article was written, a new branch, the Marine branch, has been set up in the R.A.F. Its main duties are the command of R.A.F. vessels and Marine Units, and some related staff and marine engineering posts.

Under long-term plans, most permanent officers will be drawn from regular N.C.O. coxswains. If necessary, additional officers may be drawn from other sources, such as other Air Force officers with the necessary qualifications, or from Merchant Navy officers. For the present, permanent officers will be chosen from marine officers holding emergency or extended service commissions.

[Air Ministry Photograph

R.A.F. flying-boats operate from Ceylon. Sailing as relaxation.

H.M.S. ILLUSTRIOUS.

Photo : Charles Brown

H.M.S. INDEFATIGABLE.

De Havilland Hornet deck landing.

NAVAL FLYING AS A CAREER

At this, our entry into the air age, I commend the article which follows to the attention of the youth of our maritime race.

VICE-ADMIRAL SIR PHILIP VIAN,
FIFTH SEA LORD

FOR CENTURIES the call of the sea has challenged youth. Young men of Britain went with Drake to plunder the riches of Spain, with Cook to map the eastern sea-board of the Australian continent, with Nelson to smash the arrogance of Napoleon. But in the twentieth century the adventure of the sea is challenged by the adventure of the air and youth has had to make a vital choice. If the attraction of the sea has been strong, then the Royal Navy or the Merchant Navy won another recruit; if the appeal of the air rode rough shod over the desire to 'see the world', then the R.A.F. benefited.

In no Service has it been possible in peace-time to embrace the adventure of the sea and the thrill of the air in a fully-fledged sea-air career. A youth could join the Navy as officer or rating, hoping to specialise in flying later, or he could join the R.A.F. hoping for subsequent posting to Coastal Command. During the war he could volunteer for 'hostilities only' flying duties in the Navy, but this job for sea-going pilots finished when war ended.

To-day the Royal Navy seeks to bridge the peace-time gap between the sea and the air by offering a full career to those whose bent is sea-going aviation. If you are between the ages of seventeen and nineteen you can now join the Navy as a pilot.

Henceforth the majority of naval pilots will be recruited direct from civil life and it is the purpose of this article to describe how one may enlist in the ranks of this pioneering branch of naval service—a branch in which one may see the world from the cockpit of a naval plane soaring thousands of feet above the panorama of some foreign scene, and not with the perspiration of the boiler-room or the sweat of the tropics on one's brow.

About two-thirds of the Royal Navy's future pilots will be ratings, whom it is recognised must have special conditions of service. Their qualifications for entry will be high, their duties will not be in the same category as those of any other naval branch, and consequently some distinction will be made between them and other ratings.

This will be achieved by the simple descriptive title of 'Pilot', a high standard of pay, chances of promotion and good living and working conditions. Their conditions will be at least as good as those of the R.A.F.'s new category of Airman Pilots and much better than those of most other naval branches. There will be no hammock slinging for them. Instead they will have multiple bunk sleeping compartments, and both ashore and afloat they will have their own messes.

In this new era of naval flying no one can enlist as an Officer Pilot. Officer Pilots will be 'made' within the Navy. One must become an officer first then take one's chance of becoming a pilot. If this route is preferred and a candidate is too old to compete for a Dartmouth Cadetship, it is still open to apply under the Navy's Special Entry Scheme, details of which may be obtained from the Secretary of the Admiralty (C.W. Branch). Under this scheme, however, there is no guarantee that an applicant will become a pilot or that he will have anything directly to do with naval aviation.

The Standards Expected

In return for the 'special status' granted to pilots, the Navy expects entries with ability and fairly high qualifications. If *you* wish to become a naval pilot and join in this adventure in the air you must comply with certain standards.

You must pass a medical test of the usual high standard set for all pilots in the Navy and R.A.F. You must possess a Schools Certificate with four passes, one of which must be in mathematics. You must produce evidence of British nationality and testimonials as to good character. If you have these preliminary requirements you will be well on your way to becoming a naval pilot.

A youth who has made formal application and reported to a recruiting centre will appear for a brief interview and preliminary medical examination. If the authorities are satisfied with the details supplied on his application form he will be asked to attend a Selection Board at one of the naval air bases, probably about a month later. Here he will have a thorough medical examination and appear before a Board of officers. Before he leaves he will be informed of the result.

If provisionally accepted he will be asked to report to another air station for assessment of 'Pilot Suitability'. Everyone has heard of the variety of tests which prospective pilots had to undergo during the war. At present there are 'Aptitude Tests' and 'Grading Tests', but new tests are being devised constantly and it is likely that a much simpler system will be devised to find out whether a young man will make a good pilot or not.

It is if, and when, an applicant has survived the 'Suitability Test' that he can relax. His worries are over. He is 'in'.

The First Stages

He will then set out on the long journey to become a proficient naval pilot. Instructions will be received to join a naval training establishment and the young hopeful will become a 'Probationary Pilot'.

The first two months' service of the Probationary Pilot is spent learning the manners and customs of the Navy; one custom, that of being regarded exactly as other 'entries', will be observed. This is 'Part I Training'. Following it is the first stage of 'Pilot' training, which will be carried out at another air training establishment.

Here the new entry begins to learn his trade—the trade of a specialised pilot. He learns the 'whys' and 'wherefores' of aeronautics and assimilates the rules of flying. He also learns what he must not do if he values his career and his life. The principles of flight, air navigation, signals and aero engines are among the subjects in which he will receive instruction in this 'pre-flight' training.

De Havilland Sea Mosquito.

After these two months' training the new entry's whole class may be sent to sea for a few days in an aircraft carrier to observe what is expected of the qualified naval pilot under actual service conditions. This glimpse of the sea, the hangar and the flight deck will whet the aeronautical appetite of the entrant during the next two years of his training, years in which he will receive instructions in all stages of naval training necessary to qualify as a carrier pilot.

Basic flying training takes six months and at the end of this time the Probationary Pilot will be able to put his basic training aircraft through all the aerobatics, blind flying and night flying tests that it is possible for a training aircraft to do.

The next six months of the training period is spent in close association with the advanced trainer, learning to do more than merely fly it. Air firing, bombing, formation flying and all the basic requirements of a proper operational pilot will be studied and put into practice in this training aircraft.

The Qualified Pilot

Not until he has completed these stages of his training is the entrant a qualified pilot, and he has still more training to do before he is a qualified operational pilot. Another year of training is necessary, a year in which he will learn to fly Service aircraft—fighter and bomber—and reach a proficiency standard in the use of all aircraft weapons, known as the 'marksmanship standard'.

Not until the end of this second twelve months of his training, when he qualifies as a deck landing pilot, is the recruit ready to join his unit as a fully qualified naval pilot.

Flying in the peace-time Navy is largely a matter of training; there is no enemy to intercept, except the enemy 'inefficiency'; there are no reconnaissance or bombing operations to be carried out, except at the practice range. But the pilot in the most important arm of the modern Navy has a twofold responsibility: to keep himself at the highest standard of efficiency, and to help improve the standard of efficiency of naval aviation as a whole.

Whatever form the pilot's training may have taken, whether he has developed as a bomber or a fighter pilot, he is assured of a colourful existence. Life in a carrier is seldom boring. There is lively company in which to enjoy off-duty hours, and plenty of interesting, exciting work to do in periods of duty. Flying will be undertaken under varying conditions of geography, climate and weather.

If this life appeals to *you*, you may be able to make it yours for at least twelve

De Havilland Sea Vampire.

M

years, with a gratuity if you then wish to leave the Service; and if you still like it, you can stay on for another ten years and qualify for a pension.

Prospects of promotion are good in the Air branch. At the age of twenty-three a young man can be a Pilot II, the equivalent rating to a Petty Officer. At twenty-seven he can be a Pilot I or on the same footing as a Chief Petty Officer. And, with ability and personality, it is possible to become a commissioned officer at an early date. The Admiralty give no promises about commissions but the quota of promotions from the Pilot branch is expected to be large in view of the high entry qualifications, and in any new branch opportunities are always numerous.

Officer Pilot, Pilot I or Pilot II—the men of the Pilot branch—will serve their country as skilful aviators in the most interesting and fast-developing branch of the Navy.

Fairey Firefly Mk. I.

CAREERS IN THE BRITISH AIRCRAFT INDUSTRY

by

E. C. Bowyer

Director, Society of British Aircraft Constructors

NOT MANY years ago aircraft engineering as a profession was not popular with parents who assessed the merits of an industry on its stability and traditions. The trade of the aircraft builder in this country was small in the pioneering days between 1909 and 1914; it flourished for a spell during the 1914–18 war, and then languished for fifteen years. It seemed that only war could bring prosperity.

There has now arisen a new cause which the aircraft builder must serve—the cause of air commerce. The struggle for supremacy on the airways of the world is fierce and unrelenting and the demands of the airline companies are exacting. So long as an industry can meet those demands that long it may hope to be prosperous. What is the outlook for the British aircraft industry?

Hard times after the 1914–18 war neither checked the flow of new recruits to the British aircraft industry nor extinguished the genius of the engineers who had made British aeroplanes famous in every land. Paucity of orders and poverty of resources sharpened ingenuity and stimulated invention; in the inter-war years many novel devices and notable aeroplanes—landmarks of aeronautical progress—came from factories and workshops owned and run by British companies. The young men who, with or without parental consent, implemented their resolve to become aeronautical engineers found abundant scope for their skill and knowledge and no dearth of good jobs.

The fertility of mind and liveliness of imagination displayed in that period of comparative adversity proved to be no false augury. When war demanded air weapons superior to those of an enemy by no means destitute of imagination and engineering skill, they were supplied; and now that peace calls for first-class airliners to meet world-wide competition they, too, are being supplied from British factories.

Since the end of 1945, the industry has lost much of its war-time girth—in 1943, at the peak of war production effort it employed no fewer than 1,821,000 men and women—but it is still much bigger than in 1935, when, belatedly, the re-armament of the R.A.F. began.

Even now, conditions are exceptional. Manufacturers are being pressed as urgently for the delivery of airliners and air transports of all kinds as they were for bombers and fighters from 1939 to 1945. The world is in desperate need of air transports of all types. In time, the more pressing of these needs will be met, but it is safe to assume that the development of air commerce, progress in airframe and engine design, and rivalry on the world's air routes, will keep many British drawing offices and factories busy for years. Orders worth more than fifty million pounds are already assured from the civil market alone. To them must be added substantial military contracts.

It may well prove that the coming of the gas turbine and other new aircraft propulsion units, the helicopter and radar, have opened a new chapter in the history of aeronautics. All that is written in the chapter now closing may be merely a preamble to the true story of aeronautical achievement. Those now starting their training as aeronautical engineers with British firms, schools and universities have before them a fair prospect of steady employment in the industry for a long time to come.

Training

As in every other profession, success in aeronautical engineering does not spring from natural gifts alone. The most talented student must pass through a long and strenuous period of practical and academic training—lasting perhaps for five years or more—before he can embark upon his career. Enthusiasm alone is a small asset. Aptitude must be allied with a readiness to undergo weeks and months of basic training remote from the positions of responsibility to which the student may aspire.

The greasy overalls of the mechanic lack the dignity of the white smock of the laboratory and research worker, but the wise pupil is as diligent and conscientious at the bench learning to handle a file, and in the machine shop learning the art of the turner and millwright, as he is in the drawing office and research laboratory. Academic honours are puny and meaningless if they have been won at the sacrifice of practical training. The designer who is unfamiliar with workshop technique will all too frequently impose unnecessary burdens upon the production engineer through ignorance of manufacturing processes. In turn, the production engineer may, from the same cause, plan a production sequence that adds unnecessary hours, days or weeks to the completion of a contract.

Too much stress cannot be laid upon practical training. It gives substance and meaning to the classroom lectures and 'book learning' that form an essential part of the student's training. It puts a keener edge on the imagination and curbs any tendency towards over-daring experiment. Only the soundly-trained aeronautical engineer can strike an exact balance between the ideal and the practicable, and yet avoid being enslaved by convention.

A deep and wide practical training loses none of its value from the increasing trend towards specialisation which arises from the growing complexity of the aeroplane. No one would set out to-day to acquire a full

A major component assembly shop where students spend about six months of their training period.

and expert knowledge of every aspect of aircraft design and construction, and of the design and construction of the innumerable accessories which go to make up the large modern aeroplane; but that does not exempt the beginner from learning broad first principles.

Nor is an ability to fly to be despised. The student often becomes a better engineer if he is also a pilot. After all, the flight of an aeroplane is the culmination and test of many men's work, and engineers who are familiar with the forces of flight and the technique of aeroplane control bring to their work an understanding which cannot be acquired from books, lectures or films. A course in flight training may also disclose an analytical attitude and a critical faculty which stamp the 'natural' test pilot and mark him out for one of the most specialised appointments in the industry.

The Way Ahead

The highest ranks of the profession can be reached by many roads. Which road the pupil takes will often depend upon the amount of money available for his training, and the standard of his earlier education. He can enter a university, study at a technical college or school, or sign an apprentice agreement with an aircraft company, according to his circumstances.

Scores of young men (and a few young women) sign aircraft apprenticeships with the manufacturing companies every year. Until 1944, apprentices were trained under schemes drawn up by each company. These schemes varied to a greater or lesser extent according to the available facilities. In 1944, the Society of British Aircraft Constructors—on which are represented all the principal aircraft, aero-engine and accessory manufacturers and suppliers of materials—decided that the time was ripe for the issue of a standard syllabus to be recommended for adoption by all aircraft companies offering aircraft apprentice training.

Another three years must elapse before the first trainees under the standardised scheme are launched on their careers, but the new plan has already proved its worth and by 1949 will provide the industry with a continuous stream of men and women engineers all trained to approximately the same high level of efficiency.

Under the S.B.A.C. scheme pupils between the ages of 16 and 18 are accepted for training either as aircraft apprentices or (where facilities are provided) as engine apprentices. The syllabus of practical training for aircraft apprentices, which runs concurrently with theoretical training, covers:

(a) Pattern making and foundry work.
(b) Fitting work.
(c) Machining.
(d) Tool room work.
(e) Sheet metal work.
(f) Aircraft electrical installation.
(g) Bench equipment and jig assembly.
(h) Final erection.
(i) Materials testing and inspection.
(j) The experimental and research department.
(k) The laboratory.
(l) Design office or jig and tool drawing office.
(m) Rate fixing department.
(n) Estimating and planning department.

Instruction in subjects (i) to (n) depends upon the aptitude of the pupil. These are 'specialist' subjects, and though all are taken, the periods spent on each will be governed by the degree of interest or fitness the pupil shows for them.

Engine apprentices pass through a similar syllabus, taking:

(a) Pattern making and foundry work.
(b) Machining.
(c) Fitting work.
(d) Tool room work.
(e) Engine testing.
(f) Materials testing and inspection.
(g) Experimental and research work.
(h) Laboratory work.
(i) Design office or jig and tool drawing office.
(j) Rate fixing department.
(k) Estimating department.

Under this scheme, the specialist subjects are those from (f) to (k) inclusive.

While gaining practical experience in the workshops and the associated offices, the student is expected to pass specified examinations at fixed intervals, finishing with the B.Sc. (Engineering) and the Higher National Certificate Examinations for admission to the Royal Aeronautical Society or the Institution of Production Engineers. The National Certificate Course for aeronautical students, taken in combined part-time and evening classes, is given in the table at the foot of the page.

Some aircraft companies offer more than one type of training. One, for instance, has a training course for the aeronautical engineer whose interests lie in the study of the science of aeronautics, aerodynamics, methods and problems of design and manufacture, production methods and control and administration, and another for the trade apprentice. The first course has two separate parts: (a) A Graduate Apprenticeship Course, which provides practical instruction in the company's works for students taking a full-time Engineering Degree Course at a university or engineering college, and (b) a Five-Year Technical Apprenticeship Course, combining practical instruction in the works with part-time theoretical instruction at an engineering college.

The second course is for the skilled craftsman. Under this scheme, training is offered through a five-year Trade Apprenticeship Course in one of the particular trades practised in the company's works.

The Graduate Apprenticeship Course is designed to provide practical workshop training for engineering students both during their period of study for, and after the attainment of, a University Degree. Students are enrolled under agreement to work in the factory during the whole of the two summer vacation periods of their three-year Degree Course, and for a further two years after obtaining a degree. No premium is required and students are paid wages on a rising scale.

The Technical Apprenticeship Course covers extensive practical training in the company's works with concurrent theoretical training at a day engineering college. The apprenticeship is for a period of five years, including an initial six months' probation, and is covered by an agreement signed by the parent or guardian, the apprentice and the company.

NATIONAL CERTIFICATE COURSE FOR AERONAUTICAL STUDENTS

	DAY	EVENING
First year . . .	Engineering Science (Mechanics, Heat, Electricity), Chemistry.	Mathematics, Engineering and Aeronautical Drawing.
Second year . . .	Applied Mechanics, Aeronautics, Heat Engines.	Mathematics, Engineering and Aeronautical Drawing.
Third year . . .	Applied Mechanics, Aeronautics, Heat Engines.	Mathematics, Aeronautical Drawing and Design.
Fourth year:		
Aircraft Course .	Materials and Structures, Metallurgy, Aeronautics.	Mathematics, Aircraft Design.
Engine course .	Materials and Structures, Metallurgy, I.C. Engines, Theory of Machines.	Mathematics, Aero-Engine Design.
Fifth year.		

At least three subjects from the following group:

Mathematics
Aerodynamics
Materials and Structures (Aeronautical)
Aircraft Design
Aero-Engine Design
Theory of Machines

Again, no premium is required, and wages are paid on a rising scale as the apprenticeship proceeds.

The Trade Apprenticeship Course is designed to train skilled artisans in one of the particular trades listed below, selected by the apprentice.

Detail fittings.   A student learning to work from blueprints.

The apprenticeship is for a period of five years, including an initial six months' probation, and is covered by an agreement signed by the parent or guardian, the apprentice and the company. No premium is required, and wages are paid from the start. The selection of candidates is made from (a) shop and office boys in the company's employment on general duties since leaving elementary or central schools, who have undergone a course of engineering training or manual work and who are physically fit and have mechanical aptitude. Candidates must not be more than sixteen years of age. The trades in which training is offered are: aircraft fitting (including jig and template making), turning, milling (universal), machining, tool making, sheet metal working and millwright.

Trade apprentices who show outstanding capabilities during their training and who receive satisfactory reports from the technical colleges may be considered for promotion to the *Technical Apprentice Scheme.*

That is a brief outline of one company's training programme. Similar schemes, differing only in matters of detail, are in operation at the majority of aircraft factories in the United Kingdom. The courses are stiff, and students are encouraged to make use of recreational and cultural facilities provided by the companies' Sports Clubs, Debating Societies and other organisations, to prevent their becoming stale, physically and mentally, through overstudy.

The Financial Aspect

Although apprentices pay no premium, and draw wages, they remain to some extent a financial liability to their parents. This is a liability most parents willingly accept, but many a boy whose heart is set upon a career in the aircraft industry is forced to take work which brings in bigger money—simply because his parents cannot afford to support him beyond his schooldays. For boys so placed the Society of British Aircraft Constructors offers annually a number of grants which solve the parents' financial difficulties. The fund from which these grants are made is administered by the Royal Aeronautical Society, and provides successful applicants with a training identical with that offered to young men more fortunately placed. One scholarship, given in

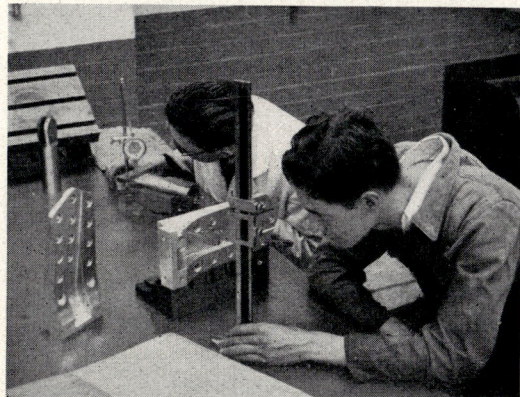

The surface table.   Students marking off and using precision tools.

memory of the famous airwoman, Amy Johnson, goes every year to a girl.

Apprentices who show unusual talents (and this includes those apprenticed under the S.B.A.C. 'grant' scheme) are sometimes sent by their training company to a university for further training, the company paying the fees and residential expenses. Other university scholarships are provided each year by the S.B.A.C., varying in number from five to ten, and each worth £250 a year. Candidates (who must not have reached their twenty-third birthday) are chosen from among engineering apprentices in the industry who have successfully passed a Higher National Certificate examination after a five-year course of training, preferably with aeronautical subjects, or a recognised alternative. In certain circumstances, a degree is not an essential qualification.

The College of Aeronautics

An important addition was made to the number of training establishments when the government set up the College of Aeronautics at Cranfield, near Bletchley, Bucks, ' to provide a high-grade engineering, technical and scientific training in aeronautics to fit students for leadership in the aircraft industry, civil aviation, the Services, education and research '. The curriculum, as originally drawn up, covered six main subjects :

    (i) Flight.
   (ii) Aircraft equipment.
  (iii) Aircraft structures, engineering and design.
   (iv) Aerodynamics.
    (v) Engines and systems of propulsion.
   (vi) Production, administration and maintenance.

The first course, which began in October 1946, was limited to three main subjects: (a) Aerodynamics, (b) Aircraft design and (c) Aircraft propulsion.

Candidates for admission to the College are expected to have had a sound engineering training, not necessarily aeronautical. The course normally lasts for two years, but other shorter courses are provided for specialisation purposes, and there are also refresher courses on various subjects for those wishing to bring their knowledge up to date from time to time. Flight experiments and flight training play a big part in the College's syllabus. The fee for the two-year course has

been fixed at £75 a year, but the authorities expect, soon, to be able to offer a number of scholarships. Living-in expenses are between £100 and £150. (See note at end.)

Fees at other universities and training colleges vary, ranging for a full course from slightly less to rather more than £100 per

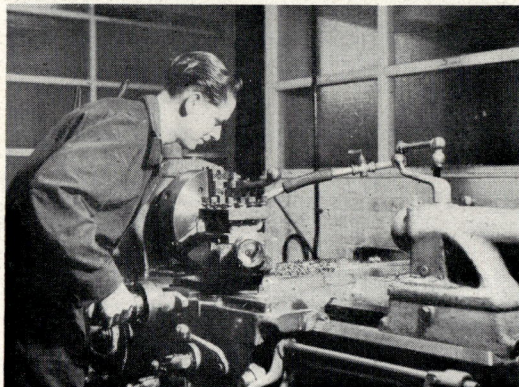

Machine shop training. An aircraft apprentice operating a centre lathe.

annum. Where instruction is taken in evening classes the cost per year is usually lower. For those who have not the time or money to take the practical and theoretical courses offered by aircraft companies, schools, colleges and universities, there are correspondence courses.

Most aeronautical engineers have the ambition to qualify for one of the technical grades of the Royal Aeronautical Society, or of the Institution of Aeronautical Engineers. Most become members of the Students' Section of the R.Ae.S. as soon as they have completed their probationary term of training. The Society has many branches, both at home and overseas. Those who specialise in production normally qualify for membership of the Institution of Production Engineers.

Greater stress has been laid in this survey on aeronautical engineering training than upon the openings in the profession itself. Experience has shown that it is not until a pupil is well advanced in his training that he displays the talents and aptitudes that do much to determine his ultimate career. It is therefore inadvisable for a young man, or young woman, to begin training with a fixed goal in mind. It is better to let natural gifts show themselves so that they can be fostered and cultivated. In that way, the pupil finds congenial employment, and the industry has the benefit of natural talents brought to full fruition by careful coaching.

As a career, the profession of aircraft design and construction and its many subsidiary professions have a powerful appeal. They are new, growing, and always changing. They are modern and progressive. They are directed on the one hand to a vehicle that belongs to commerce and to travel, and on the other to a vital part of a country's defences. It seems certain that far more has yet to be achieved than has been accomplished in the past half-century. Unless the signs and tokens are misleading, many laurels and many big prizes will be won before the industry and profession of aircraft manufacture begin to decline.

NOTE.—Another Government institution for aircraft apprentices is the Royal Aircraft Establishment Technical College which has been set up in association with the work of the R.A.E. The College was formally opened by Sir Stafford Cripps, the Chancellor of the Exchequer, on 18th February 1948, although it had been in active existence at that time for more than four years. It caters for engineering apprentices, craft apprentices, scientific assistants, drawing office tracers and junior clerks, and is intended to provide scientists, technicians and craftsmen for the aircraft industry and for the Government aviation centres.

Students have to be between 16 and 18 years of age and are chosen as a result of competitive examinations, aptitude tests and interviews. The standard of examination is approximately between General Schools Certificate and Higher Schools Certificate.

From the start the students are divided into two groups. The members of one group are trained for the R.A.E. Diploma and are expected to get the London degree in engineering at the end of their fourth year. The others go for the Higher National Certificates in mechanics and production engineering. All students spend their first year at the College. Their second and third years are spent in the various workshops of the Royal Aircraft Establishment and their fourth and fifth years in the research departments and drawing offices. In this last year the Diploma group goes towards work in the research departments while the National Certificate group goes towards design and development in the workshops and drawing offices. Craft apprentices, scientific assistants and drawing office tracers have different conditions of entry and different courses of study.

*   *   *

The drawing office. Students taking the technical apprenticeship course spend upwards of twelve months in the drawing office, the stress office or aerodynamics department.

The jet-propelled de Havilland 108, experimental forerunner of 550 m.p.h. jet transatlantic airliners.

THE LITERATURE OF FLIGHT

LET the admiring world be told, that these two men were launched to swim in air—or meet inevitable death; and from this precipice, to the rapturous astonishment of thousands of spectators, these bold adventurers floated safe in the atmosphere, buoyed up by a power lighter than air itself.

> Reporter in the *Gentleman's Magazine* on
> the first Channel flight by Blanchard and
> Jeffries on 7th January 1785

THE ROYAL AERONAUTICAL SOCIETY
ITS WORK AND ACTIVITIES

by

Captain John Laurence Pritchard, Hon. F.R.Ae.S.

Secretary-General, Royal Aeronautical Society. Author of ' Aero-plane Structures', 1920; 'The Story of the Aeroplane', 1927.

THE FUTURE of travel and transport generally lies in the air. The time is not far distant when few people will think of taking any journey of over a hundred miles or so except by air. The young man now at school will wish to own his own aeroplane and to know how it works just as much as an earlier generation expected to have a motor-cycle or car.

There will, indeed, be a great future in the air for all those who have learnt not only how to pilot an aeroplane, but how to look after it. And to those, too, who will be concerned in its design and production, aviation will be one of the major industries of the world and those who enter it now will see it grow until its ramifications are world-wide. Never before has such an opportunity presented itself for a young man, with enthusiasm and ability, to enter a profession which will grow more and more in importance during the next fifty years.

It is in the field of aircraft design and aero-engine design particularly that the Royal Aeronautical Society and its members have played and are playing a supreme role. It is not only the actual design with which the Society is concerned. Among its members are the leaders in the design and manufacture of aircraft instruments, research into new fuels, the training and education of aeronautical engineers, the study of meteorology and air flow, radar, and research on new materials for construction.

Indeed the work of members of the Society covers a very wide field, including that of mechanical, civil and electrical engineering, physics, mathematics, navigation, maintenance and so on.

Founded on 12th January 1866 the Royal Aeronautical Society is the oldest aeronautical society in the world. Its objects are simple, to promote the advancement of aeronautical engineering and science, and it has done its best to do so for over eighty years.

The very first lecture read before it in 1866 was by F. H. Wenham, a member of the first Council and a well-known engineer. This first lecture was not only significant because it was the first meeting, but was of outstanding importance in that the first public lecture read before the members was on heavier-than-air aircraft. This was at a time when there was no apparent hope of a mechanically driven heavier-than-air aircraft becoming a possibility in the lifetime of those present. In his paper Wenham laid down the engineering principles of flight, and pointed out that progress could only be made on sound engineering lines.

Since that day over eighty years ago practically all chief designers and constructors of aircraft have been members of the Society, and have led the world in the conquest of the air. In the summer of 1868 just over two years after the founding of the Society, the Society held the first aeronautical exhibition in the world. At the exhibition, John Stringfellow, for many years a leading member, flew a model of an aeroplane powered by a steam engine which was the lightest of its day. His flying model, the first mechanically driven model ever to fly, was a close forecast of the present day machines and clearly demonstrated the possibility of flight once the motive power could be made light enough.

It was the Society which first began, in 1870, to study in a scientific way the lift and resistance of various wing shapes, and to forecast, in 1886, the coming of jet-propulsion.

Behind the design and construction of every well-known British aeroplane, civil or military, since 1909, has been a member of the Royal Aeronautical Society, a tribute in itself to the authority the Society now wields in aviation. Members of the Society designed the Vickers Vimy which was the first machine to fly the Atlantic in 1919; the Spitfire and the Hurricane, which played such a large part in winning the Battle of Britain; the great bombers which devastated Germany; and the Empire flying-boats and modern transport aeroplanes which are steadily putting Britain first in the air.

Before the Society every year is read a series of lectures on all sides of aeronautical development, and many of these papers have become standard reference papers for further progress. The pages of the journal of the Society, indeed, not only provide a history of aviation during the past eighty years, but are pointers to the future, pointers made by some of the outstanding engineers in aviation.

Qualifications for Membership

With this long tradition behind it of constant progress the Society has become the leading society in the world on the engineering and scientific side of aviation, and to be an Associate Fellow or Fellow of the Society has become an acknowledged qualification.

Students may join the Society at the age of eighteen and they immediately become eligible for all the benefits of the Society, to receive the monthly journal, to consult or borrow books from the library, and to be free to attend all lectures read before the Society.

There is a special Students' and Graduates' Section of the Society, organised by the students and graduates themselves. This section arranges for its own lectures, in addition to those before the Society itself, by well-known aeronautical engineers as well as the students and graduates themselves. The section also arranges for a number of informal discussions on subjects of topical interest in design, production or research,

and visits to various aircraft firms and official government establishments.

The only requirements of a student of the Society are that he shall signify that he intends to make aviation his career and shall have passed the Common Preliminary Examination or its equivalent.

The next step, apart from his training in an aircraft works or elsewhere, is to become a Graduate of the Society. A graduate is required to pass the Associate Fellowship Examination of the Society or be exempted from it by reason of other examinations he has passed. These examinations are held twice a year, in May and December, and are roughly of the standard of an honours degree.

A graduate, over the age of twenty-six, can become an Associate Fellow of the Society, if he has had five years' experience in aeronautical engineering, or science or research as applied to aviation. His period of training does not count as experience, so that anyone who is elected an Associate Fellow is known not only to possess the practical experience required of him, but also to have the necessary theoretical engineering knowledge.

The qualifications for Associate Fellowship are high, but aircraft engineering calls for them, and it is most unlikely these qualifications will ever be lowered. Aeronautical engineering, indeed, demands a higher efficiency than most other forms of engineering, since the aeronautical engineer is compelled all the time to make the very best use possible of the materials he is called upon to use.

There is another class of membership, that of Associate Member, which is of great importance. There are many students who find it difficult to pass the necessary severe examinations for Associate Fellowship, but who have, nevertheless, an excellent mechanical ability. This class can take charge of construction and production of aircraft and aero engines and be responsible for the management of works or sections of works. They must have a thorough practical training and have at least five years' experience before they can be considered for election as Associate Member.

Fellowship of the Society is the highest

THE GRAND ENGLISH AIR BALLOON.

With the *GALLANT LUNARDI* ascending the Atmosphere from the Artillery Ground LONDON Sep 15 1784 at 2 O'Clock in the Afternoon, and was wafted an immense height, till about 5 in the Evening, when he safely descended at Colliers End near Ware, in Hertfordshire, 20 Miles from London.—

Pub.ᵈ 20 Oct.ʳ 1784 by H.Humphreys Nᵒ 3, Bedford Court Cov.Garden.

The first aerial voyage in England, September 1784.   (*See* page 219.)

grade of all and is awarded to those members, Associate Fellows and Associate Members, who have reached a considerable degree of eminence and have had a long experience in aviation.

Advantages of Membership

For those who wish to make a career in aviation, particularly on the engineering, scientific or research side, it is invaluable for them to become members of the Society as soon as possible. The Society exists to help them and encourages in every way possible their education and training. The Society is in constant contact with the Society of British Aircraft Constructors, the body controlling the industry, and from them receives considerable help to carry out its work.

The Society has a technical staff which is concerned with the issue of data sheets, special monographs and other forms of information of direct use to members of the Society. The library of the Society is one of the finest aeronautical technical libraries in the world and there is a large technical index which enables members to find and study the available information on any subject of aeronautical interest.

For those members of the Society whose work is chiefly in the provinces or abroad, there are branches which enable them to get together and hold lectures and other meetings. These branches are in convenient centres throughout the country and there are branches in Canada, South Africa, New Zealand and Australia.

The Society is in close touch with corresponding bodies throughout the world and through them is able to provide introductions and other facilities for members who go abroad for a short or a long period. The Society also subscribes to the leading aviation technical journals and other publications throughout the world and so enables its members to keep in close touch with the aeronautical developments in other countries.

Finally the Society offers each year a number of valuable prizes and premium awards for papers in the journal or papers read before the Society, or its branches.

It is not possible in a short summary such as this to give full details of the Society and its work, or of the qualifications for membership in any grade. These, however, may be obtained by writing to the Secretary, Royal Aeronautical Society, No. 4 Hamilton Place, London, W.1.

THE LITERATURE OF FLIGHT

A Prophecy Of Air War

I, WHOSE Genius and desire hath always prompted me to endeavour to my utmost, to find out difficult Inventions, do hope at length, I have light upon a way of making such an Engine as shall not only by its being lighter than the Air raise itself in the Air, but together, with itself, Buoy up and carry into the Air Men or any other weight. Nor do I believe I deceive myself, since I conjure the thing both by certain Experiments and by Demonstration, drawn from the

Eleventh Book of Euclid, hitherto thought infallible of all Mathematicians. . . .

Other difficulties I see not which may be objected against this Invention, beside one which to me seems greater than all the rest, and that is, That it may be thought, that God will never suffer this Invention to take effect because of the many consequences which may disturb the civil Government of Men. For who sees not, that no City can be secure against attack since our Ship may at any

[*Photo: Charles Brown*

An experimental Avro Lancastrian with two nene jet engines, showing the plane flying by jet power only, with piston engines stopped.

time be placed directly over it, and descending down may discharge Soldiers; the same would happen to private Houses, and Ships on the Sea; for our Ship descending out of the Air to the sails of Sea Ships, it may cut their ropes, yea without descending by casting Grapples it may over-set them, kill their men, burn their Ships by artificial Fireworks and Fire-balls. And this they may do, not only to Ships but to great buildings, Castles, Cities, with such security that they which cast these things down from a height out of Gunshot, cannot on the other side be offended by those from below.

FRANCESCO LANA, *Prodromo overo saggio di alcune invenzione nuove premesso all' Arte Maestra,* 1670

191

AEROMODELLING

by

D. A. Russell, M.I.Mech.E.

*Managing Editor of ' The Aeromodeller '; author of ' The
Design and Construction of Flying Model Aircraft ', etc.*

EVER SINCE the day when Sir George Cayley flew his model glider in 1804, the small scale aircraft has been of great service in the history of aviation, perhaps the most famous being Langley's successful petrol-driven machine of 1896, the full-sized version of which unfortunately crashed on taking off. However, once flight became a practical possibility designers abandoned the model as a testing device and hastened to put machine after machine into the air almost from the drawing-board, with consequent cost in both lives and still scant capital. As the aeroplane grew in power and strength the cost of such hazardous experiments became too great to be borne by any but the wealthiest of manufacturers and once more models took their place in the hierarchy of full-size aviation. Small precision models were built for display to directors and others interested in new projects, and for use in wind tunnel experiments, which could forecast with tolerable accuracy the performance of the prototype under varied conditions of weather and load. Other manufacturers developed man-size scaled-down replicas of their larger ventures, such as the single-seater Pobjoy engined machine that first flew as a quarter-size edition of what was to be the famous Short Stirling. During the 1939–45 war, research on radio-controlled models has developed to such an extent that a number of firms are now using such machines before proceeding to final production. First in the field are the Stout Corporation of America who have published interesting data on their researches. It may be mentioned that this firm have long sponsored model aviation activities—the Stout Trophy being offered for annual competition in the U.S.A.—and it is fitting that they should therefore be the first to appreciate and make use of this new medium.

Sport and Hobby

But it is as a sport and hobby and as a training ground for the student of aeronautics that aeromodelling, as it has come to be known, has achieved national recognition from a fast growing band of enthusiasts that are now said to number one in every twenty-three of the population of the British Isles—a total approaching the two million mark. To cater for their needs a large industry has sprung up, together with special literature created to satisfy their demand for knowledge. Two monthly journals are published—one now in its eleventh year of publication, and, even in these times, able to publish certified sales of over sixty thousand copies per issue—exclusively devoted to aeromodelling, while a number of other journals devote space to the subject. Even the Air Correspondent of *The Times* has reported on the activities of various groups from time to time. Whilst this article is primarily intended as a general treatise on the subject, it is as well to draw attention to the spread of model aeronautics on a world-wide rather than a purely national basis. Every country without exception has followed, to a greater or lesser degree, the example set by the English-speaking nations.

Until about 1930, activities were confined in the main to the British Isles and U.S.A., but the support of the late Lord Wakefield of Hythe, who presented a Trophy for annual international competition between aeromodellers of all countries, brought about a great surge of interest on the Continent. Entrants from France, Holland, Belgium, Germany, the Scandinavian countries and most of the Balkan States showed their enthusiasm. By 1938, when a French model won the coveted Trophy, it may be said to have become firmly established. King Peter of Yugoslavia gave a similar International Trophy that embraced sailplanes in addition to rubber powered machines, which, in the two years before the war in which contests were held, bid fair to equal the 'Wakefield' in popularity. In the same way as in this country and the U.S.A. an extensive foreign literature on the subject has developed, though generally the technical standard is not so high as here. Unfortunately some of the continental enthusiasts were absorbed into political groups run ostensibly for aero-modelling such as the National Socialist Flieger Korps in Germany and a similar body in Italy, but in the main the more liberal minded countries, though, in many instances, giving it State support—lacking in Great Britain—have been content to develop it as a useful adjunct to full-size aviation without forcing on it political aims.

Model aeronautics can broadly speaking be sub-divided into two main groups—flying and non-flying aircraft.

Non-Flying Models

Non-flying models are usually exact replicas in outline of full-size machines to certain fixed scales, the most popular being 1/72nd full size and 1/48th full size. Such models, measuring a few inches only in span for a modern fighter aircraft, have enjoyed an immense measure of popularity during the

[Photo : 'Aeromodeller'

Solid model Typhoon to the popular 1/48 scale. An amazing amount of detail can be incorporated and, with suitable backgrounds, it is extremely difficult in photographs to detect a well-built model from the real thing.

war years. Small in size and requiring the simplest possible tools to produce, they proved an excellent escapist occupation for men and women in all parts of the world engaged in more or less hazardous occupa-tions. The writer was recently shown a perfect little 1/72nd Focke Wulf 190 carved by a member of the Forces whilst sheltering

[Photo : 'Aeromodeller'

A solid scale flying-boat that demonstrates the value of these models for aircraft recognition purposes and display.

for twenty-four hours in a Normandy bomb-hole on D-Day plus one. It was made entirely from scraps he had in his pockets or found within a range of about one yard ! More normal model-makers devote a great deal of time and care to producing as exact a model as possible, going to much pain to ensure that camouflage colouring, insignia and squadron markings are correct. Small moulded cockpit covers are fixed in place and every detail faithfully portrayed. In the very small sizes—some have even been made to 1/144th scale—it is not possible to embody such details as retracting under-carriages, sliding cockpit covers and fully detailed ' office '. For those desiring these refinements 1/48th is the minimum practical scale which gives scope for a reasonable degree of detail without risk of the completed model ' looking like a Christmas tree '.

During the war something like eighty per cent. of aeromodellers were spending all or most of their leisure on ' solids ', as such replicas were rather obviously called. From somewhat rough but recognisable versions of their early efforts a real craft appeared, so that their work became truly a thing of beauty

N

to be compared with the work of old crafts-men prisoners in Napoleonic days who produced those delightful ship models now so highly prized. With the development of their skill the more ambitious sought for more and more detail and this led to the final stage of non-flying models which were then made as built-up replicas, employing in many cases rib and former construction identical with the prototype. These are usually of 1/24th scale, though a few have been built to 1/12th, but this size is unwieldy for display purposes, besides requiring more elaborate tools and greater attention to detail finish. Such built-up models, though winning a new popularity towards the end of the war, are really by no means new, as enthusiasts have been producing them in small numbers for very many years.

With the end of hostilities the need for 'escapist' occupation became less, and interest in solid models has somewhat declined, until now not more than twenty per cent. of aeromodellers are building them. Many newcomers to the hobby, however, who had never before built flying models are finding new enthusiasm in this other outlet for their skill.

There continues to be a market for the few specialist firms producing precision replicas of aircraft for manufacturers and private individuals. A well-built model, made by a reputable company, will command a commissioned price of anything from £20 to £75 depending on the degree of detail required. These serve a useful purpose to convince directors who would never under-stand a blueprint, to keep the public informed of new ventures, and to serve as a memento of some favourite aircraft.

It must not be forgotten, too, that solid models played their by no means insignificant part in final victory. Hundreds of thousands of plastic recognition solids were made for the R.A.F. and A.A. batteries, while the United States mobilised their modellers in schools and colleges to turn out thousands of Japanese models for training in the Pacific field. Large-size solids were used extensively to secure 'air-to-air' shots of new enemy aircraft from the scant particulars offered by returning aircrews who had encountered new machines in the course of their trips.

Many illustrations appearing in war-time numbers of *Flight* and *The Aeroplane* would have deceived but for the tell-tale caption, '. . . from a model'.

Flying Models

Flying models cannot be considered in so convenient a classification. First they must be subdivided into powered models and sail-planes, which again break down into a variety of groups. Under the heading 'powered' can be placed rubber-powered, petrol-engined, compressed-air or dry-ice driven, and diesel-engined, rocket and jet-propelled machines. Sailplanes can be split into light-weight types of a wing-loading up to say, 5 oz. per square foot, and heavy-weight designs of anything up to 16 oz. or more wing-loading to the square foot. Then again they can be grouped as tow-line launched models and slope-soaring models. Such subdivisions are purely arbitrary and take no account of countless other variants such as unconventional types, 'pushers,' tailless models, canards, tandems, scale models, semi-scale design, and so on *ad infinitum*. Each commands an enthusiastic following prepared to defend their particular branch against any suggestion that other fields remain to be explored !

Duration Types

It is probable that the most popular class—certainly the most numerous—is the so-called 'duration' type. This, its detractors declare, has no resemblance whatever to a full-size aircraft, and is condemned by them on that account without further ado. But it cannot be so lightly dismissed: its lack of family likeness is intentional, for all those necessary features in a full-size aircraft that in them-selves lend no aerodynamic aid have been ruthlessly excluded, until in fact the model is a flying embodiment of theoretical perfection. In the search for pure aerodynamics highly skilled exponents have removed cockpits and canopies and all drag-producing non-essentials such as undercarriage legs and wheels. The modern highly efficient competition model in this class has a streamlined body, single-blade folding airscrew, and retracting undercarriage. In the ultra lightweight class streamlining is not carried to finality, merely a fairing-in of the entry, but the undercarriage has shrunk to a wire of about 18 s.w.g. which serves merely as a support until the airscrew picks up speed enough to lift the aircraft in an almost vertical climb.

It has a ' poor relation ' in the shape of the commercial duration kit model, where the manufacturer is offering extreme simplification, such as slabsided box construction of fuselage, constant chord wings and flat plate tail surfaces, at a low price within reach of his younger customers. These kits serve a

[Photo : ' Aeromodeller

Models in flight during a recent national competition. These are petrol engined designs produced mainly for contest work and lack the finish and refinements encountered in scale and semi-scale models.

Exactly the same aerodynamic principles are devoted to the design of such monstrosities —to alien eyes—as go to make the latest civil transport produced in a full-size drawing office. The designer has, however, no problems of payload, engine placing, design specification or pilot's visibility. He is concerned only in making a machine that will stay up in the air for the maximum length of time, achieve the greatest height with the lowest possible expenditure of power ; and when this power is expended return to earth with the flattest possible glide. Added to this he must build-in automatic stability that will tend to keep the model on its correct flight path in spite of vagaries of wind, gusty pockets and the like, for no pilot is carried to swing over the controls. Hence the ugly duckling of model aeronautics that nevertheless enjoys a keen following amongst competition enthusiasts the world over.

very useful purpose in introducing a real flying model at an impressionable age, but are by no means indicative of the highly skilled work that goes to make a successful contest model. Only too often the youngster has that initial prejudice against a model that does not ' look like the real thing ', and insists on commencing his flying career with a small-scale replica of some full-size aircraft that will indeed fly, but requires more skill to achieve that end than he can bring to bear.

Such success has attended this search after duration that designers have now produced a dethermaliser which automatically spoils the flight after a set duration, and causes the model to glide prematurely to earth. This is necessary in view of the usual contest rule that requires three flights to be made in a competition. One long flight may sometimes win, but it is safer to have two flights of reasonable duration, recovering the model safely after each attempt, and then go all out for the longest possible duration on the third and final flight. Most dethermalisers work on the air-leak system, whereby a small arm actuates the spoiling device after anything from five to twenty minutes. This spoiler may take the form of a change in tail trim or a movement of some ballast weight. A simpler variant is a small Japanese-tissue parachute folded and tied to the fuselage, attached to which is a touch paper designed to burn for a set time, and then release the retaining cotton; the parachute opens and being attached to the tail thus upsets the trim. This device is extremely light in weight, but not so reliable in action as the air-leak type which itself may weigh as little as 1/8th oz.

Scale Flying Models

The more thoughtful aeromodeller is not content for long with this curious state of affairs, where the only object is duration, and the loss of a model, unless restrained from giving that duration by some artificial flight limitation. He will ultimately fall under the spell of the scale or semi-scale model, where resemblance to a full-size prototype is the aim. This requires a high degree of skill, for while any handyman can produce, say, a model Spitfire, it needs an expert to make it fly! The absence of a pilot, the high wing-loading of modern aircraft, and the change of trim necessitated by the substitution of a rubber motor the full length of the fuselage for an engine located at the front, present a puzzling series of problems to the builder. To build a scale model he must obviously keep to the outline of the prototype, and yet make a number of subtle adjustments calculated to overcome these problems. The automatic stability is best achieved by increasing the amount of dihedral in the model, which if skilfully done does not displease the eye by striking an obvious false note. Next, the high wing-loading is conquered by changing the aerofoil from the high-speed section employed to one more suitable for the low speeds at which the model will fly; probably at the same time the angle of incidence is changed to comply with the optimum efficiency of the new aerofoil. The change of trim involved in using

a rubber motor is overcome by making it as short as possible, putting a gear train in the nose, and adding further skeins of rubber to carry the required power. Finally by building the empennage as lightly as possible, and perhaps increasing the area of tail surfaces slightly, the design is completed. The result is a model that looks in outline very like the prototype, the amount of detail fittings being dependent on the scale used. The usual size of such models is 1/12th scale, or one inch to the foot. This gives a pleasing size, large enough to allow robust construction and a fair degree of detail without being unwieldy for transport.

The next problem of the scale model-builder is to produce flights in the style of the prototype. Nothing would look less real than a Spitfire wafted on the evening breeze. Accordingly, high speed of anything up to thirty or forty miles per hour is aimed at, and the model trimmed to perform such simple evolutions as a 'Victory roll', a zooming dive and a banked turn. This requires a high degree of patience, and a number of disappointments, but it can be done—and the builder can then rightly feel he has made something worth while.

Much of the success of scale model flying depends on the choice of a suitable prototype. While pleasing to look at, the highly stream-lined modern aircraft is not a very happy example, except in skilled hands. Far better are some of the 'old-timers', such as the range of Bristol biplanes, the Hawker biplanes and the high-wing monoplanes, such as the Westland Widgeon and the A.B.C. Robin. The most successful types for copying amongst recent aircraft are the Lysander and the Auster, both of which produce stable models with a minimum of alteration to their full-size characteristics.

Before leaving the subject of flying scale models, mention must be made of the progress shown in recent years in the reproduction of multi-engined aircraft. Bearing in mind the limitations imposed by rubber motors this would seem to be a class outside the scope of model building. These difficulties have aroused the interest of a select band of enthusiasts who, working on different lines, have achieved surprisingly good results. Here the problem has been to find some remote drive that will turn the airscrews situated often on nacelles too short to house the rubber motor. One successful method has been to employ wire coils similar to those used for expanding curtain rails, which, running in a suitable sheathing, can be made to turn a propeller at up to 180 degrees to the line of the motor skein, without undue friction losses. More recently, what has become known as the Moore Drive, after its inventor, has been perfected. This utilises a series of shafts running in bushes connected by a species of stirrup joint that enables the most

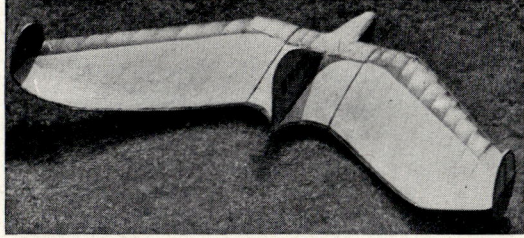

[*Photo : ' Aeromodeller '*

The Crowfly. A particularly stable model of the tailless variety. This is a formula that is attracting more and more attention as problems are overcome.

An elegant flying-boat that combines many practical features with grace of outline, and is representative of the best in modern model aircraft design. Note the slot holding the wing bracing spar that can be moved to enable minor adjustment in trim to be effected.

[*Photo : ' Aeromodeller '*

complicated engine layout to be faithfully copied at the expense of negligible friction loss and very little increase in weight. Replicas of the Short Scion and Bristol Blenheim have flown successfully using this system, their flights being almost exactly equal to a single-engined aircraft producing similar power and built to the same specification.

Semi-Scale Types

Less exacting, but of great interest, is the development of semi-scale model aircraft. These, as their name suggests, bear a likeness to full-size planes, but do not attempt an exact replica of any type. Here there is no limit to the builder's ingenuity; he may make his own idea of a new civil aircraft; he may

A good example of the semi-scale model. It looks like a real aeroplane, but of no particular type.

[*Photo : ' Aeromodeller '*

follow the general lines of some favourite aircraft, without feeling bound to include features unsuitable for model practice or he may just build as fancy dictates, yet keeping to something that looks like the real thing.

The solution of knotty problems always attracts a following and amongst aero-modellers the unconventional in layout is often accepted as the usual. Pusher types are regaining favour, usually to the Tatin layout, while canards have their supporters. When it is possible to produce some aerodynamic curiosity for the expenditure of a few hours of work and a trifling amount of money, it is easy to indulge the wildest fancies. The only type that has not been well received in this country is the ornithopter, and this had a

An experimental type athodyd jet unit for installation in model aircraft. Simplicity, combined with light weight and strength, is proving a stumbling-block, but already model designers have achieved their first successes.

great following in Germany both before and during the war. Their researches in the field were remarkable, and included the most complicated wing-testing devices in the School of Model Aeronautics at Rothenburg. Alexander Lippisch, better known as the designer of the Me 163 and a supersonic project discovered after the occupation, was the prime mover in this research. He produced a number of successful flapping-wing models, including a miniature petrol-engined design that flew, ultimately, for over half an hour.

The most popular unorthodoxy at present is undoubtedly the tailless model or flying wing. Research has been stimulated by Sir Frederick Handley Page's Prize of £50

offered in 1945 for a tailless model conforming to certain fairly broad conditions. Last year he offered a similar prize to any such type winning a National Contest against conventional models, as well as a series of smaller cash prizes for the best performance in certain other contests of models built to this formula. While full-size research follows similar lines it is interesting to note that in the model field such interest existed even before the added incentive of high cash prizes.

Jet-Propulsion

In one field aeromodellers have lagged a long way behind; this is in the achievement of successful reaction-propelled flight. A number of experimental jet units have been built, nearly all employing the Ram principle, but, so far as is known, no really outstanding performance has been put up. Rocket propulsion, on the other hand, has progressed in leaps and bounds. A well-known firm of pyrotechnicians is co-operating with the model aircraft movement in producing special rockets for use with model aircraft to definite thrust equivalents, so that the builder can install a rocket of given power that he knows will achieve its object. So far tailless models have been employed for the obvious advantage given by the absence of empennage that could be fired by the exploding propulsant. Recently a scale model Vampire made its appearance and flew quite well. Much remains to be done in this field to overcome the high initial thrust that lasts only a few seconds, after which the aircraft becomes no more than an average glider. The high thrust tends to waste itself in looping and aerobatics, rather than in straight upward flight, so that duration is very limited. A flight of even thirty seconds is considered an achievement as yet.

Gliders

Prior to 1939 the development of model gliders and sailplanes in this country lagged considerably behind that on the Continent, while in America gliders were practically unknown apart from the all-wood chuck gliders that were hardly regarded as a serious

AEROMODELLING

branch of aeromodelling. During the war, however, shortages of rubber and the light balsa wood, so invaluable to builders, led to an added interest in unpowered craft. The years have been fruitful, and it is not too much to say that this section is now the equal of any other in aeromodelling and probably as highly specialised as in any European country.

The use of hardwoods has produced a crop of medium-span models, usually not exceeding seven feet in span. This limit is an aftermath of a span limitation placed on models during the war by the Air Ministry. Only now are larger models making their presence felt, embracing a number of designs up to eleven feet in wingspan. Such a size enables true aerodynamic phenomena to be well appreciated and is an indication of the progress made in the application of scientific principles to this branch of modelling. When working in this scale it is necessary to stress the structure in exactly the same way as a full-size aircraft, and embody many of the weight-saving practices used in large gliders. An added attraction to the serious student is that a wealth of additional data becomes available at once, for in this size the published reports on a variety of airfoils become of value, as the wings are operating at Reynolds numbers more nearly akin to those at which sections were originally tested.

Many really beautiful designs have been flown successfully all over the country. Once it was realised that the fetish for low wing-loading led to a dead-end, designers became bolder and loadings of 16 oz. to the square foot are now the commonplace in high performance sailplanes, whereas six or seven years ago it was rare to find any rated at much more than the prescribed minimum of the F.A.I., 4.92 oz. per square foot. Streamlining too, has been developed, to-

[Photo: ' Aeromodeller '

A high performance sailplane with monocoque fuselage and tapered wings. The wire skid serves the dual purpose of protecting the model on landing and as a tow hook. The latter can be seen just below the wing root trailing edge. Attention to such details as bearings enables excellent performances to be put up by these models.

gether with tapered wings and all those refinements that weight limitation makes difficult of achievement in a rubber-powered model. Increasing attention has been paid to fairing-in of wing roots to the fuselage, and reduction of unnecessary drag in every way. Other points to notice in the modern sailplane are the concealed wing fixings that replace the unsightly rubber bands, formerly an inseparable part of nearly every model. From a practical point of view, greater care is now taken to design a truly crashproof model. In many instances the tailplane is located high on the fin to reduce its chances of fracture on heavy landing. Polyhedral or tip dihedral has replaced in popularity the former straight dihedral, while examples have been seen of the theoretically perfect cowhorn wing form, as well as occasional experiments with end-plates in a perfectly flat wing.

In the smaller sizes of from three-and-a-half to seven foot span equal progress has been

199

achieved. That horrible rut into which the rubber-powered duration-model has shown a tendency to slide has happily been avoided in model glider design. Every conceivable wing form and fuselage cross-section has been tried with, of course, varying degrees of success. Lifting fuselages in the side-eleva-

opinion regarding the value of this circular flight path, and a number of well-qualified flyers have now abandoned it in favour of straight flight that allows the model to wander and, so they aver, stand a better chance of encountering thermals. For small-space flying it must be admitted that the

A miniature petrol engine for use in model aircraft, compared with a threepenny piece.

[*Photo : ' Aeromodeller* '

tion shape of a thinned airfoil section have an increasing following, while the general use of a fully-planked fuselage shows that here, too, designers are not afraid of increased wing-loading, which in these smaller sizes varies from 5 to 12 oz. per square foot of wing area.

Much time has also been devoted to automatic steering devices, which in the main have provided structural problems beyond the scope of experimenters. Most involve use of some form of compass-control built to keep the model on a fixed course, with a correcting movement as soon as it deviates. Usually this produces an increasingly vicious series of turns giving the flight path a serpentine appearance. However, the less ambitious use of a spring-loaded trimming-tab on the fin has enabled gliders to be launched easily from long towlines without instability and, on their release, flown on a circular path to increase their chances of meeting thermal currents. There is some divergence of

spring-loaded tab renders chances of loss more remote.

One phenomenon that deserves comment is the enthusiasm that has greeted the introduction of inordinately high parasol wings, often placed as much as a wing chord above the upper surface of the fuselage. This innovation is American in origin and lacks any claim to a pleasing appearance. For those intent on performance at all costs it has its points but is a development to be deplored.

The lack of many suitable locations for slope-soaring has made this a somewhat neglected branch of the hobby, only one or two enthusiasts regularly producing slope-soarers. On the other hand, towline launching is the almost inevitable method employed. It is fascinating to watch a really expert man at work with a glider on perhaps three hundred feet of line, playing it like a fish until it is almost vertically overhead, and then choosing just the moment to release it at its best flying angle. Contrary to continental practice the use of complicated winches is the exception rather than the rule. The average equipment is a converted grindstone, which could be purchased for a few pence before the war, geared up about four- or five-to-one, and a suitable length of thin fishing line or carpet thread. Fine gauge spring steel wire as used abroad has never, to the author's knowledge, been used in any recognised contest in this country.

The Petrol-Driven Model

The aristocrat of all model aircraft must undoubtedly be the petrol-engined plane. As long ago as 1914 a record was established for a petrol-engined model, and this record remained unbroken until the early 'thirties when Lt.-Col., then Captain, Bowden produced his Blue Dragon. No attempt had been made until then to develop a special engine for use in model aircraft—all the early flights were made with engines adapted from model power-boat practice. Shortly afterwards, however, an American firm produced a special engine, the Brown Junior, which achieved instant popularity. (As a matter of interest one of the first such engines imported into this country in about 1933 was still

flying models as late as 1945, a testimony to the wearing qualities of these 10 c.c. miniatures.) Many other firms followed suit and just before the war a number of British manufacturers were producing engines, absorbed only too quickly by an eager public.

National Competitions attracted a big entry during the pre-war years and a number of pioneer enthusiasts produced a range of literature that brought petrol modelling within reach of any builders with skill enough to construct a simple rubber model. In those early years the same pitfalls that exist for the rubber modellers proved a trap for those making their first petrol-engined model, namely the desire to build a scale replica of some existing aircraft. Many such were made and looked very attractive standing on the tarmac at meetings in all parts. They achieved distinction at Concours d'Elégance, but, alas, never took the air. A suitable compromise was found in the semi-scale design which first showed that a pleasing appearance could be combined successfully with first-rate performance. Both high-wing and low-wing designs made their appearance in the late 'thirties, together with one or two outstanding biplanes. This layout has always enjoyed a false reputation for extreme difficulty, both in construction and trimming,

[Photo : ' Aeromodeller '

Entrants prepare their models to fly in a petrol-engined model contest. The take-off strip can be seen in the background, though a larger area of concrete is to be recommended.

but the few models produced would seem to prove the contrary. All these early models were powered with engines of from 9 to 10 c.c., with a few higher-capacity makes of 18 c.c., and even one or two of 30 c.c. This naturally involved wingspans of as much as fourteen feet and rendered transport more than a problem without a car. One enthusiast ingeniously solved it by attending the major meetings with a trailer caravan equipped as hangar and workshop, besides housing his wife and himself !

The appeal of the miniature internal combustion engine to engineers resulted in a number of free-lance engines being produced in all sizes from 1 c.c. upwards. All these were of the two-stroke variety employing coil ignition. In the very small sizes the question of weight plays such a large part that none but the most expert should attempt to build any model powered by anything smaller than 2.5 c.c. Certain items of equipment such as coil and flight batteries are exactly the same weight for the ultra-small engine as for the medium-size, and represent so much greater a proportion of the total load. In recent years this has been overcome to a great extent by the design of miniature accumulators weighing less than half the weight of dry batteries of equal capacity.

Eventually the pre-war taste settled at about the 5 c.c. to 8 c.c. capacity of engine which enabled models of reasonable proportions to be built. The maximum size accepted for record attempts was fixed at 10 c.c., so that generally speaking there ceased to be a market for any larger size. Manufacturers had taken the lead offered by amateur designers and were marketing a wide range of engines in the more popular sizes. This then was the position at the outbreak of war.

During the first few months a desultory activity amongst the few enthusiasts with time to spare continued, but in 1941, as a result of recommendations by the then principal body representing Model Aeronautic interests, the Air Ministry decided to ban the flying of all petrol-engined models during the war. This ban was subsequently lifted in 1944 following the urgent representations of the only journal then dealing with the hobby. Contrary to any beliefs

that may have been held, the three years of enforced idleness had done nothing to dull the public interest. Rather the reverse ; a greater national appreciation of the interest to be found in aircraft of all sizes led to a remarkable increase of enthusiasm. The limited numbers of petrol engines then available—none had been produced during the war years—were eagerly snapped up and typical modern prices paid for very indifferent motors. With the cessation of hostilities interest has soared to unprecedented heights and even the increasing output of old and new firms cannot cope with the demand for petrol engines. In Great Britain some six makes are now on the market or promised for early delivery, while in the U.S.A. more than sixty different makes are being produced, and presumably find customers.

The post-war trend is definitely towards smaller models. Motor transport is still limited and aeromodellers require a design that can, if necessary, be carried by train without inconvenience to themselves or other passengers. Six feet may be said to be the ordinary maximum span that finds ready appeal. True miniatures have been built of some thirty inches in span, but the difficulties of weight already mentioned still limit this size to experts. Apart from which, even if the model flies, its speed is such that a short life is indicated unless trimmed with the utmost patience.

Control-Line Flying

Another American development that is gaining ground in this country is control-line flying. Here the petrol-engined model is not allowed to fly free, but is attached to the launcher by a length of fine wire and flies in circles. A further wire which terminates in a hand grip actuates controls on the plane so that all the normal manœuvres of full-size flight may be performed at the will of the operator. This opens great possibilities for true-scale replicas ; and this is the phase that has made most appeal to American enthusiasts. The usual control fitted, for the sake of simplicity, is elevators only, but this enables a series of interesting evolutions limited only by the skill of the pilot. Other builders have concentrated on adapting this

[Photo : T. Alexander

Line up of contestants' models at a recent Control-Line Flying meeting. Scale types are very popular though in most cases the lines are spoilt by protruding non-scale cylinder heads due to the unwillingness of designers to fly their engines inverted.

branch of flying to high-speed racers—claiming speeds in excess of 100 m.p.h. Without electric timing devices it is difficult to know how reliable these figures are, but a conservative opinion would not place maximum speeds possible with present-day designs at much more than 80 to 85 m.p.h.

One of the main pleasures of aeromodelling is that nothing is ever developed to finality. After something over ten years of petrol-engined model flying it might be expected that some degree of 'sameness' would set in, but such is not the case. The sated flyer can turn his hand to yet another development that will be the commonplace of ten years hence, namely radio-controlled flying. So many of our air-minded young men now have, by virtue

One of the first radio-controlled petrol models made in the U.S.A.

[Photo : T. Alexander

of their war service, a highly developed knowledge of electronics, that they are turning to this section of their hobby well equipped to produce outstanding examples of ingenuity.

Radio Control

Leading aircraft firms, as has been mentioned, are studying this aspect with considerable interest, but without any attempt at building for full-size research it is possible to make a reliable and fascinating radio-controlled model. A number of successful attempts have already been made by amateurs who have arranged a mutual co-operation scheme with like-minded amateur wireless enthusiasts to exchange their respective skills. The Postmaster-General has recently agreed to allocate a wavelength for these remote control experiments, and will permit any *bona fide* experimenter to work without the necessity for obtaining a transmitting licence, provided that he does not use his set for transmitting messages. It is possible to build a receiver for installation in a model weighing as little as 9 oz. To this must be added the weight of the relay system employed to actuate controls. An eight selection relay complete will bring the payload up to approximately 2 lb. Once more it seems that the medium-weight model will come into its own as this payload represents a weight that will require an engine of 15 c.c. capacity, though it is possible that by attention to construction a model could be designed to fly with 10 c.c., but this is not advisable in the experimental stage, when apparatus has not yet been fined down to ultimate minimum weights. One project that has been seen is an eight-foot-span scale model Auster that, with a 10 c.c., will just not lift the required dead weight. The installation of a 15 c.c.

motor gave it power and to spare, and it is hoped to witness successful trials during this summer. The author's own 1/5th scale Lysander was built with the idea of fitting radio control and this project, too, will have

[Photo : ' Aeromodeller '

A model-aircraft diesel engine of .7 c.c., compared with a halfpenny. Constructed by Aeromodeller Research Department.

its first radio-controlled trials as soon as pressure of work permits.

Diesel Power

Perhaps the most outstanding achievement in the realm of model aeronautics is the development of the compression-ignition principle as applicable to miniature engines. During the war, rumours of these so-called ' diesel ' engines filtered through, and it was discovered that a Swiss firm was producing such a unit of 2.5 c.c. capacity that operated without any of the complicated electrical equipment that, besides being bulky, formed 90 per cent of engine failures. The occupation of Italy enabled a number of these engines, together with similar designs developed in that country, to be brought over here for research. Meanwhile it transpired that practically every European country had been making diesels, as they persist in being called, all presumably variants of the first Swiss design. The original specification was, it is learned, taken out as early as 1927, but only the shortage of electrical equipment during the war brought it into favour. Three years

of patient research has enabled a British design to be produced that employs the most efficient features of continental engines, together with improvements that place the final engine in a class of its own.

Briefly the principle which actuates these compression-ignition engines is the employment of a fuel that is, in itself, sufficiently volatile to ignite under compression without the need for any electrical firing device. The basic fuel is sulphuric ether mixed in proportions which vary according to the engine design from as little as 15 per cent. to as high as 50 per cent. of the mixture. Added to this is a proportion of engine oil for lubrication purposes and a restraining agent such as paraffin or even turpentine. Instead of the conventional fixed cylinder head employed in electrical ignition engines, a movable head or *contra-piston* is fitted which enables the degree of compression to be adjusted within fine limits. The engine is swung over with a rich mixture, adjusted by a needle-valve type of carburettor, and will fire almost immediately. The initial running will probably show every sign of four- or even eight-stroking together with a frightening pinking. The contra-piston is then screwed down until this is reduced to a minimum. Next, the mixture is weakened until pinking again commences, and the contra-piston then adjusted to the smoothest running possible. This is a matter of trial-and-error, but once the correct setting for any mixture and engine has been found, perfect performance can be duplicated indefinitely, provided that the fuel is mixed in exactly similar proportions every time. Greater care is required in constructing a diesel engine, which must be built to finer limits, than a conventional i.c. type, while steel pistons and liners are to be preferred to the lighter alloys. The result is an engine producing far greater power for weight than an i.c. engine of similar capacity. This is due to the fact that the greater precision in its construction enables the diesel to run with a compression ratio of up to sixteen to one, against an average i.c. compression ratio of not more than four to one.

Diesel engines are being produced commercially in large numbers, though as yet manufacture has hardly got under way in this country. The objections to amateur construction do not apply to mass production, for with suitable dies, engines of great precision can be fabricated without undue problems. It is likely that models of low capacity will prove most useful, the formula being most effective in very small sizes of up to 5 c.c. In France commercial engines of between 1 and 2 c.c. are usual. These miniatures serve to fly models of spans up to four feet, and, due to the saving in weight obtained by the omission of heavy coils and batteries, can have low wing-loadings, thus making a small, slow-flying, easily-trimmed machine a practical possibility.

It is felt that the prospects of attracting an even wider following for model aeronautics by this simplicity of operation are immensely increased. Detractors have predicted a short life for the diesel engine on account of the increased internal strains compared with normal petrol engines, but three years' research has not given any indication that this is in fact the case. An experimental engine that has been demonstrated to an extent far beyond its normal life still shows no sign of undue wear. The only snag yet experienced is that it is not possible to fit the usual type of mechanical timing device to limit engine run, which is the accepted fitting on petrol engines to avoid accidental flyaways and consequent risk of damage to persons and property. Even this can be counteracted by a spring-loaded choke, operated by clockwork or air-leak control, or even the simple expedient of limiting the fuel capacity of the tank. This latter solution is probably the best for lightweight models of under 1 lb. in weight.

Indoor Flying

Yet another phase of aeromodelling remains—indoor flying. These models fall into two categories — free-flight models and machines flown r.t.p. or 'round-the-pole'. A small pole about forty inches high is erected in any conveniently sized small hall, with a swivel attached to the top to which is fixed a length of up to twelve feet of cotton, terminating in a small hook. This hook is inserted into a loop or hole on the leading edge tip of the aircraft to be flown, which is wound up and released. Flights of over five minutes'

duration have been regularly achieved with the leading models, while figures of between two and three minutes are usual amongst fliers of average ability. These r.t.p. models are of lighter construction than outdoor

[Photo : ' Aeromodeller '

A lightweight model taking off round the pole. These weigh from 1–2 oz., and are capable of flights exceeding five minutes. Indoor flying provides an interesting club activity for the winter months and entails a high degree of manual skill, if no great amount of technical knowledge.

designs, and classified for contest purposes in two groups—under 1 oz., and up to 2 oz. in weight. They have practically no glide in the still air of a hall, and rely entirely on their rubber power run for duration. Owing to their extreme simplicity in construction they can hardly be described as a serious branch of the hobby, but nevertheless provide excellent entertainment for the numerous clubs throughout the country, and serve as an added attraction to keep junior members interested during the winter months. Conventional methods of building are employed, similar to the small commercial kits sold to youngsters, with all unnecessary weight avoided.

Recently experts have used microfilm for a wing covering in place of tissue to secure a more airproof wing finish. This microfilm, which is a mixture of cellulose dope and some plasticiser, such as castor oil, is the basis of most free-flight indoor models. Here a high degree of delicacy of touch is required to achieve consistent results, and the ultimate weight of models is unbelievably small. The finest possible sections of balsa wood and the lightest gauge of wire produce models where the saving of a thousandth of an ounce is worth recording on delicate scales used in building something that will just not collapse under the strain of a wound rubber motor ! It is not of universal appeal, requiring a special sort of patience, where one careless movement may destroy days of patient work ; but there is, it must be admitted, a certain fascination in seeing these midgets with transparent wings covered with what looks like soap-bubble fabric, floating through the air at less than a mile an hour ! As they come near a smoker they may be seen to rise in the hot air generated by the cigarette, while from time to time a careful flyer will gently turn his model as it approaches a wall or other obstruction. Flights of five and ten minutes are commonplace, while figures exceeding twenty minutes have been attained on occasion. But 'microfilmies' will remain the province of the specialist and afford only an attractive spectacle rather than a popular branch.

For those who like indoor flying, and yet demand something more substantial than these lightweights, there is scope in the development of electrically driven models. Nothing here is beyond the range of the builder, twin-engined scale replicas, fighter aircraft or indeed any form of flying machine that appeals. The method employed is an improvement of the r.t.p. system already outlined, but in this instance a stouter pole is set up and through this is fed an electric current of 6 to 20 volts, which passes down a light lead to the aircraft, which houses one or more small electric motors, weighing from 2 oz. to $\frac{1}{2}$ lb. A forty-inch Vickers Viking was flown continuously every day for over a month at the Second National Model Aircraft Exhibition at Dorland Hall in 1946. This exquisite model also incorporated a retracting undercarriage which could be operated electrically from the control panel, while each engine had separate throttle control. The pilot would switch on engines and allow them to rev up. The model would race round its perspex landing strip until flying speed was attained, when it would take off, and the throttle would be eased back. A further movement and the undercarriage would retract into the nacelles. Any attempt to land with wheels up was rendered impossible by a special wiring circuit—except in the event of engine failure. Similar models are quite within the scope of any modeller of ordinary ability. Variations include the addition of elevator controls

An excellent example of 'round-the-pole' flying. A scale model of a Vickers Viking with electrically driven airscrews and retractable undercarriage flying indoors anchored to a central column.

[Photo : ' Aeromodeller '

worked manually. Altogether an excellent field for further study, and one that is attracting increased attention. Enquiries have been made by full-size aircraft concerns who see the possibilities in this for popular-

[Photo : ' Aeromodeller'

An experimental speed model designed to be flown indoors round the pole. A monocoque fuselage is employed and sheet balsa wood wings and empennage. Speeds of nearly 40 m.p.h. are possible with these r.t.p. racing models.

ising air travel by flying model demonstrations in their showrooms.

Aeromodel Clubs

Before concluding this brief survey of aeromodelling, something must be said of the extensive club movement and the principal controlling bodies, as well as the research side of communal activities. Until 1944 one body only claimed to represent the aero-modelling movement—the Society of Model Aeronautical Engineers, which had developed from the long defunct Kite and Model Aircraft Association of the early part of the century. This body is run on an entirely voluntary basis, without paid officers or permanent headquarters, although arrangements are now in hand for office accommodation to be provided by the Royal Aero Club. Under these handicaps it performs a valuable service, particularly to the club movement, in fostering competitions through-out the country.

In 1944 a number of aeromodellers felt the need for a body employing a paid secretary and occupying permanent London head-quarters, which could voice the needs of adult enthusiasts and at the same time give attention to the more youthful enthusiasts who might, or might not, be members of any existing club. So the Association of British Aeromodellers was born. In the

short period since its inception it has more than carried out the promises of its promoters —its membership stands at some thousands and includes several affiliated bodies and a considerable number of clubs. It has sponsored National Contests and organ-ised the first post-war team to compete in an international event outside Great Britain.

Outside the club movement as such, and yet not to be considered as a controlling body, is the Low Speed Aerodynamics Research Association, which is of recent foundation. This body exists solely for the mutual collaboration of its members in research work affecting low-speed flying. It had been appreciated for many years that little or nothing was known of the performance of airfoils and other parts of an aircraft at very low speeds and a group of interested enthusiasts decided to launch this association. Apart from unrelated experiments with small and comparatively inefficient wind tunnels, such as that constructed by the author before the war, nothing had been done to draw up data on the very many unknowns. Formulæ were mainly empirical, and results achieved by an often painful pro-cess of trial and error. This the L.S.A.R.A. sought to ameliorate and threw open their ranks to any serious student able and willing to conduct original research or follow up lines outlined by the Director of Research and his assistants. First results were surprising. Response was immediate, and early findings were of such a nature as to interest the Ministry of Aircraft Production, relating as they did to laminar flow wing sections. Here low-speed results tallied with supersonic speed research and led the Ministry to bestow its blessing on the project. Since then a number of informative papers have been issued that contribute much to the science of aeromodelling, while membership has been swollen by applications from experts in all parts of the world. Added to this, improved facilities have been placed at the disposal of the directors of research by full-size aircraft firms, including a specially adapted low-speed wind tunnel of an accuracy hitherto unattained.

Aeromodelling as a hobby has come to stay. What ultimate part it will play in the development of full-size aeronautics remains to be seen. If it remains a simple hobby it will achieve object enough, for already many of the leading figures of the industry to-day have sprung from its ranks, including—to name but a few—A. V. Roe, Sidney Camm, Desoutter and countless 'back-room boys' working in design departments all over the country. To those who would still name it 'child's play' it can but be said that this same child's play proved the training ground of literally thousands of the young men who fought the Battle of Britain and brought final destruction to a vicious enemy.

[Photo : 'Aeromodeller'

Members of a club group co-operate in the construction of a model. This scene is from a class organised by the L.C.C. Men's Evening Institutes which affords both instruction and communal activities to its members.

AIR STAMPS OF THE EMPIRE

by

Arthur Blair

*Editor of the McAlpine Press. Owns one of the largest collections of stamps
in the country and is a contributor to the leading philatelic magazines.*

COLLECTING THE stamps of the world is now such a complicated affair that the newcomer to the hobby, faced with thousands of collectable stamps from so many countries, is wise if he starts to concentrate on a particular group right at the beginning.

One of the finest of such groups is aerophilately; no other subject collection depicts such historical and thrilling events as air mail stamps; the 'story behind the stamp' plays a very prominent part in this branch of the hobby and, except for a number of unnecessary issues emanating from certain foreign countries, most air stamps are issued for use on a vital service in the postal communications of the world.

However, even in this group, one has to set a limit to the specimens to be collected, and to divide the material into British Empire and Foreign stamps and Flown Covers. A further subdivision is usual by separating official government issues from the semi-official stamps. If the collector decides on the official government stamps issued by the British Empire, then one of the finest groups will have been chosen.

Australia

We will briefly describe some outstanding specimens in an ' Empire ' collection which, for interest, value and beauty, cannot be surpassed.

First on the list comes AUSTRALIA. On 20th May 1929, the Dominion issued a very picturesque stamp, showing a plane flying over typical Australian countryside; this 3d. value was recess-printed in green.

The famous Kingsford-Smith issue followed on 19th March 1931. In May 1928, Captain Kingsford-Smith, with Keith Anrid-son (co-pilot), William Todd and Charles Ulm (navigators) left the Oakland Airport, California, in their Fokker monoplane the *Southern Cross*, for Sydney, Australia. This amazing flight of 9,000 miles was carried out successfully in four ' hops '—Honolulu, Fiji Islands, Brisbane and Sydney. Three stamps appeared later to commemorate this achievement, a 2d. and 3d. for ordinary postage, and a 6d. inscribed ' Air Mail Service ' and used for that purpose. The design shows the *Southern Cross* above the hemispheres, with ' Kingsford-Smith World Flights ' below.

Two million each of the 2d. and 3d., and 200,000 of the 6d. were printed. The latter is priced at 4s. mint and 3s. used and will increase still further, as will most Australian issues. One should always be on the alert for a re-entry, which shows as a doubling of ' FO ' in ' KINGSFORD ' and ' LD ' in ' WORLD ', and as this changes a 3s. stamp into a £2 item, it is well worth finding. The colour of this 6d. stamp was violet, and on 4th November 1931 it was reissued in sepia, inscribed, ' Air Mail Service ' on the bottom tablet and first used for Christmas mail carried to England by Captain Kingsford-Smith, piloting an Australian National Airways machine.

A particularly striking design is the 1s. 6d. purple that came in 1934 to frank mail on the Australia–England flights, inaugurated 8th December 1934. Hermes is shown between the two hemispheres, and here again it pays to be observant, for there are two similar issues: one issued on 1st December 1934, on unwatermarked paper perforate 11, and another on 22nd October 1937, watermarked small crowns and ' C of A ', and perforate $13\frac{1}{2} \times 14$; specimens of the earlier issue are catalogued at 10d. used and 3s.

mint, whereas the stamp that followed later is worth more used (1s. 6d.), yet less mint (1s. 8d.).

Canadian Stamps

The stamps of CANADA are always in such demand that it is wise to try and complete the issues while they are current. The air stamps in particular are desirable items and a small collection of them can open with the 5 cents depicting 'Allegory of Flight'.

one specimen minus the surcharge, and a pair showing a diagonal surcharge on one specimen and the adjoining one without the surcharge.

To commemorate the Conference of Great Britain and the Dominions held at Ottawa in 1932, the 5 cent showing Mercury and the Western Hemisphere was overprinted '6 OTTAWA CONFERENCE 1932' in dark blue and first used to frank mail on a flight from Ottawa to Bradore Bay, Quebec, on 12th July 1932.

Daedalus we know as the mythical Greek

Right.—Australia. 1929. Australian Scene.

Below left.—Australia. 1931. Kingsford Smith's World Flights.

Below centre.—Australia. 1931. Regular issue.

Below right.—Australia. 1934. Hermes.

Issued 21st September 1928, for use first on a flight from Toronto to Montreal; the stamp is perforate 12, and worth a few pence, but there are three very scarce varieties, viz. imperforate (catalogued at £20 mint), horizontal pair imperforate between, and vertical pair imperforate between (both listed at £40 each mint).

Mercury and the Western Hemisphere was the design for the next 5 cent stamp, which appeared on 4th December 1930, followed on 22nd February 1932, by a provisional issue, made necessary by the sudden increase in the air mail fees; for this two million of the 5 cent 'Allegory of Flight' stamps of 1928 were surcharged in black '6' (and bars cancelling the original value) by the British American Bank Note Company. Scarce varieties of the surcharge exist; inverted, double, triple, diagonal, a pair of stamps with

architect and sculptor who created the Labyrinth in Crete and, in order to escape from the island, made wings for himself and flew to Sicily. He makes an imposing appearance on a 6 cent red-brown that was issued 1st June 1935. These stamps were printed by the Canadian Bank Note Company in sheets of 200, divided into four panes of 50, and for the collector who likes searching for minor varieties the fourteenth stamp in the bottom right pane has a line in the colour of the stamp above the left leg of Daedalus. A horizontal pair, imperforate between, is a known rare error.

A grand model of a seaplane flying over S.S. *Discoverer* on the Mackenzie River is the picture on the next 6 cent blue air stamp that came on 15th June 1938, followed four years later by a modern design—a view of an air training camp, on the 6 cent and 7 cent

Left.—Canada. 1930. Air Mail circles the World.
Centre.—Canada. 1932. Provisional Surcharge on ' Allegory of Flight '.
Right.—Canada. 1938. Seaplane over S.S. *Discoverer* on Mackenzie River.

air stamps, and a magnificent picture of the trans-Canadian plane in flight on the 16 cent and 17 cent air express stamps.

Egypt

Although EGYPT is politically separated from Britain, stamp collectors still customarily include the fine stamps of that ancient country in their Empire collections, and so many fine air issues have come from her that Egypt will continue to be a favourite country with collectors of British Empire emissions.

Since August 1923 there had been a regular air mail service between Cairo and Baghdad and on 10th March 1926 a special stamp was issued. The value was a 27 millieme deep violet depicting a de Havilland in flight over the Nile. Three years later this stamp was reissued in chestnut colour.

The giant *Graf Zeppelin* made its mark on Egyptian stamps when the dirigible paid a visit to the country in 1931. To commemorate the occasion 25,000 sets of the 1929 air stamps received an overprint ' GRAF ZEPPELIN AVRIL 1931 ' and a value, in French and Arabic; the 50 millieme surcharge was in blue, the 100 millieme in violet. Letters bearing these stamps were carried by the airship during her flight over Egypt, and they are very much sought after. Mint and used specimens are priced at 50s. each.

A very long set of air post stamps came from Egypt on 15th February 1933, when twenty values (from 1 to 200 milliemes) appeared. The design, in two colours, shows a Handley Page 4-motor biplane over the Pyramids.

A set which increases in value with each new catalogue is the one that came out on 20th December 1933 to commemorate the International Aviation Congress held at Cairo. The issue was said to have been sold out on the first day—and no wonder, for the designs would appeal to both philatelist and non-collector: 5 millieme and 10 millieme, Imperial Airways' 4-engine monoplane; 13 millieme and 15 millieme, the famous German 12-engined flying-boat Dornier Do X; 20 millieme, the *Graf Zeppelin*.

India

For the aerial route from India to Great Britain special stamps were created by INDIA and issued on 22nd October 1929. The oblong design has a picture of a heavy 3-engined biplane over an Indian lake and a portrait of King George V in a medallion on the right. There were five values (3, 4, 6, 8 and 12 annas), with a 2 anna joining the set on 2nd December.

When a set of eight handsome pictorial stamps appeared in 1937 to illustrate the various methods of conveying mail in India —Native Runner, Bullock Cart, Dak Tonga, Camel, Train, Steamer, Lorry—the aeroplane was not forgotten, and it appeared on the 12 anna, an Armstrong Whitworth aircraft that was used by the Indian Post Office for air mails. A portrait of King George VI is on the right of the design.

In 1928 the postal service from MALTA to India, 'Iraq and Persia was considerably hastened by the introduction of the air post. The Maltese Post Office used the Imperial Line to Lower Asia. The mails went by boat to Egypt and were then transferred to plane. To prepay the air fee, a George V

Left.—Egypt. 1933. Aeroplane over Pyramids.
Centre.—India. 1929. Biplane over Lake.
Right.—India. 1937. Mail plane used by Indian Post Office.

6d. of the 1926 regular issue was overprinted 'AIR MAIL', 1st April 1928, being the first day of issue.

Transatlantic Air Mail

Of all the countries issuing air mails NEWFOUNDLAND is easily the most popular. True, one would have to be a rich person to try and complete this group, but the wise collector will at least get the more recent, and cheaper, specimens before they, too, move from the 'shillings' to the 'pounds' class. However, it is very doubtful if any recent issues will ever have the historical interest and attain the immense popularity of the early Newfoundland air stamps—the 'classics' of aero-philately.

When H. G. Hawker and K. M. Grieve left Newfoundland on 18th May 1919 in an effort to fly the Atlantic and so win a prize

ATLANTIC AIR POST, APRIL 1919'. After completing 1,100 miles of the journey, a mechanical defect forced the plane into the sea, but fortunately a ship rescued the aviators and took them to Scotland. Later the machine, with its bag of mail containing ninety-five covers franked with the special stamps, was salvaged and landed at Falmouth. Many of the covers were badly damaged by sea water. To-day a mint copy of a 'Hawker' is worth £450, a used one £275.

The same day that Hawker made his flight, a second machine, with Messrs. Morgan and Raynham at the controls, left Newfoundland to attempt the Atlantic crossing, but it crashed as it took off. This ill-fated plane, a Martinsyde, had on board sixty letters franked with special stamps—the 3 cent Caribou, on the face of which the postmaster had written in ink, 'Aerial Atlantic Mail J.A.R.'. The mail was taken from the

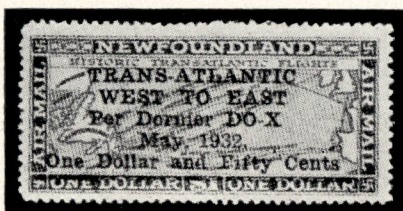

Newfoundland. 1932. Dornier
Do X issue.

Newfoundland. 1933. General
Balbo Flight.

of £10,000, they carried with them mail franked with special stamps that were to become even more valuable than the prize offered for a successful flight ! We refer, of course, to the famous 'Hawker' stamps, created by the Newfoundland postmaster, J. A. Robinson, who had 200 copies of the 3 cents Caribou overprinted 'FIRST TRANS-

plane and sent to its destination by the ordinary sea routes. Only eight used and two unused copies of this provisional exist, so naturally they are extremely rare.

Another attempt to conquer the Atlantic by air was made, this time by Captain John Alcock and Lieutenant A. Whitten Brown, who left St. John's, Newfoundland, on 14th

June 1919. The postmaster had prepared a large supply of special stamps to be ready to frank mail on any further Atlantic flights, and on 9th June 1919, he issued 10,000 of the 15 cent of 1897 (showing a group of seals) overprinted ' Trans-Atlantic AIR POST, 1919. ONE DOLLAR '. Alcock and Brown successfully crossed the Atlantic, touching down at Clifden, Ireland, fifteen hours, fifty-seven minutes after taking off from St. John's.

This ' Alcock-Brown ' issue has been steadily increasing in price, and in 1946 it fetched from £7 to £9. There are two scarce errors: no comma after ' POST ', and no stop after ' 1919 '. A cover carried on the successful flight is now worth about £50. Their machine, a Vickers Vimy biplane, is shown on the 15 cent of the 1928 ' Publicity ' issue.

When a mail service between Botwood, Newfoundland and Halifax, Nova Scotia, was planned, 14,000 of the 35 cent ' Iceberg ' stamps of 1897 were overprinted ' AIR MAIL to HALIFAX, N.S. 1921 '. The first attempt at the flight took place in December 1921, but was unsuccessful, as was the next attempt the following month. The project was given up and the 5,000 letters that were to have been flown were despatched through the usual postal service. There were a few varieties in the overprint, such as missing periods and inverted surcharge, and these are very scarce. Normal specimens are cheap at the listed price of £2.

Commander Francesco de Pinedo also left his mark in aero-philately. In his seaplane *Santa Maria II*, he made a gallant effort in 1927 to fly from Newfoundland to Rome; unfortunately his engine failed as he was nearing his native land and he finished up in the sea; but his machine kept afloat and he was eventually towed to the Azores, where the machine was repaired and he then continued his flight in ' hops ', arriving in Rome on 1st June. A special issue was created and issued 21st May 1927, for this European flight by overprinting 300 of the 60 cent (Henry VII) of 1897 ' Air Mail DE PINEDO 1927 ' in red. Unused the ' De Pinedo ' is a rarity (£600); used it is worth £100, which is roughly the value of a flown cover.

Another transatlantic crossing, Newfound-land-England, was made in 1930, when Captain J. Erroll-Boyd and Lieutenant Harry Connor, in the monoplane *Miss Columbia*, left Harbour Grace on 9th October at 1.15 p.m., arriving at Croydon, London, approximately 3.15 p.m. the next day. To frank the correspondence which they carried, 300 of the 36 cent ' Caribou ' of 1919 were overprinted, ' Trans-Atlantic AIR MAIL by B.M. " Columbia " September 1930 Fifty Cents '; £160 mint and £125 used are the catalogue quotations for these rarities.

As a change from overprints, Newfound-land's regular air issue appeared on 2nd January 1931. The 15 cent chocolate (the local air fee) has as its design a ' Dart ' single-engine biplane with skis, flying above a dog-team in the snow. The 50 cent green shows the Vickers Vimy biplane leaving St. John's with the first transatlantic air mail and passing over an early sailing-boat, and was to frank mail to the U.S.A. and Canada. The $1 deep blue has a map of the North Atlantic Ocean with the routes of historic transatlantic flights clearly marked; this value was for transatlantic mail. Quantities printed were not large: 15 cent, 55,000; 50 cent, and $1, 30,000 of each. The set can sometimes be picked up for about £3. The issue first appeared on unwatermarked paper, then on 13th March 1931, it was reissued on paper watermarked with the Colony's Coat of Arms.

The Dornier Do X had a special issue when this flying-boat journeyed from New-foundland to Germany in May 1932. The $1 ' Routes of Historic Trans-Atlantic Flights ' (with watermark) received a surcharge reading, ' TRANS-ATLANTIC WEST TO EAST Per Dornier Do X May, 1932. One Dollar and Fifty Cents '. Eight thousand were thus surcharged and 1,804 used on the special flight. Twenty received an inverted surcharge. Mint and used copies of the normal specimen are priced at £12 and £14 respectively, while the ' invert ' often realises £200.

Another regular issue came out on 31st May 1933. The designs are attractive: 5 cent brown, a Douglas-type biplane putting wild birds to flight; 10 cent yellow, a monoplane skimming the waters of ' Land of Heart's Delight '; 30 cent blue, a biplane

Left.—New Zealand. 1935. Aeroplane over Bell Block Aerodrome.
Centre.—New Zealand. 1946. 'Peace' issue. Badge of Royal New Zealand Air Force, with Lancaster bomber
and Spitfire fighter (*left*), Empire flying-boat and York transport aeroplane (*right*).
Right.—Sudan. 1931. Aeroplane passing statue of General Gordon.

spotting the herd in the icy wastes; 60 cent green, a seaplane approaching a ship with 'News from Home'; 75 cent brown, planes above Labrador, the Land of Gold.

Another flight that thrilled the public was the squadron of Italian seaplanes that made such historical flights under the command of General Italo Balbo. When the mass formation flight made the return journey from Chicago to Rome in 1933, 8,000 copies of the 75 cent 'Labrador, Land of Gold' stamp were surcharged '1933 GEN. BALBO FLIGHT $4.50' and issued on 24th July. Used copies are priced at £14, and unused £12.

A particularly fine-looking specimen is the 7 cent blue of June 1943 showing a plane over St. John's; obtainable to-day at a few pence mint or used.

albums have a good chance of increasing in value. The few 'airs' of NEW ZEALAND appear to fall into the good investment class. First there are the 3d., 4d. and 7d. values that were issued on 11th November 1931, showing an aeroplane over Lake Manapouri. These were followed by a provisional, created on 18th December of that year by surcharging the 3d. with 'FIVE CENTS'. Then the first official mail flight between New Zealand and Australia was commemorated by overprinting the 7d. air stamp with 'TRANS-TASMAN AIR MAIL "FAITH IN AUSTRALIA"'.

One of the most attractive of air designs is that employed for the 1d., 3d. and 6d. denomination of the regular issue of 1935; this shows an aeroplane over the landing field of the Bell Block aerodrome.

New Zealand

To many collectors the word 'investment' when applied to stamps is against the true principles of the hobby, yet we all like to think that the stamps that go into our

South Africa

For the air mail route between Cape Town and Durban four special stamps depicting a single-engine Blackburn biplane in flight were issued on 25th February 1925. The

Left.—South Africa. 1929. Mail plane.
Centre.—New Guinea. 1939. Aeroplane above the Bulolo Gold-Fields.
Right.—South West Africa. 1930. Large overprint.

service was discontinued three months later and the stamps on hand destroyed.

Two further air stamps with a picture of a mail plane in the clouds appeared on 16th August 1929.

In the 1942 ' War Effort ' series the 1s. 3d. value, showing a radio signaller, was used as an air stamp.

Catalogues

To collect air stamps successfully one should have an air mail catalogue. Although the general catalogues list all official air stamps, it is best to have a book devoted to this branch of the hobby, so that one does not have to search through thousands of non-air issues to pick out the air stamps.

Musson's Air Mail Catalogue for 1946 is the only specialised book published on the subject in Britain to-day. This is a fine book and is issued in three parts (Europe, The Americas, Rest of the World) and is published at 5s. per volume. It is well illustrated and gives plenty of information about all official and semi-official air stamps, together with prices for both mint and used copies.

A somewhat similar work, in one volume, is the American catalogue *Sanabria's Air Post Catalogue* published yearly in the United States. This has plenty of useful information about U.S. air stamps and details of famous flights. The whole world is covered in one volume, and like the English work, gives numbers printed and both official and semi-official issues.

* * *

The Saab Scandia—first Swedish-designed airliner.

The Firefly Trainer is an instructional version of the Firefly Naval fighter.

THE LITERATURE OF FLIGHT

Faith Of A Pioneer

THE human being shall take his first flight, filling the world with amazement, all writings with his fame, and bringing eternal glory to the nest whence he sprang.

LEONARDO DA VINCI
(about 1500)

CHRONOLOGY OF AERONAUTICS

FROM THE EARLIEST TIMES TO 1909

by

C. H. Gibbs-Smith

Companion, Royal Aeronautical Society ; author of ' Basic Aircraft Recognition';
' The Aircraft Recognition Manual ' ; ' German Aircraft ' ; ' Ballooning ', etc.

NOTES: The history of aeronautics consists of two distinct streams, the lighter-than-air stream (aerostation) and the heavier-than-air (aviation). The latter has occupied humanity for most of its history, as it is natural that birds should inspire envy and escape. The mythologies and religions of the world display a variety of flying figures, but the story of Daedalus and Icarus forms the central flying myth, the symbol of the desire to fly.

Most countries have also semi-fictional traditions of flying-men, some of which might well have started with a basis of real effort on the part of adventurers with artificial wings.

The floating, as opposed to the flapping, principle arrived much later, as will be seen from the chronology, despite the ever-present forms of the clouds which seldom seemed to have inspired the ancient world. But it was in lighter-than-air craft that man was first to fly.

The history of flight is a strange mixture of actual scientific discovery; events and people who (although insignificant in themselves) yet provided stimulus for later experimenters; and just plain displays of courage and the adventurous spirit. All are important, each acting and re-acting on the other.

The best introduction to the history of flight is in the galleries of the Science Museum South Kensington, London, which display a fine collection of models and original aircraft, including (owing to a tragic quarrel in the U.S.A.) the original Wright biplane—perhaps the most prized historic object in the whole field of aeronautics. A note has been added to the entries below if there is a relevant exhibit in the Museum.

c. 400 B.C.	ARCHYTAS of Tarentum is said to have made his mechanical flying pigeon.
c. 200 B.C.	Kites in use by the Chinese. The kite is the earliest form of aircraft.
c. 1020	OLIVER OF MALMESBURY attempts to fly from a tower, and is badly injured. The story is probably apocryphal.
c. 1250	ROGER BACON speculates upon human flight, and in his *Secrets of Art and Nature* makes the first specific speculation about lighter-than-air flight. He describes a large sphere which when fitted with ' ethereal air or liquid fire ' would float on the upper surface of the atmosphere. Further speculation was made by Francisco di Mendoza (d. 1626), Gaspar Schottus (1608–66) and John Wilkins, Bishop of Chester (1614–72).
c. 1490	G. B. DANTI (Italian), a Perugian mathematician, is said to have attempted to fly over Lake Trasimeno in Umbria.

217

c. 1500	. .	LEONARDO DA VINCI'S researches into aeronautical problems. He invents the helicopter (lifting airscrew), the parachute, designs a number of ornithopters, investigates bird flight, and one contemporary description may refer to a lighter-than-air model; in which case he is the inventor of the hot-air balloon. (Models of the ornithopters and parachute in the Science Museum.)
1507	. .	J. DAMIAN (Italian settled in Scotland) attempts to fly from Stirling Castle, and is injured.
1634	. .	J. BATE (British) publishes his book *The Mysteries of Nature and Art,* which illustrates the earliest known form of kite in England.
1640	. .	Bishop WILKINS (British) discusses the possibilities and difficulties of mechanical flight in a discourse appended to his *Discovery of a New World.*
1655	. .	ROBERT HOOKE (British) conducts experiments with artificial wings. No proper record exists. In 1679, in his *Philosophical Collections*, he discusses flying and gives an excerpt from Lana (*see* 1670).
c. 1660	. .	The French tight-rope dancer ALLARD was injured when attempting to fly before Louis XIV at St. Germain.
1670	. .	Father FRANCESCO LANA (or DE LANA) publishes his *Prodromo* at Brescia, in which he describes his aerial ship, to be supported by four evacuated copper spheres. Also gives the first, vivid description of bombing raids. There was never any attempt to build the aircraft, but it is one of the most widely ' publicised ' of early ideas. (Model in Science Museum.)
1678	. .	The French locksmith BESNIER alleged to have made wings with which he glided short distances. The only surviving illustration is obviously misleading.
1680	. .	*De Motu Animalium* of G. A. BORELLI (Italian) published at Rome. This includes a full discussion of bird flight and a refutation of the idea of man being able to lift himself by his muscles.
1709	. .	Father LAURENCO DE GUSMAO (Portuguese) experiments with flying machines at Lisbon. It is difficult to estimate exactly what happened, but it is fairly certain he made a successful model hot-air balloon, and a model glider.
1742	. .	The Marquis DE BACQUEVILLE (French) makes his celebrated attempt to fly across the Seine. He is alleged to have launched himself from a balcony and crashed, breaking a leg, on a washerwoman's barge a short distance out in the river.
1755	. .	Father J. GALIEN (French) publishes his book *L'Art de Naviger dans les Airs*, in which he envisages lighter-than-air flight, but gives no proper explanation of how it could be done.
1766	. .	HENRY CAVENDISH (British) discovers hydrogen.
1781	. .	T. CAVALLO (Italian, settled in England) blows soap-bubbles with hydrogen.
1782	. .	The brothers JOSEPH and ETIENNE MONTGOLFIER (French) experiment with paper bags filled with hot-air at Avignon. In the same year they send up a large silk bag, inflated over a fire of straw and wool (at Annonay, near Lyons, where they own a paper works).
1783 (June 5)	.	The MONTGOLFIERS give their first public demonstration at Annonay. Hot-air balloon is of linen lined with paper and of 23,430 cubic feet. This ranks as the first proper balloon ascent in history. No attempt to attach basket, etc.

1783	.	.	Professor J. A. C. CHARLES (French) is commissioned by the Academy to design a balloon after reports of the Montgolfier experiments. Not knowing what raised the balloons he assumed it must have been hydrogen, so designed his balloon accordingly. It is a small bag of lutestring varnished with rubber, built by the brothers Robert at Paris.
1783 (Aug. 27)	.	.	Professor CHARLES' small hydrogen balloon is sent up from the Champ de Mars and descends, terrifying the villagers, at Gonesse (15 miles). Hydrogen balloons become known as ' Charlières '.
1783 (Sept. 19)	.	.	The MONTGOLFIERS, at Versailles, send up a balloon with a basket containing a sheep, cock and duck. Hot-air balloons become known as ' Montgolfières ', and for some time are built only by the brothers.
1783 (Oct. 15)	.	.	PILÂTRE DE ROZIER is the first human being to make an ascent (from the Reveillon Garden near Paris). Balloon was a ' Montgolfière ', but was captive.
1783 (Nov. 21)	.	.	**THE FIRST AERIAL VOYAGE OF HISTORY.** ROZIER and the Marquis D'ARLANDES ascend from the Château de la Muette in the Bois de Boulogne, in a Montgolfière. They fly over Paris and land $5\frac{1}{2}$ miles from the start after 25 minutes in the air. (*See* p. 47.)
1783 (Dec. 1)	.	.	The first aerial voyage in a hydrogen balloon, and the true beginning of aerial travel. This balloon also designed by CHARLES and built by the ROBERTS, was complete with basket, ballast, valve and barometer. It ascended with Charles and one of the Robert brothers from the Tuileries Gardens and landed at Nesle (27 miles).
1783	.	.	The first human parachute descent (from a tower at Lyons) by LENORMAND (French). BLANCHARD later in the same year lets go a dog from a balloon and then tries himself, but breaks a leg.
1784	.	.	J. P. BLANCHARD (French) tries his ' moulinet ', or revolving fan, in an unsuccessful effort to propel a balloon, and is therefore the first to apply the airscrew to an aircraft. Meusnier was the first (*see below*) to design a practical application of the airscrew to aircraft.
1784	.	.	J. B. M. MEUSNIER (French) is the first to design a practical dirigible airship, with elongated envelope, gondola, airscrews, rudder and ballonets. It was too expensive to build, but the drawings (which are preserved at Chalais-Meudon in France) represent one of the great feats of aeronautical history.
1784	.	.	MIOLAN and JANINET (French) ; a Montgolfière designed to be navigated by hot-air jets from ports in the envelope. Balloon destroyed during inflation.
1784 (June 4)	.	.	The first woman to fly; Madame THIBLE at Lyons, as passenger in the hot-air balloon *Le Gustave*.
1784 (Sept. 15)	.	.	The first aerial voyage in England, by VINCENT LUNARDI (Neapolitan), from Moorfields, London. Balloon was hydrogen-filled.
1784 (Oct. 4)	.	.	The first English aeronaut, JAMES SADLER, ascends for the first time, at Oxford. Sadler and his two sons became well-known aeronauts.
1784	.	.	LANNOY and BIENVENU (French) are the first to make practical tests of a model helicopter. It consisted of two superimposed screws revolving in opposite directions, worked by a bow-string.
1784	.	.	During the year a variety of methods were suggested of directing and propelling balloons—sails, oars, propellers, jets of air or steam, gunpowder rockets and even trained birds ! The sails and oars were tried without success, as also the revolving fan, but the last held the germ of success.

1785 (Jan. 7)	.	The first Channel crossing by air (Dover to the forest of Guînes, near Calais) by Dr. J. JEFFRIES (American) and BLANCHARD (French) who was pilot.
1785 (June 15)	.	The first aerial fatalities. P. DE ROZIER and M. ROMAINE (French) attempt a Channel crossing in a combined hot-air and hydrogen balloon, which catches fire and crashes near Boulogne. Both are killed.
1786	.	The first night flight, by TESTU-BRISSY (French).
1793	.	First aerial voyage in the U.S.A. by BLANCHARD (French) at Philadelphia.
1794	.	The first military air reconnaissance. The French send up a captive hydrogen balloon at the Siege of Maubeuge. Balloons are thereafter used for military spotting throughout the nineteenth and twentieth centuries.
1796	.	Sir GEORGE CAYLEY starts his researches into aeronautics with experiments with a Chinese (aerial) top.
1797	.	The first successful human parachute descent from a balloon, by A. J. GARNERIN (French) at Paris. Animals had been sent down since 1783.
1802	.	The first parachute descent in England (over London) by GARNERIN (French).
1804	.	The first aeroplane proper. Sir GEORGE CAYLEY successfully flies his large model glider (replica in Science Museum). (See 1809.)
1809	.	Sir GEORGE CAYLEY (British) publishes his first written contribution to aeronautics (in the *Journal of Natural Philosophy*), which he had begun studying in 1796. He was perhaps the greatest of the early pioneers in aerodynamics and his researches and experiments dealt with both aviation and aerostation. M. Dollfus has described him as ' le plus grand génie de l'aviation . . . le véritable inventeur de l'aéroplane '. He contributed to periodicals at intervals from 1809 to 1852.
1821	.	C. GREEN (British) first uses coal-gas for balloons.
1836	.	The most famous long-distance flight of the century. CHARLES GREEN (pilot), R. HOLLOND and M. MASON fly from London to near Weilburg in the Duchy of Nassau (500 miles) in the balloon *Vauxhall*, later re-christened the *Great Balloon of Nassau*.
1837	.	The first parachute fatality. R. COCKING (British) invents an inverted cone parachute which is taken up beneath a balloon. The parachute is released and soon collapses and crashes, killing Cocking (at Lee in Kent). This event which did not deter the conventional parachutists was one of the most publicised tragedies of the century.
1839	.	The American balloonist JOHN WISE invents the ripping panel for rapid deflation of the envelope on landing.
1842	.	W. S. HENSON (British) patents the designs for his ' Aerial Steam Carriage ', a steam-driven twin-screw monoplane. Widespread publication of these designs, with fanciful flying views (in 1843), made this the best-known design for a flying-machine in the nineteenth century. Construction of a model started in 1843.
1844	.	Dr. LE BERRIER (French) exhibits in Paris a model dirigible with screws driven by a steam engine. This is the first application of an engine to an aircraft.
1847	.	HENSON, in collaboration with J. STRINGFELLOW (British) completes the model ' Aerial Steam Carriage ' (original in Science Museum). The tests are unsuccessful, only a shallow glide being achieved. Henson abandons the experiments and emigrates to the U.S.A. Stringfellow was chiefly concerned with the engine, but from then on studied the whole subject.

1848 . . The first powered aeroplane to fly. STRINGFELLOW completes and tests his twin-screw steam-driven model monoplane (original and replica in Science Museum). It achieves sustained flight at Chard, Somerset, and later in London.

1849 . . The first bombing raid in history. The Austrians send pilotless bomb-carrying hot-air balloons against Venice, with negligible damage.

1849 . . The Alps crossed by air for the first time, by F. ARBAN (French) from Marseilles to Stubini, near Turin.

1850 . . P. JULLIEN (French) constructs a working model of a dirigible airship, at Paris, which he named *Le Précurseur*. Equipped with fins and rudder, a streamlined envelope, a clockwork motor driving port and starboard screws. A full-sized craft was never built. It followed the unsuccessful efforts of Scott (1789), Pauly and Egg (1816), Lennox (1834), Mason (1843) and Bell (1850), and is a landmark in airship design. It influenced the successful design of Giffard (*see* 1852).

1852 . . The first successful airship. The French engineer H. GIFFARD constructs and flies his semi-rigid dirigible at Paris. It was filled with 88,000 cubic feet of coal-gas and driven by a 3 h.p. steam engine at about $5\frac{1}{2}$ m.p.h. (Model in Science Museum.)

1852 . . Rocket propulsion suggested (but not tried) for airships by J. NYE (British).

1855–57 . . J. M. LE BRIS (French) tests his full-sized glider, built after a study of the albatross. He piloted it himself and was launched from a cart. It seems certain that he was not only airborne, but did achieve gliding flight (and is therefore the first successful glider pioneer). Information is rather scant about this achievement as also about his second machine which he tested in 1868, although a photograph exists of the latter.

1857 . . F. DU TEMPLE (French) patents his designs for an aeroplane, the first comprehensive idea in France. He later made a model which is alleged to have taken off under its own power.

1858 . . The first aerial photograph is taken by NADAR (French) from a balloon over Paris.

1861–3 . . Balloons successfully used by the Federals for observation in the American Civil War, especially at the Battle of Fair Oaks, 1862.

1862 . . H. COXWELL (pilot) and J. GLAISHER (both British) ascend from Wolverhampton on a meteorological flight which became one of the most publicised ascents in history. Glaisher (who became unconscious at one point) alleges they reached 37,000 feet, which they certainly could not have done without oxygen. From the evidence it was probably about 20,000 feet.

1863 . . Foundation of the first French aeronautical society, later to become the Soc. Française de Navigation Aérienne.

1863 . . PONTON D'AMECOURT (French) builds an ingenious but unsuccessful model steam helicopter.

1866 . . Foundation of the Aeronautical Society (later Royal) of Great Britain.

1866 . . F. H. WENHAM (British) reads his influential paper on ' Aerial Locomotion ' to the first meeting of the Aeronautical Society. In this, he advocates superimposed planes, high aspect-ratio wings, cambered surfaces, etc.

1866 . . R. BOYMAN (British) granted a patent for an all-metal airship to be driven by jet-propulsion (air or steam). It was never built.

1868 . . The first aeronautical exhibition in England, at the Crystal Palace. STRINGFELLOW shows his model triplane (original in Science Museum) which aroused great interest, but was never fully tested.

1870–71	. .	More than sixty balloons sent out of besieged Paris with refugees, letters and carrier pigeons. The last were flown back with microfilmed letters. Over 160 persons were carried.
1871	. .	A. PÉNAUD (French) makes a successful model aeroplane driven by a pusher airscrew worked by twisted rubber. Pénaud made many experiments and was to become one of the greatest pioneers of the aeroplane (*see below*).
1872	. .	The first use of an internal combustion engine to propel an aircraft. P. HENLEIN (German) builds and flies his airship at Brünn, using a Lenoir gas engine. Important as a forerunner. It was not until 1896 that the German Wolfert used a petrol engine in an airship.
1874	. .	E. J. MAREY (French) publishes his book *Animal Mechanism*, which was one of the first books to influence the Wright brothers.
1875	. .	T. MOY (British) tests his ' Aerial Steamer ', a model monoplane, in a circular tethered flight at the Crystal Palace. It was powered by a steam-engine driving large twin-screws, and it is said to have risen a few inches (model in Science Museum).
1876	. .	Dr. N. A. OTTO (German) introduces the high-speed internal combustion engine. This invention ultimately made possible aeroplane flight.
1876	. .	A. PÉNAUD patents his designs for a remarkable aeroplane. It was a twin-screw monoplane, with cambered, double-surfaced wings, elevators and wing-warping device. He dies without being able to build it.
1879	. .	V. TATIN (French) makes a successful twin-screw compressed-air-driven model, which rose and flew under its own power. It flew tethered to a central pole, as with modern indoor flying-models.
1881	. .	L. P. MOUILLARD (French) publishes his book *L'Empire de l'Air* which contains the results of many years study of flight. He also constructed an unsuccessful glider. He ranks chiefly as an inspirer of subsequent inventors.
1883	. .	First use of electric propulsion. A. and G. TISSANDIER (French) construct (1882) and first fly their airship with a $1\frac{1}{2}$ h.p. motor, at Auteuil. (Model in Science Museum).
1883	. .	J. J. MONTGOMERY (American) starts his researches by constructing an ornithopter. He soon went over to fixed-wing gliders and had some limited success. Totally unmerited claims have recently been put forward for him, and American experts have rightly discounted them. (*See* also 1905.)
1884	. .	L. HARGRAVE (Australian) starts his many aeronautical experiments. Until 1893 he worked on flapping-wing and airscrew models with clock-work, rubber and compressor air drives. One model flew 120 feet. (One original model in Science Museum.) He is credited with inventing the rotary engine.
1884	. .	The turning point in airship design comes with the construction and flight of the dirigible *La France* by C. RENARD and Captain A. C. KREBS (both French) at Chalais-Meudon. It was properly navigable, being able to return to its starting-place. A 9 h.p. electric motor was used and a speed of 13 m.p.h. attained. It showed that practical airships could now be made and operated.
1889	. .	OTTO LILIENTHAL (German) publishes in Berlin his book *Der Vogelflug als Grundlage der Fliegekunst*, one of the classic studies of bird-flight and one of the starting-points of modern aviation. It led directly to his successful gliding experiments (*see* 1890).

| 1890 | . | . | LILIENTHAL starts his great series of gliding experiments. He is one of the greatest men in the history of flying and his work paved the way for the Wright brothers. His tests went on until he was killed in 1896. (Original glider in Science Museum.) |

1890 . . C. ADER (French) claimed to have risen in his steam-powered bat-like aeroplane *Eole*. It was not proved. Ader then went on to make two other aircraft (*see* 1897).

1891 . . Professor S. P. LANGLEY (American) publishes his book *Experiments in Aerodynamics*, which describes his work with inclined planes, etc. He is to become a major figure in aviation (*see below*).

1892 . . The first use of small balloons to carry meteorological instruments into the upper air. Such balloons, also for other ' met ' uses, have been used universally ever since.

1893 . . HARGRAVE starts his experiments with kites, which ended in 1909. He invents the box-kite, which was later adopted by Santos-Dumont for his aeroplane wings, also by Archdeacon and Voisin.

1893 . . H. PHILLIPS (British) tests his aeroplane at Harrow. It was made to test the cambered wing, which particularly interested him, and 50 narrow cambered wings set one above each other like a Venetian blind formed the lifting surfaces. In circular tethered tests, powered by a steam-driven airscrew, it is said to have nearly left the ground. (Model in Science Museum.)

1894 . . OCTAVE CHANUTE (American) publishes his classic work *Progress in Flying Machines*. He was one of the inspirers of the Wrights, and himself made gliding experiments after first studying Lilienthal. His work on stability was of major importance and his biplane glider inspired later aircraft in England and America. (An original glider in Science Museum.)

1894 . . Sir H. MAXIM (British) after years of experiment, tests his full-sized steam-driven biplane at Baldwins Park. The test was made on a rail track with an upper guard rail to limit its rise. The machine definitely raised itself, but on its third trial was wrecked owing to a structural failure. He had been interested in aeronautics since 1856, and wrote a book *Artificial and Natural Flight*, published in 1909. (Maxim's original model in the Science Museum.)

1895 . . PERCY PILCHER (British) constructs his first glider, the *Bat*. He followed Lilienthal's ideas and was the chief British gliding pioneer. He crashed and was killed in 1899.

1896 . . LILIENTHAL killed when one of his gliders got out of control and crashed near Stöllen. He had achieved glides of more than 750 feet. (An original Lilienthal glider is in the Science Museum.)

1896 . . The first application of the petrol engine to aeronautics. Dr. WÖLFERT (German) successfully flies his dirigible *Deutschland* at Berlin.

1896 . . LANGLEY, after many experiments, makes a successful model aeroplane driven by a petrol engine. It covers 3,200 feet, at about 30 m.p.h. He repeats and betters this performance, but does not attempt to build a full-sized machine until 1899 (*see below*). He calls his models ' aerodromes '.

1896 . . WILBUR and ORVILLE WRIGHT (American) start their study of aeronautics, inspired by the work of Lilienthal.

1896 . . J. WEISS (French) starts his researches with model gliders. He was interested especially in achieving automatic stability, and between 1902 and 1907 made about 200 models. He later experimented successfully with full-sized craft. (Original model in Science Museum.)

| 1896 | . | . | The German Army introduce the ' Drachen ' captive observation balloon, the first of the ' sausage ' balloons, to avoid the movement of captive sphericals. |

1897 . . C. ADER (French) tests the third of his powered aeroplanes, *Avion III*, at Satory. The French Army observer stated that it made several hops, but was not satisfactory. There are still a number of people who claim Ader as the first to fly, but it is *sustained* powered flight that counts and that honour belongs without any argument to the Wright brothers.

1897 . . D. SCHWARZ (German) tests his dirigible at Berlin, the first completely rigid design and built entirely of aluminium. It was powered by a Daimler petrol engine. An accident caused its destruction before proper trials could be carried out.

1897 . . The first Arctic exploration by air. S. A. ANDRÉE (Swedish) and two companions set off in a balloon from Spitzbergen hoping to cross the North Pole. They disappeared and were not heard of until 1930, when the bodies and equipment (in perfect condition) were discovered by accident in the ice on White Island, Franz Josef Land.

1898 . . A. SANTOS DUMONT (Brazilian) constructs and flies his first small non-rigid airship at Paris. He builds 14 small airships between 1898 and 1906, and does much to create interest and enthusiasm for flying. He changed to aeroplanes in 1906 (*which see*).

1899 . . LANGLEY, requested and financed by the U.S. Government in 1898, starts construction of his full-sized ' aerodrome ' (*see* 1903).

1900 . . The WRIGHTS build and test their first glider at Kitty Hawk, N. Carolina. The machine was a Chanute type biplane. Glider No. 2 was built in 1901, and No. 3 in 1902. With the last they made nearly 1,000 test flights.

1900 . . The first Zeppelin is tested successfully at Lake Constance. It was designed by Count F. VON ZEPPELIN and commenced in 1898. It had two 16 h.p. engines and flew at about 20 m.p.h.

1901 . . The first attempt to drive a full-sized aeroplane by a petrol engine, by W. KRESS (Austrain) at Tullnerbach. The machine, of his own design, was destroyed when taxi-ing on the water.

1901 . . The Mediterranean crossed by balloon (Toulon to Algeria) by the Comte DE LA VAULX (French).

1901 . . Aero Club (later Royal) of Great Britain founded, in a balloon.

1903 . . LANGLEY finishes construction of his full-sized ' aerodrome '. In this year it is twice launched from a house-boat on the Potomac, but on both occasions there was a hitch in the launching and it crashed into the river. The U.S. Government would not advance further funds. In 1914, this machine (after alterations) was piloted by Glenn Curtiss and just managed to get airborne. This was used in a rightly unsuccessful, and very acrimonious, claim to antedate the Wright brothers' achievement.

1903 (Dec. 17) . **THE FIRST CONTROLLED AND SUSTAINED POWERED FLIGHT.** This historic event occurred when ORVILLE WRIGHT flew for twelve seconds at Kitty Hawk, N. Carolina. Three more flights were made by the brothers that day. The machine and engine were constructed by the brothers. It was a biplane with a span of forty feet and an 8–12 h.p. petrol engine driving two screws. It was controlled by a forward elevator, a rear rudder and by wing warping. Their achievement went virtually unrecognised until 1906. (The original aircraft is in the Science Museum.) The Wrights' work, with that of Chanute, became the main basis of practical aviation in Europe.

| 1905 | . | . | The first flight of over thirty minutes, by ORVILLE WRIGHT, at Dayton, U.S.A. (33 minutes 17 seconds). |

1905 . . MONTGOMERY builds a glider which is launched with another pilot from a balloon at 4,000 feet. He himself was killed in a gliding accident in 1911.

1905 . . E. ARCHDEACON (French) and G. VOISIN (French) collaborate, and after many experiments succeed in making good flights in a box-kite biplane glider when towed by a motor-boat on the Seine.

1906 . . The first powered flight in Europe. A. SANTOS-DUMONT (Brazilian) successfully flies his powered box-kite biplane ' 14 *bis* ' at Bagatelle in France. He then wins, in the same year, the Archdeacon Cup for the first sustained flight in Europe. (Model in Science Museum.)

1906 . . Inauguration of the Gordon-Bennett international balloon races. The first was started from Paris.

1907 . . The VOISIN brothers (Gabriel and Charles) start making aeroplanes and after early trouble the first aircraft makes a successful flight, piloted by L. Delagrange.

1907 . . L. BLÉRIOT (French), after collaborating with G. Voisin on gliders, constructs his own first machine, a monoplane. He later introduced the aileron for lateral control.

1907 . . The first free ascent of a helicopter with a pilot, by P. CORNU (French), near Lisieux.

1908 . . H. FARMAN (French) on a Voisin biplane wins the Deutsch Archdeacon Cup for a circular flight of a mile. This flight may be said to mark the entry of practical flying in Europe. (Model of a Voisin biplane in the Science Museum.)

1908 . . The first flight of over an hour, by ORVILLE WRIGHT, at Fort Myers (1 hour 2 minutes 30 seconds).

1908 . . The first aviation fatality. Lt. SELFRIDGE (U.S. Army) is killed when a machine piloted by Orville Wright crashes at Fort Myers, U.S.A.

1908 . . The WRIGHT brothers visit France and give many flights. This event gave tremendous impetus to aviation as no such achievements had seemed possible till then.

1908 . . S. F. CODY (American settled in England) makes and flies his aeroplane, based on his kite designs, near Farnborough. Like Blériot, he employed ailerons for lateral control.

1908 . . J. W. DUNNE (British) tests his swept-back wing monoplane, built in 1906. It was the first attempt at an inherently stable aeroplane but was not successful in free flight.

1909 . . The first aviation meetings are held, the most famous being at Rheims.

1909 . . The first Englishman to fly in England. J. T. C. MOORE-BRABAZON (later Lord Brabazon) flies a Voisin biplane at Leysdown, Isle of Sheppey.

1909 . . A. V. ROE (British) builds and successfully flies his triplane at Lea Marshes. He had made a biplane in 1908 which was partially successful.

1909 (July 25) . The first cross-Channel aeroplane flight, by L. BLÉRIOT (French) from Baraques to Dover. Aviation has now ' arrived ' both scientifically, and in the popular imagination. Research and development proceed everywhere.

[Copyright : The Associated Press

The first aircraft to break the sonic barrier—the American Bell XS–1. The speed of sound at sea-level is approximately 760 m.p.h., which decreases with altitude owing to the decreasing density of the air. This remarkable piloted aircraft broke the barrier at some 80,000 feet, but the actual speed attained has not been disclosed. The world of aviation has been awaiting with intense interest the result of flying an aircraft through the transition barrier at speeds greater than sound. This achievement opens up the possibilities of supersonic flight at ultimate speeds of over a thousand miles an hour.

THE WORLD'S AIRCRAFT

THE WORLD'S AIRCRAFT

Compiled by

JOHN STROUD

BRITISH AIRCRAFT

THE BRITISH aircraft dealt with in this section are for the most part the aircraft in production at the time of compilation, or types in wide-scale service or shortly due to enter service. Many of these types are standard equipment in the squadrons of the Royal Air Force and the Royal Navy, while the civil types are mainly in service on the world's airlines, with charter operators or as private owners' and club aircraft.

In addition a number of experimental aircraft have been included, such as the Armstrong Whitworth A.W.52G and the de Havilland 108, as these types will have a large influence on transport aircraft now in the design and early construction stages.

Airspeed AMBASSADOR

Country of origin	.	Britain
Designing company	.	Airspeed Ltd.
Name and type number	.	Ambassador, A.S.57 (Brabazon IIA)
Duty	. .	Passenger transport
Motors	. .	Two 2,200 h.p. Bristol Centaurus 57
Span	.	115 feet
Loaded weight	.	45,000 lb.
Cruising speed	.	180–298 m.p.h.
Range	. .	1,000–2,000 miles
Accommodation	.	24–40 passengers

Note :—A pressure cabin version powered by gas turbines will be built.

[*Photo : John Stroud*

Airspeed CONSUL

Country of origin	.	Britain
Designing company	.	Airspeed Ltd.
Name and type number	.	Consul, A.S.65
Duty	. .	Feeder line transport
Motors	. .	Two 395 h.p. Armstrong-Siddeley Cheetah X
Span	. .	53 feet 4 inches
Loaded weight	.	8,250 lb.
Cruising speed	.	155 m.p.h.
Maximum speed	.	192 m.p.h.
Range	.	635 miles
Accommodation	.	5 passengers

Country of origin	.	Britain
Designing company	.	Sir W. G. Armstrong Whit- worth Aircraft Ltd.
Type number	.	A.W.52G
Duty	.	Experimental tailless glider
Span	.	53 feet 4 inches
Loaded weight	.	6,000 lb.
Maximum speed	.	250 m.p.h.
Accommodation	.	Crew of two

Note :—Normally towed by a powered aircraft. Research type for A.W.52 two-jet tailless aeroplane weighing 30,000 lb. (*See* p. 272.)

[*Photo : Charles Brown*

Armstrong Whitworth A.W.52G

Country of origin	.	Britain
Designing company	.	Auster Aircraft Ltd.
Name and type number	.	Autocrat, J.1
Duty	.	Light private type
Motor	.	One 100 h.p. Cirrus Minor II
Span	.	36 feet
Loaded weight	.	1,850 lb.
Cruising speed	.	100 m.p.h.
Maximum speed	.	120 m.p.h.
Range	.	280 miles
Accommodation	.	Pilot and two passengers

[*Photo : John Stroud*

Auster AUTOCRAT

Country of origin	.	Britain
Designing company	.	A. V. Roe & Co. Ltd.
Name and type number	.	Lancaster, Avro 683
Duty	.	Heavy bomber
Motors	.	Four 1,280 h.p. Rolls-Royce Merlin XX
Span	.	102 feet
Loaded weight	.	68,000 lb.
Maximum speed	.	275 m.p.h.
Maximum range	.	About 3,000 miles
Armament	.	Ten .303-inch machine-guns in four turrets and up to 22,000 lb. bomb load

Note :—Figures quoted are for Mk. I; Mk. II has Bristol Hercules radial motors; Mk. III has Packard-built Merlins.

[*Photo : John Stroud*

Avro LANCASTER

[Photo : John Stroud

Avro LANCASTRIAN

Country of origin	.	Britain
Designing company	.	A. V. Roe & Co. Ltd.
Name and type number	.	Lancastrian, Avro 691
Duty	. . .	High-speed long-range transport
Motors	. .	Four 1,640 h.p. Rolls-Royce Merlin 24
Span	. .	102 feet
Loaded weight	.	65,000 lb.
Cruising speed	.	280 m.p.h.
Maximum speed	.	315 m.p.h.
Maximum range	.	4,100 miles
Accommodation	.	9 day or 6 night passengers

Note:—Figures are for Mk. I, in service with B.O.A.C.; the Mk. II is in service with R.A.F. Transport Command and the 12–14 seat Mk. III is in service with B.S.A.A.C. A Lancastrian powered by two Merlins and two Nene turbo-jets is now flying.

Avro LINCOLN

Country of origin	.	Britain
Designing company	.	A. V. Roe & Co. Ltd.
Name and type number	.	Lincoln, Avro 694
Duty	. . .	Heavy bomber
Motors	. .	Four 1,680 h.p. Rolls-Royce Merlin 85
Span	. .	120 feet
Loaded weight	.	75,000 lb.
Cruising speed	.	263 m.p.h.
Maximum speed	.	310 m.p.h.
Range	. .	4,000 miles
Armament	.	Seven .5-inch machine-guns, later marks have five machine-guns and two 20 m.m. cannon

Avro TUDOR I

Country of origin	.	Britain
Designing company	.	A. V. Roe & Co. Ltd.
Name and type number	.	Tudor I, Avro 688
Duty	. . .	Long-range passenger transport
Motors	. .	Four 1,670 h.p. Rolls-Royce Merlin 600 series
Span	. .	120 feet
Loaded weight	.	77,000 lb.
Cruising speed	.	300 m.p.h.
Maximum speed	.	346 m.p.h.
Maximum range	.	4,890 miles
Accommodation	.	12–24 passengers

Note :—Fitted with pressure cabin.

THE WORLD'S AIRCRAFT

Country of origin .	Britain
Designing company .	A. V. Roe & Co. Ltd.
Name and type number .	Tudor II, Avro 689
Duty . .	Medium-range passenger transport
Motors . .	Four 1,770 h.p. Rolls-Royce Merlin 621
Span . .	120 feet
Loaded weight .	80,000 lb.
Cruising speed .	285 m.p.h.
Maximum speed .	330 m.p.h.
Range . .	2,600 miles with 40 passengers
Accommodation .	40–60 passengers or up to 9 tons of freight

Note :—Fitted with pressure cabin.

Avro TUDOR II

Country of origin .	Britain
Designing company .	A. V. Roe & Co. Ltd.
Name and type number .	York, Avro 685
Duty . .	Military and civil transport
Motors . .	Four 1,280 h.p. Rolls-Royce Merlin 24
Span . .	102 feet
Loaded weight .	65,000 lb.
Maximum speed .	290 m.p.h.
Maximum range .	3,100 miles
Accommodation .	12–56 passengers

Note :—In service with R.A.F. Transport Command, B.O.A.C., B.S.A.A.C., South African Airways and F.A.M.A.

Avro YORK

Country of origin .	Britain
Designing company .	A. V. Roe & Co. Ltd.
Name and type number .	XIX, Avro 652A
Duty . .	Feeder line transport
Motors . .	Two 420 h.p. Armstrong-Siddeley Cheetah XV
Span . .	56 feet 6 inches
Loaded weight .	10,401 lb.
Cruising speed .	164 m.p.h.
Maximum speed .	190 m.p.h.
Range . .	400 miles
Accommodation .	6–9 passengers

Note :—In service with the R.A.F. and the Irish Air Force.

[*Photo : John Stroud*

Avro XIX

Blackburn FIREBRAND

Country of origin .	Britain
Designing company .	Blackburn Aircraft Ltd.
Name and type number .	Firebrand T.F. Mk. IV., Blackburn B.37
Duty . . .	Single-seat torpedo-carrier fighter
Motor . . .	One 2,500 h.p. Bristol Centaurus IX
Span . . .	51 feet 3½ inches
Loaded weight .	15,671–16,227 lb.
Cruising speed .	256–289 m.p.h.
Maximum speed .	350 m.p.h.
Range . . .	745–1,250 miles
Armament . .	Four 20 mm. cannon and one 1,850 lb. torpedo

Note :—Mk. I and Mk. II had Napier Sabre inline motor, Mk. III had Bristol Centaurus.

Bristol BRIGAND

Country of origin .	Britain
Designing company .	The Bristol Aeroplane Co.
Name and type number .	Brigand T.F. Mk. I, Bristol 164
Duty . . .	Three-seat torpedo-carrier fighter
Motors . .	Two 2,200 h.p. Bristol Centaurus 57
Span . . .	72 feet 4 inches
Loaded weight .	38,200 lb.
Cruising speed .	292 m.p.h.
Maximum speed .	323 m.p.h.
Range . . .	1,980–2,770 miles
Armament . .	Offensive: four 20 mm. cannon and 16 rocket projectiles or 1,000 lb. bomb, or externally-slung torpedo. Defensive: .5-inch machine-gun

[*Photo : John Stroud*

Bristol WAYFARER/FREIGHTER

Country of origin .	Britain
Designing company .	The Bristol Aeroplane Co. Ltd.
Name and type number .	Wayfarer/Freighter, Bristol 170
Duty . . .	Wayfarer: Passenger transport. Freighter: Freight transport
Motors . .	Two 1,675 h.p. Bristol Hercules 630
Span . . .	98 feet
Loaded weight .	36,500 lb.
Cruising speed .	180 m.p.h.
Maximum speed .	236 m.p.h.
Range . . .	1,085–1,200 miles
Accommodation .	Wayfarer: 32–36 passengers

Note :—This type can be powered by two Bristol Theseus gas turbines driving airscrews.

Country of origin .	Britain
Designing company .	The Bristol Aeroplane Co. Ltd.
Type number . .	Bristol 167 (Brabazon I)
Duty . . .	Transatlantic passenger transport
Motors . . .	Eight 2,500 h.p. Bristol Centaurus (paired)
Span . . .	250 feet
Loaded weight .	284,000 lb.
Cruising speed .	250 m.p.h.
Range . .	5,000 miles
Accommodation .	Pressurised cabins for 180–224 day passengers or 72 night passengers

Note :—A version powered by Bristol Proteus gas turbines will be built.

Bristol 167 (Brabazon I)

Country of origin .	Britain
Designing company .	The de Havilland Aircraft Co. Ltd.
Name and type number .	Dove, D.H.104
Duty . . .	Feeder line transport
Motors . . .	Two 330 h.p. de Havilland Gipsy Queen 71
Span . . .	57 feet
Loaded weight .	8,500 lb.
Cruising speed .	155 m.p.h.
Maximum speed .	222 m.p.h.
Range . . .	500 miles
Accommodation .	8–11 passengers

Note :—Now entering world-wide service. A version powered by gas turbines may be built.

De Havilland DOVE

Country of origin .	Britain
Designing company .	The de Havilland Aircraft Co. Ltd.
Name and type number .	Dragon Rapide, D.H.89A
Duty . . .	Feeder line transport
Motors . . .	Two 200 h.p. de Havilland Gipsy Six
Span . . .	48 feet
Loaded weight .	5,550 lb.
Cruising speed .	132 m.p.h.
Maximum speed .	157 m.p.h.
Range . . .	556 miles
Accommodation .	5–8 passengers

Note :—In service on British internal airlines and throughout the world.

[*Photo : John Stroud*

De Havilland DRAGON RAPIDE

Country of origin .	Britain
Designing company .	The de Havilland Aircraft Co. Ltd.
Name and type number .	Hornet F.Mk. I, D.H.103
Duty . . .	Single-seat fighter
Motors . .	Two 2,080 h.p. Rolls-Royce Merlin 130 series
Span . . .	45 feet
Loaded weight .	17,600 lb.
Maximum speed .	Over 470 m.p.h.
Range . .	Over 2,500 miles
Armament .	Four 20 mm. cannon

Note :—The Mk. II is an unarmed reconnaissance type. The Naval version is the Sea Hornet XX.

De Havilland HORNET

Country of origin .	Britain
Designing company	The de Havilland Aircraft Co. Ltd.
Name and type number .	Mosquito, D.H.98
Duty . . .	Fighter, bomber, photographic reconnaissance, fighter - bomber, trainer and transport
Motors . .	Two Rolls-Royce Merlin. Varying according to Mk. number of the aeroplane
Span . . .	54 feet 2 inches
Maximum speed .	Over 400 m.p.h.
Range . .	Over 2,000 miles
Armament .	Varies widely over the range from Mk. I to Mk. 36. Some Mks. are unarmed

Note :—The Mk. 33 Naval version is called the Sea Mosquito.

De Havilland MOSQUITO

[Photo : John Stroud

Country of origin .	Britain
Designing company .	The de Havilland Aircraft Co. Ltd.
Name and type number .	Tiger Moth, D.H.82A
Duty . . .	Primary trainer
Motor . . .	One 130 h.p. de Havilland Gipsy Major
Span . . .	29 feet 4 inches
Loaded weight .	1,770–1,825 lb.
Cruising speed .	93 m.p.h.
Maximum speed .	109 m.p.h.
Accommodation .	Open cockpits for pupil and instructor

De Havilland TIGER MOTH

THE WORLD'S AIRCRAFT

Country of origin .	Britain
Designing company	The de Havilland Aircraft Co. Ltd.
Name and type number .	Vampire F.Mk. I, D.H.100
Duty . .	Single-seat fighter
Motor . .	One 3,000 lb. thrust de Havilland Goblin turbo-jet
Span . .	40 feet
Loaded weight .	10,298 lb.
Cruising speed .	400–450 m.p.h.
Maximum speed .	540 m.p.h.
Range . .	500–1,050 miles
Armament .	Four 20 mm. cannon

Note :—In service with the R.A.F., Swedish Air Force and Swiss Air Force. There is a Naval version called the Sea Vampire.

De Havilland VAMPIRE

Country of origin .	Britain
Designing company .	The de Havilland Aircraft Co. Ltd.
Type number .	D.H.108
Duty . .	Research
Motor . .	One de Havilland Goblin turbo-jet
Span, loaded weight and performance . .	Not released for publication

Note :—This aeroplane was designed for high-speed research prior to the construction of the de Havilland 106, a 75,000 lb. flying-wing transatlantic passenger transport powered by four jet motors.

[*Photo : S.B.A.C.*
De Havilland 108

Country of origin .	Britain
Designing company .	The Fairey Aviation Co.
Name . .	Firefly IV
Duty . .	Two-seat Naval reconnaissance-fighter
Motor . .	One 2,245 h.p. Rolls-Royce Griffon 74
Span . .	41 feet 2 inches
Loaded weight .	13,200 lb.
Cruising speed .	220 m.p.h.
Maximum speed .	386 m.p.h.
Range . .	Up to 1,070 miles
Armament .	Four 20 mm. cannon. Can also carry eight pairs of rocket projectiles or two 1,000 lb. bombs

Note :—The Mk. I is also in service with the Royal Navy and with the Royal Netherlands Naval Air Service.

Fairey FIREFLY IV

235

Country of origin	.	Britain
Designing company	.	The Fairey Aviation Co. Ltd.
Name . .	.	Spearfish I
Duty . .	.	Two-seat Naval torpedo-dive-bomber-reconnaissance
Motor . .	.	One 2,585 h.p. Bristol Centaurus 58, 59 or 60
Span . .	.	60 feet
Loaded weight .	.	24,000 lb.
Maximum speed	.	301 m.p.h.
Range . .	.	900 miles
Armament .	.	Four .5-inch machine-guns. Can carry one 18-inch torpedo, bombs, mines or depth charges up to 2,000 lb.

Fairey SPEARFISH

Country of origin	.	Britain
Designing company	.	General Aircraft Ltd.
Name and type number	.	Hamilcar X, G.A.L.58
Duty . .	.	Powered glider transport
Motors . .	.	Two 965 h.p. Bristol Mercury 31
Span . .	.	110 feet
Loaded weight .	.	45,500–47,000 lb.
Cruising speed .	.	120 m.p.h.
Maximum speed	.	145 m.p.h.
Range . .	.	700 miles with 3,000 lb. load

[*Photo : Air Transport*

General Aircraft HAMILCAR X

Note :—This is a powered version of the Hamilcar glider. It is normally towed off by a Handley Page Halifax.

Country of origin	.	Britain
Designing company	.	Gloster Aircraft Co. Ltd.
Name . .	.	Meteor IV
Duty . .	.	Single-seat fighter
Motors . .	.	Two 3,500 lb. thrust Rolls-Royce Derwent V turbo-jets
Span . .	.	43 feet
Maximum speed	.	Over 620 m.p.h.
Armament .	.	Four 20 mm. cannon

[*Photo : S.B.A.C.*

Gloster METEOR

Note :—A Meteor of the R.A.F. held the world's air-speed record with a speed of 616 m.p.h. The production Meteor IV now has a reduced span of 37 feet 2 inches.

Country of origin .	Britain
Designing company .	Handley Page Ltd.
Name and type number .	Halton, H.P.70
Duty . . .	Passenger transport
Motors . .	Four 1,650 h.p. Bristol Hercules
Span . . .	103 feet 8 inches
Loaded weight . .	65,000 lb.
Cruising speed . .	260 m.p.h.
Maximum speed .	320 m.p.h.
Range . . .	2,700 miles
Accommodation .	10 passengers

Note :—Twelve of these aircraft are in service with B.O.A.C. The Halton is the civil passenger version of the Halifax C.VIII.

[*Photo : B.O.A.C.*

Handley Page HALTON

Country of origin .	Britain
Designing company .	Handley Page Ltd.
Name and type number .	Hermes I, H.P.68
Duty . . .	Passenger transport
Motors . .	Four 1,675 h.p. Bristol Hercules
Span . .	113 feet
Loaded weight . .	75,000 lb.
Cruising speed . .	194–281 m.p.h.
Maximum speed .	337 m.p.h.
Range . . .	Up to 3,030 miles
Accommodation .	32–50 passengers

Note :—Mk. II will have an extended fuselage, Mk. III will be powered by four Bristol Theseus gas turbines driving airscrews, Mk. IV will have a tricycle undercarriage. The military version, the H.P.67 Hastings, is illustrated.

Handley Page HASTINGS

Country of origin .	Britain
Designing company .	Hawker Aircraft Ltd.
Name . .	Fury F.Mk. I
Duty . .	Single-seat fighter
Motor . .	One 3,000 h.p. Napier Sabre VII
Span . .	38 feet 5 inches
Loaded weight .	12,010 lb.
Maximum speed .	485 m.p.h.
Range . .	450–1,790 miles
Armament .	Four 20 mm. cannon. Can carry two 1,000 lb. bombs or rocket projectiles

Note :—In production for the R.A.F.

Hawker FURY

Hawker SEA FURY

Country of origin	.	Britain
Designing company	.	Hawker Aircraft Ltd.
Name . .	.	Sea Fury F.Mk. X
Duty . .	.	Carrier-borne single-seat fighter
Motor . .	.	One 2,400 h.p. Bristol Centaurus XVIII
Span . .	.	38 feet 5 inches
Loaded weight .	.	12,030 lb.
Maximum speed	.	435 m.p.h.
Range . .	.	1,160 miles
Armament .	.	Four 20 mm. cannon and two 1,000 lb. bombs or twelve rocket projectiles

Hawker TEMPEST

Country of origin	.	Britain
Designing company	.	Hawker Aircraft Ltd.
Name . .	.	Tempest F.Mk. VI
Duty . .	.	Single-seat fighter
Motor . .	.	One 2,600 h.p. Napier Sabre VA
Span . .	.	41 feet
Loaded weight .	.	11,400 lb. (Mk. V fighter version)
Maximum speed	.	Over 435 m.p.h.
Armament .	.	Four 20 mm. cannon

Note :—Developed from and almost identical with the Mk. V with Sabre IIB motor (illustrated). The Mk. II also in service has a Bristol Centaurus V radial motor.

[*Photo : John Stroud*

Miles AEROVAN

Country of origin	.	Britain
Designing company	.	Miles Aircraft Ltd.
Name and type number	.	Aerovan, M.57
Duty . .	.	Light cargo and passenger transport
Motors . .	.	Two 150 h.p. Cirrus Major
Span . .	.	50 feet
Loaded weight .	.	6,000 lb.
Cruising speed .	.	112 m.p.h.
Maximum speed	.	127 m.p.h.
Range . .	.	400 miles
Accommodation	.	Up to 10 passengers or 1 ton of freight

Note :—A larger development is called the Merchantman.

Country of origin	.	Britain
Designing company	.	Miles Aircraft Ltd.
Name and type number	.	Gemini, M.65
Duty	. .	Light passenger transport
Motors	.	Two 100 h.p. Cirrus Minor II
Span	. .	36 feet 2 inches
Loaded weight	.	3,000 lb.
Cruising speed	.	130 m.p.h.
Maximum speed		150 m.p.h.
Range	. .	520–820 miles
Accommodation	.	Pilot and three passengers

Miles GEMINI

Country of origin	.	Britain
Designing company	.	Miles Aircraft Ltd.
Name and type number	.	Marathon, M.60
Duty	. .	Passenger transport
Motors	.	Four 330 h.p. de Havilland Gipsy Queen 71
Span	.	65 feet
Loaded weight	.	16,000 lb.
Cruising speed	.	175–208 m.p.h.
Maximum speed	.	230 m.p.h.
Range	. .	300–1,000 miles
Accommodation	.	14–20 passengers

Note :—A gas-turbine-powered version may be built.

Miles MARATHON

Country of origin	.	Britain
Designing company	.	Miles Aircraft Ltd.
Name and type number	.	Martinet, M.25
Duty	. .	Target tug
Motor	. .	One 835–870 h.p. Bristol Mercury XX
Span	. .	39 feet
Loaded weight	.	6,600 lb.
Cruising speed	.	225 m.p.h.
Maximum speed	.	237 m.p.h.
Accommodation	.	Crew of two

Note :—In service with the R.A.F., the Royal Navy and a Swedish private company. A two-seat trainer version is illustrated.

[*Photo : John Stroud*]

Miles MARTINET TRAINER

Miles MESSENGER

Country of origin .	Britain
Designing Company .	Miles Aircraft Ltd.
Name and type number .	Messenger, M.38
Duty . .	Light transport
Motor . .	One 150 h.p. Cirrus Major III
Span . .	36 feet 2 inches
Loaded weight .	2,400 lb.
Cruising speed .	112 m.p.h.
Maximum speed .	120 m.p.h.
Range . .	250–500 miles
Accommodation	Pilot and three passengers

Percival PRENTICE

Country of origin .	Britain
Designing company .	Percival Aircraft Ltd.
Name . .	Prentice
Duty . .	Elementary trainer
Motor . .	One 250 h.p. de Havilland Gipsy Queen 32 or 295 h.p. supercharged Gipsy Queen 51
Span . .	46 feet
Loaded weight .	3,790 lb. (Gipsy Queen 32) 3,860 lb. (Gipsy Queen 51)
Cruising speed .	136–149 m.p.h. (Gipsy Queen 32) 129–160 m.p.h. (Gipsy Queen 51)
Maximum speed .	155 m.p.h. (Gipsy Queen 32) 171 m.p.h. (Gipsy Queen 51)
Range . .	495 miles (Gipsy Queen 32) 517 miles (Gipsy Queen 51)

[*Photo : John Stroud*]

Percival PROCTOR V

Country of origin .	Britain
Designing company .	Percival Aircraft Ltd.
Name . .	Proctor V
Duty . .	Light transport
Motor . .	One 208 h.p. de Havilland Gipsy Queen II
Span . .	39 feet 6 inches
Loaded weight .	3,500 lb.
Cruising speed .	135–146 m.p.h.
Maximum speed .	157 m.p.h.
Range . .	500–780 miles
Accommodation .	Pilot and 3 passengers

Country of origin .	Britain
Designing company .	Reid and Sigrist Ltd.
Name and type number .	Desford, R.S.3
Duty . .	Advanced trainer
Motors . .	Two 130 h.p. de Havilland Gipsy Major
Span . .	34 feet
Loaded weight .	3,300 lb.
Cruising speed .	148 m.p.h.
Maximum speed .	162 m.p.h.
Range . .	463 miles
Accommodation .	Pupil and instructor

[*Photo : John Stroud*

Reid and Sigrist DESFORD

Country of origin .	Britain
Designing company .	Short Brothers (Rochester & Bedford) Ltd.
Name . .	Sealand
Duty . .	Passenger transport amphibian
Motors . .	Two 330 h.p. de Havilland Gipsy Queen 71
Span . .	59 feet
Loaded weight .	8,500 lb.
Cruising speed .	132–165 m.p.h.
Maximum speed .	193.2 m.p.h.
Range . .	594–775 miles
Accommodation .	5–7 passengers

Short SEALAND

Country of origin .	Britain
Designing company .	Short Brothers (Rochester & Bedford) Ltd.
Name and type number .	Shetland, S.35
Duty . .	Passenger transport flying-boat
Motors . .	Four 2,500 h.p. Bristol Centaurus
Span . .	150 feet 4 inches
Loaded weight .	130,000 lb.
Cruising speed .	188 m.p.h.
Maximum speed .	267 m.p.h.
Range . .	4,650 miles
Accommodation .	24–40 passengers

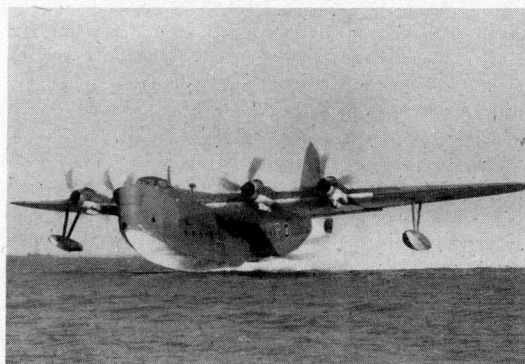

Short SHETLAND

Q

[Photo : B.O.A.C.

Short SOLENT

Country of origin .	Britain
Designing company .	Short Brothers (Rochester & Bedford) Ltd.
Name and type number .	Solent, S.45
Duty . . .	Passenger transport flying-boat
Motors . . .	Four 1,675 h.p. Bristol Hercules
Span . . .	112 feet
Loaded weight .	75,000 lb.
Cruising speed .	208 m.p.h.
Maximum speed .	236 m.p.h.
Range . . .	2,200 miles
Accommodation .	24–36 day passengers, 24 night passengers

Note:—A fleet of Solents is in service with B.O.A.C.

[Photo : John Stroud

Short STURGEON

Country of origin .	Britain
Designing company .	Short Brothers (Rochester & Bedford) Ltd.
Name and type number .	Sturgeon P.R.Mk. I, S.A.1
Duty . . .	Three-seat Naval reconnaissance
Motors . . .	Two 2,080 h.p. Rolls-Royce Merlin 140
Span . . .	60 feet
Loaded weight .	21,800 lb.
Cruising speed .	About 200 m.p.h.
Maximum speed .	Over 350 m.p.h.
Range . . .	Over 1,000 miles
Armament . .	Four .5-inch machine-guns and eight 60 lb. rocket projectiles

Note :—A target-towing version is the Short S.A.II, Sturgeon T.T.Mk. II.

[Photo : B.O.A.C.

Short HYTHE

Country of origin .	Britain
Designing company .	Short Brothers (Rochester & Bedford) Ltd.
Name and type number .	Hythe, S.25 (Sunderland III)
Duty . . .	Passenger transport flying-boat
Motors . . .	Four 1,050 h.p. Bristol Pegasus XVIII
Span . . .	112 feet 9½ inches
Loaded weight .	56,000 lb.
Cruising speed .	178 m.p.h.
Maximum speed .	210 m.p.h.
Range . . .	1,780 miles
Accommodation .	16–22 passengers

Note :—B.O.A.C. civil version of military Sunderland III. A purely civil version is in production as the Sandringham.

Country of origin	.	Britain
Designing company	.	Vickers - Armstrongs Ltd. (Supermarine Works)
Name	. . .	Seafire F.Mk. 46
Duty	. .	Single-seat Naval fighter
Motor	. .	One 2,050 h.p. Rolls-Royce Griffon 61, 64 or 85
Span	. .	36 feet 11 inches
Loaded weight	.	10,080 lb.
Maximum speed	.	450 m.p.h.
Armament	.	Four 20 mm. cannon

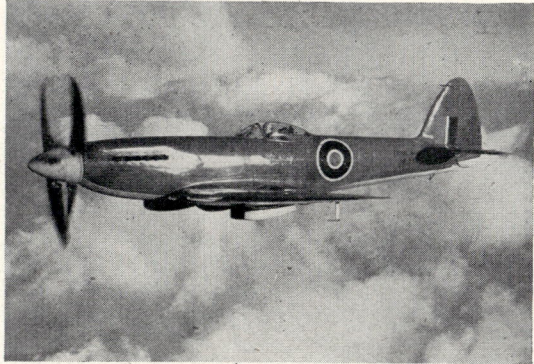

Supermarine SEAFIRE 46

Country of origin	.	Britain
Designing company	.	Vickers - Armstrongs Ltd. (Supermarine Works)
Name	.	Seafang
Duty	.	Carrier - borne single - seat fighter
Motor	.	One 2,050 h.p. Rolls-Royce Griffon 69 or 89
Span	.	35 feet
Loaded weight	.	10,450 lb.
Maximum speed	.	475 m.p.h.
Range	.	About 730 miles maximum
Armament	.	Four 20 mm. cannon and three 500 lb. bombs or rocket projectiles

*Note :—*The Seafang is the Naval version of the Spiteful.

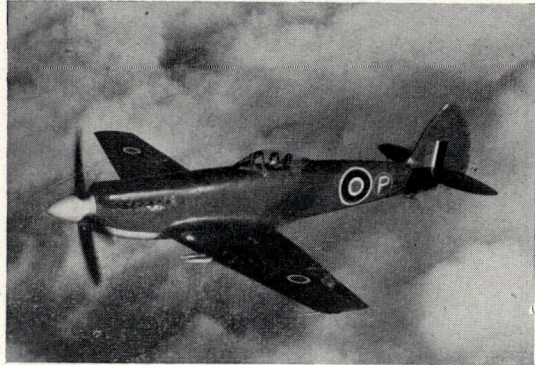

Supermarine SEAFANG

Country of origin	.	Britain
Designing company	.	Vickers - Armstrongs Ltd. (Supermarine Works)
Name	. .	Spiteful
Duty	. .	Single-seat fighter
Motor	. .	One 2,050 h.p. Rolls-Royce Griffon
Span	. .	35 feet
Loaded weight	.	9,950 lb.
Maximum speed	.	483 m.p.h.
Armament	.	Four 20 mm. cannon and two 1,000 lb. bombs or four 300 lb. rockets

Supermarine SPITEFUL

243

Supermarine SPITFIRE 22

Country of origin	.	Britain
Designing company	.	Vickers - Armstrongs Ltd. (Supermarine Works)
Name	. . .	Spitfire F.Mk. 22
Duty	. . .	Single-seat fighter
Motor	. . .	One 2,050 h.p. Rolls-Royce Griffon 61, 64 or 85
Span	. . .	36 feet 11 inches
Loaded weight	.	9,900 lb.
Maximum speed	.	450 m.p.h.
Armament	.	Four 20 mm. cannon. Three 500 lb. bombs or rocket projectiles can be carried

Note :—The Mks. 21, 22 and 24 are the latest. An even later Spitfire is the two-seat trainer.

[*Photo :* S.B.A.C.

Supermarine ATTACKER

Country of origin	.	Britain
Designing company	.	Vickers - Armstrongs Ltd. (Supermarine Works)
Name and type number	.	Attacker, E.10/44
Duty	. .	Single-seat fighter
Motor	. .	One 5,000 lb. thrust Rolls-Royce Nene I turbo-jet
Span	. .	36 feet 11 inches
Maximum speed	.	Over 600 m.p.h.
Armament	.	Four 20 mm. cannon

Vickers-Armstrongs VIKING

Country of origin	.	Britain
Designing company	.	Vickers-Armstrongs Ltd.
Name and type number	.	Viking, V.C.1
Duty	. .	Passenger transport
Motors	. .	Two 1,690 h.p. Bristol Hercules 630
Span	. .	89 feet 3 inches
Loaded weight	.	34,000 lb.
Cruising speed	.	210 m.p.h.
Maximum cruising speed		252 m.p.h.
Range	. .	Up to 1,920 miles
Accommodation	.	21–27 passengers

Note :—The Viking is in service with B.E.A.C., R.A.F. Transport Command, and many overseas airlines. Four of this type are also in the King's Flight. A version of the Viking powered by two Nene turbo-jets is in the project stage—its speed will exceed 400 m.p.h.

Country of origin	.	Britain
Designing company	.	Westland Aircraft Ltd.
Name	. .	Welkin I
Duty	. .	High-altitude single-seat fighter
Motors	. .	Two 1,650 plus h.p. Rolls-Royce Merlin
Span	. .	70 feet
Loaded weight	.	17,500 lb.
Maximum speed	.	385 m.p.h.
Range	. .	About 1,500 miles
Armament	.	Four 20 mm. cannon

[*Photo : S.B.A.C.*

Westland WELKIN

Note :—The Mk. II two-seat version is illustrated.

UNITED STATES AIRCRAFT

THIS SECTION on United States aircraft is constituted much in the same way as the British section. It will prove to be an interesting record of United States military aircraft of the orthodox type, for in most classes of military aircraft the U.S. Army and Navy are intending to replace existing types with jet-propelled aeroplanes. Many prototypes are already flying, while such types as the Lockheed P-80 Shooting Star and the McDonnell FD-1 are already in service.

Unfortunately when this work was compiled security forbade the inclusion of most of these jet types.

Country of origin	.	U.S.A.
Designing company	.	The Aeronca Aircraft Corporation
Name	. .	Chief
Duty	. .	Private owner type
Motor	. .	One 65 h.p. Continental A.65
Span	. .	36 feet
Loaded weight	.	1,250 lb.
Cruising speed	.	90 m.p.h.
Maximum speed	.	100 m.p.h.
Range	.	420 miles
Accommodation	.	Pilot and 1 passenger

Aeronca CHIEF

245

Beech BONANZA

Country of origin	.	U.S.A.
Designing company	.	Beech Aircraft Corporation
Name	. .	Bonanza
Duty	. .	Private owner type
Motor	. .	One 165 h.p. Continental E.165
Span	. .	32 feet 8 inches
Loaded weight	.	2,545 lb.
Cruising speed	.	175 m.p.h.
Maximum speed	.	183 m.p.h.
Range	. .	745 miles
Accommodation	.	Pilot and 3 passengers

Beech 18S

Country of origin	.	U.S.A.
Designing company	.	Beech Aircraft Corporation
Name	. .	Model 18S
Duty	. .	Light transport
Motors	. .	Two 450 h.p. Pratt & Whitney R–985
Span	. .	47 feet 8 inches
Loaded weight	.	7,500 lb.
Cruising speed	.	160 m.p.h.
Maximum speed	.	225 m.p.h.
Range	. .	1,200 miles
Accommodation	.	6 passengers

Bell 47

Country of origin	.	U.S.A.
Designing company	.	Bell Aircraft Corporation
Name	. .	Model 47
Duty	. .	Commercial helicopter
Motor	. .	One 175 h.p. Franklin
Rotor diameter	.	33 feet
Cruising speed	.	85 m.p.h.
Maximum speed	.	100–110 m.p.h.
Range	. .	250 miles
Accommodation	.	Pilot and passenger or 612 lb. load

Note :—Deliveries are being made.

Country of origin .	U.S.A.
Designing company .	The Boeing Aircraft Company
Name and type number .	Stratocruiser, Boeing 377
Duty . . .	Passenger transport
Motors . .	Four 3,500 h.p. Pratt & Whitney
Span . .	141 feet 3 inches
Loaded weight .	130,000 lb.
Cruising speed .	340 m.p.h.
Maximum speed .	About 400 m.p.h.
Range . .	3,500 miles
Accommodation .	Up to 114 passengers

Note :—The Stratocruiser has pressure cabins and is on order for B.O.A.C., S.A.S. and some U.S. airlines. A freight version is the Stratofreighter. The U.S. Army version is the C–97 (illustrated here).

Boeing C–97

Country of origin .	U.S.A.
Designing company .	The Boeing Aircraft Company
Name and type number .	Superfortress, Boeing 345, U.S. Army B–29
Duty . . .	Heavy bomber
Motors . .	Four 2,200 h.p. Wright R–3350–23
Span . .	141 feet 3 inches
Loaded weight .	135,000 lb.
Maximum speed .	Over 350 m.p.h.
Range . .	Over 4,100 miles
Armament . .	Ten .5-inch machine-guns and one 20 mm. cannon. Bomb load up to 22,000 lb.

Note:—A B–29 named *Pacusan Dreamboat*, in 1946, flew non-stop from Honolulu over the North Pole to Cairo, a distance of 9,500 miles.

Boeing SUPERFORTRESS

Country of origin .	U.S.A.
Designing company .	The Cessna Aircraft Co. Inc.
Name . . .	Model 140
Duty . . .	Private owner type
Motor . .	One 85 h.p. Continental C–85
Span . .	32 feet 10 inches
Loaded weight .	1,450 lb.
Cruising speed .	100 m.p.h.
Maximum speed .	125 m.p.h.
Range . .	420 miles
Accommodation .	Pilot and passenger

Cessna MODEL 140

Convair L–13

Country of origin	U.S.A.
Designing company	The Consolidated Vultee Aircraft Corporation
Type number	U.S. Army L–13
Duty	Liaison and ambulance
Motor	One 245 h.p. Franklin O–425–5
Span	40 feet 5½ inches
Loaded weight	2,900 lb.
Cruising speed	92 m.p.h.
Maximum speed	115 m.p.h.
Range	368 miles
Accommodation	Two crew and two stretcher cases. Maximum load six persons

Convair XB–36

Country of origin	U.S.A.
Designing company	The Consolidated Vultee Aircraft Corporation
Type number	XB–36
Duty	Heavy bomber
Motors	Six 3,000 h.p. Pratt & Whitney Wasp Major R–4360
Span	230 feet
Loaded weight	About 260,000 lb.
Cruising speed	About 340 m.p.h.
Range	10,000 miles
Bomb load	60,000 lb.

Note :—A civil transport version with accommodation for 204 passengers will be known as the Convair Model 37.

Culver MODEL V

Country of origin	U.S.A.
Designing company	Culver Aircraft Corporation
Name	Model V
Duty	Private owner type
Motor	One 85 h.p. Continental C–85
Span	29 feet
Loaded weight	1,305 lb.
Maximum speed	140 m.p.h.
Range	700 miles
Accommodation	Pilot and passenger

Country of origin	.	U.S.A.
Designing company	.	The Curtiss-Wright Corporation, Airplane Division
Name and type number	.	Seahawk, U.S. Navy SC–1
Duty	.	Single-seat shipborne scout
Motor	.	One 1,350 h.p. Wright R–1820–62
Span	.	41 feet
Loaded weight	.	7,936 lb.
Cruising speed	.	125 m.p.h.
Maximum speed	.	238 m.p.h.
Range	.	1,090 miles
Armament	.	Two .5-inch machine-guns. Bombs or depth charges can be carried in the central float

Curtiss SEAHAWK

Country of origin	.	U.S.A.
Designing company	.	The Curtiss-Wright Corporation, Airplane Division
Type number	.	U.S. Navy XBT2C–1
Duty	.	Single - seat carrier - borne torpedo-bomber
Motor	.	One 2,500 h.p. Wright Cyclone R–3350
Span	.	Not available
Loaded weight	.	Over 18,000 lb.
Range	.	Over 1,400 miles
Armament	.	Internal stowage for torpedo, bombs or large aerial rocket. Two 20 mm. cannon are mounted in the wing

Note :—Other performance figures not available.

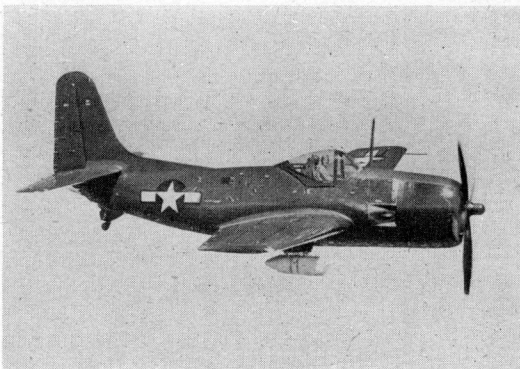

Curtiss XBT2C–1

Country of origin	.	U.S.A.
Designing company	.	The Douglas Aircraft Company Inc.
Name and type number	.	Dakota, Douglas DC 3, U.S. Army C–47, U.S. Navy R4D
Duty	.	Transport
Motors	.	Two 1,200 h.p. Pratt & Whitney Twin Wasp R–1830–92
Span	.	95 feet
Loaded weight	.	26,000 lb.
Cruising speed	.	185 m.p.h.
Maximum speed	.	229 m.p.h.
Range	.	1,500 miles
Accommodation	.	DC 3 normally 21 passengers. C–47 up to 28 troops

Douglas DAKOTA

Douglas DC 6

Country of origin	.	U.S.A.
Designing company	.	The Douglas Aircraft Company Inc.
Type number	.	DC 6
Duty	.	Passenger transport
Motors	.	Four 2,100 h.p. Pratt & Whitney Twin Wasp R–2000–C
Span	.	117 feet 6 inches
Loaded weight	.	80,500 lb.
Cruising speed	.	278–334 m.p.h.
Maximum range	.	Over 3,000 miles
Accommodation	.	52 day passengers, 26 night passengers

Note :—The DC 6 is a development of the DC 4. (*See* Skymaster.)

Douglas GLOBEMASTER

Country of origin	.	U.S.A.
Designing company	.	The Douglas Aircraft Company Inc.
Name and type number	.	Globemaster, Douglas DC 7, U.S. Army XC–74
Duty	.	Transport
Motors	.	Four 3,650 h.p. Pratt & Whitney Wasp Major R–4360
Span	.	173 feet 3 inches
Loaded weight	.	162,000 lb.
Cruising speed	.	275 m.p.h.
Maximum speed	.	Over 300 m.p.h.
Range	.	4,000–7,800 miles
Accommodation	.	96–108 passengers

Douglas INVADER

Country of origin	.	U.S.A.
Designing company	.	The Douglas Aircraft Company Inc.
Name and type number	.	Invader, U.S. Army A–26, U.S. Navy JD1
Duty	.	Three-seat attack bomber
Motors	.	Two 2,000 h.p. Pratt & Whitney Double Wasp R–2800–71
Span	.	70 feet
Loaded weight	.	27,000 lb.
Maximum speed	.	345 m.p.h.
Armament	.	Varies. A–26B has six .5-inch machine-guns in nose and eight .5-inch machine-guns under wings

Country of origin .	U.S.A.
Designing company .	The Douglas Aircraft Company Inc.
Name and type number .	Skymaster, Douglas DC 4, U.S. Army C–54, U.S. Navy R5D
Duty . .	Transport
Motors . .	Four 1,100 h.p. Pratt & Whitney Twin Wasp R–2000
Span . .	117 feet 6 inches
Loaded weight .	65,000 lb.
Cruising speed . .	239 m.p.h.
Maximum speed .	274 m.p.h.
Range . .	1,500 miles
Accommodation .	28–44 passengers

Note :—In service on the world's airlines. A Merlin-powered DC 4M is produced in Canada.

Douglas SKYMASTER

Country of origin .	U.S.A.
Designing company .	The Douglas Aircraft Company Inc.
Name and type number .	Skyraider, U.S. Navy AD–1
Duty . .	Carrier-based dive-bomber
Motor . .	One 3,650 h.p. Pratt & Whitney Wasp Major R–4360
Span . .	50 feet
Loaded weight .	16,120 lb.
Performance .	Not released for publication
Armament .	Two .5-inch machine-guns and bombs or torpedo carried externally. Provision for eight rocket projectiles. Maximum load 6,000 lb.

Douglas SKYRAIDER

Country of origin .	U.S.A.
Designing company .	The Douglas Aircraft Company Inc.
Type number .	U.S. Army XB–42
Duty . .	Bomber
Motors .	Two 1,800 h.p. Allison V–1710–125
Span . .	70 feet 7 inches
Loaded weight .	33,308 lb.
Maximum speed .	Over 380 m.p.h.

Note :—A development is the XB–43, powered by two General Electric TG–180 (J–35) turbo-jets each of 4,000 lb. thrust. The span is 71 feet 2 inches; the loaded weight 35,000 lb. and the maximum speed is estimated to be over 500 m.p.h.

Douglas XB–42

ERCOUPE

Country of origin	.	U.S.A.
Designing company	.	Engineering & Research Corporation
Name . .	.	Ercoupe
Duty . .	.	Private owner type
Motor . .	.	One 65 h.p. Continental A–65
Span . .	.	30 feet
Loaded weight .	.	1,175 lb.
Cruising speed .	.	106 m.p.h.
Maximum speed .	.	117 m.p.h.
Range . .	.	320 miles
Accommodation	.	Pilot and passenger

Fairchild PACKET

Country of origin	.	U.S.A.
Designing company	.	The Fairchild Aircraft Division of the Fairchild Engine & Airplane Corp.
Name and type number .		Packet, U.S. Army C–82
Duty . .	.	Military transport
Motors . .	.	Two 2,100 h.p. Pratt & Whitney Double Wasp R–2800C
Span . .	.	106 feet 5 inches
Loaded weight .	.	56,000 lb.
Cruising speed .	.	Over 200 m.p.h.
Maximum range .	.	4,000 miles
Accommodation	.	42 parachute troops or 34 stretchers

Note :—Some are now becoming available for civil use and at least one is in service in the United States as a flying post-office sorting-office and mail carrier.

Fairchild XNQ–1

Country of origin	.	U.S.A.
Designing company	.	The Fairchild Aircraft Division of the Fairchild Engine & Airplane Corporation
Type number .		U.S. Navy XNQ–1
Duty . .	.	Primary trainer
Motor . .	.	One 320 h.p. Lycoming
Span . .	.	41 feet 5 inches
Loaded weight .	.	3,700 lb.
Maximum speed .	.	About 170 m.p.h.
Accommodation	.	Instructor and pupil

Note :—No other information available.

Country of origin	.	U.S.A.
Designing company	.	The Globe Aircraft Corporation
Name and type number	.	Swift, GC–1A
Duty . .	.	Private owner type
Motor . .	.	One 85 h.p. Continental C–85–12
Span . .	.	29 feet 4 inches
Loaded weight .	.	1,570 lb.
Cruising speed .	.	125 m.p.h.
Maximum speed .	.	135 m.p.h.
Range . .	.	600 miles
Accommodation	.	Pilot and passenger

Globe SWIFT

Country of origin	.	U.S.A.
Designing company	.	The Grumman Aircraft Engineering Corporation
Name and type number	.	Bearcat, U.S. Navy F8F–1
Duty . .	.	Single-seat carrier-borne fighter
Motor .	.	One 2,000 h.p. Pratt & Whitney Double Wasp R–2800
Span . .	.	35 feet 6 inches
Maximum speed	.	450 m.p.h.
Maximum range	.	2,200 miles
Armament .	.	F8F–1, four .5-inch machine-guns; F8F–1C, four 20 mm. cannon. Both can carry 4 rocket projectiles.

Note :—When built by the Eastern Aircraft Division of the General Motors Corp. the Bearcat is called the F3M.

Grumman BEARCAT

Country of origin	.	U.S.A.
Designing company	.	The Grumman Aircraft Engineering Corporation
Name and type number	.	Tigercat, U.S. Navy F7F–2
Duty . .	.	Single-seat carrier-borne fighter
Motors .	.	Two 2,000 h.p. Pratt & Whitney Double Wasp R–2800
Span . .	.	51 feet 6 inches
Performance :	.	Not available for publication
Armament .	.	Cannon in the nose

Note :—Used on Midway class 45,000 ton U.S. Navy carriers. There is a two-seat night fighter version, the F7F–2N.

Grumman TIGERCAT

[Photo : John Stroud

Grumman WIDGEON

Country of origin	U.S.A.
Designing company	The Grumman Aircraft Engineering Corporation
Name and type number	Widgeon, Grumman G–44, U.S. Army OA–14, U.S. Navy J4F, Royal Navy Gosling
Duty	General utility amphibian
Motors	Two 200 h.p. Ranger L–440–5
Span	40 feet
Loaded weight	4,500 lb.
Cruising speed	138 m.p.h.
Maximum speed	153 m.p.h.
Maximum range	920 miles
Accommodation	Pilot and 3–4 passengers

[Photo : Pan American Airways Inc.

Lockheed CONSTELLATION

Country of origin	U.S.A.
Designing company	The Lockheed Aircraft Corporation
Name and type number	Constellation, Lockheed Model 49, U.S. Army C–69
Duty	Transport
Motors	Four 2,200 h.p. Wright Cyclone GR–3350
Span	123 feet
Loaded weight	102,000 lb.
Cruising speed	300 m.p.h.
Maximum speed	340 m.p.h.
Maximum range	4,000 miles
Accommodation	43–60 passengers in pressure cabin

[Photo : Central Press

Lockheed CONSTITUTION

Country of origin	U.S.A.
Designing company	The Lockheed Aircraft Corporation
Name and type number	Constitution, U.S. Navy XR60–1
Duty	Transport
Motors	Four 3,000 h.p. Pratt & Whitney Wasp Major R–4360
Span	189 feet
Loaded weight	184,000 lb.
Cruising speed	260 m.p.h.
Range	About 4,000 miles
Accommodation	108–120 passengers in pressure cabins

Country of origin	U.S.A.
Designing company	The Lockheed Aircraft Corporation
Name and type number	Neptune, U.S. Navy P2V-1
Duty	Long-range patrol
Motors	Two 2,300 h.p. Wright Duplex Cyclone R-3350-8
Span	100 feet
Loaded weight	58,000 lb.
Maximum speed	Over 300 m.p.h.
Range	3,500-5,000 miles
Armament	Various layouts.

Note :—A modified Neptune named *Truculent Turtle* left Perth, Australia and flew non-stop for 11,237 miles to Columbus, U.S.A. in 55 hours 18 minutes.

Lockheed NEPTUNE

Country of origin	U.S.A.
Designing company	The Lockheed Aircraft Corporation
Name and type number	Saturn, Lockheed Model 75
Duty	Feeder line transport
Motors	Two 800 h.p. Wright Cyclone 7BA1 or two 600 h.p. Continental GR-9A
Span	74 feet
Loaded weight	16,000 lb.
Cruising speed	206 m.p.h.
Range	600 miles
Accommodation	14 passengers

Note :—Production may not be continued.

Lockheed SATURN

Country of origin	U.S.A.
Designing company	The Lockheed Aircraft Corporation
Name and type number	Shooting Star, U.S. Army P-80A
Duty	Single-seat fighter
Motor	One General Electric I-40 turbo-jet
Span	38 feet 10½ inches
Loaded weight	14,000 lb.
Maximum speed	Over 550 m.p.h.
Armament	Six .5-inch machine-guns. Bombs can be carried

[*Photo : U.S.A.A.F.*

Lockheed SHOOTING STAR

Luscombe SILVAIR

Country of origin	.	U.S.A.
Designing company	.	Luscombe Airplane Corporation
Name	. . .	Silvair
Duty	. .	Private owner type
Motor	. .	One 75 h.p. Continental A–75
Span	. .	35 feet
Loaded weight	.	1,310 lb.
Cruising speed	.	110 m.p.h.
Maximum speed	.	115 m.p.h.
Range	. .	500 miles
Accommodation	.	Pilot and passenger

Martin MARS

Country of origin	.	U.S.A.
Designing company	.	The Glenn Martin Company
Name and type number	.	Mars, U.S. Navy JRM–1 and JRM–2
Duty	. .	Long-range transport flying-boat
Motors	.	JRM–1, four 2,100 h.p. Wright Duplex Cyclone; JRM–2, four 2,500 h.p. Pratt & Whitney Wasp Major
Span	.	200 feet
Loaded weight	.	JRM–1, 145,000 lb.; JRM–2, 165,000 lb.
Cruising speed	.	152 m.p.h.
Range	. .	About 4,000 miles
Accommodation	.	132 troops, or 84 stretchers or 50 passengers

Martin MAULER

Country of origin	.	U.S.A.
Designing company	.	The Glenn Martin Company
Name and type number	.	Mauler, U.S. Navy BTM–1
Duty	. .	Single-seat carrier-borne dive-torpedo-bomber
Motor	. .	One 3,000 h.p. Pratt & Whitney Wasp Major R–4360
Span	. .	50 feet
Maximum speed	.	Over 400 m.p.h.
Range	. .	1,700 miles
Armament	.	4,000 lb. bomb or torpedo load

Country of origin	U.S.A.
Designing company	McDonnell Aircraft Corporation
Type number	U.S. Navy FD–1
Duty	Single-seat interceptor fighter
Motors	Two 1,400 lb. thrust Westinghouse Yankee 19–B turbo-jets.
Span	42 feet
Loaded weight	About 10,000 lb.
Maximum speed	Over 500 m.p.h.
Range	About 1,000 miles
Armament	Four .5-inch machine-guns and eight rocket projectiles

Note :—First U.S. Navy jet-propelled fighter.

McDonnell FD–1

Country of origin	U.S.A.
Designing company	North American Aviation Inc.
Name and type number	Texan, U.S. Army AT–6D, U.S. Navy SNJ–5, R.A.F. Harvard III
Duty	Advanced trainer
Motor	One 550 h.p. Pratt & Whitney Wasp R–1340
Span	42 feet 0¼ inches
Loaded weight	5,300 lb.
Cruising speed	170 m.p.h.
Maximum speed	205 m.p.h.
Range	750 miles
Accommodation	Instructor and pupil

[*Photo : John Stroud*

North American HARVARD

Country of origin	U.S.A.
Designing company	North American Aviation Inc.
Name and type number	Mustang IV, U.S. Army P–51D
Duty	Single-seat fighter
Motor	One 1,590 h.p. Packard-Rolls-Royce Merlin V–1650–7
Span	37 feet 0 5/16 inches
Loaded weight	About 10,000 lb.
Maximum speed	445 m.p.h.
Armament	Six .5-inch machine-guns and 1,000 lb. bomb load or rocket projectiles

Note :—This type is in service also with the Swedish Air Force.

North American MUSTANG

R

North American NAVION

Country of origin	.	U.S.A.
Designing company	.	North American Aviation Inc.
Name . .	.	Navion
Duty . .	.	Private owner type
Motor . .	.	One 185 h.p. Continental E–185
Span . .	.	33 feet 5 inches
Loaded weight .	.	2,576 lb.
Cruising speed .	.	150 m.p.h.
Maximum speed	.	160 m.p.h.
Range . .	.	580–700 miles
Accommodation	.	Pilot and 3 passengers

North American P–82 B

Country of origin	.	U.S.A.
Designing company	.	North American Aviation Inc.
Type number .	.	U.S. Army P–82B
Duty . .	.	Two-seat fighter
Motors . .	.	Two 1,380 h.p. Packard-Rolls-Royce Merlin V–1650–23
Span . .	.	51 feet 3 inches
Loaded weight .	.	24,800 lb.
Maximum speed	.	Over 475 m.p.h.

Note :—No other information available.

Northrop REPORTER

Country of origin	.	U.S.A.
Designing company	.	Northrop Aircraft Inc.
Name and type number	.	Reporter, U.S. Army F–15
Duty . .	.	Photographic reconnaissance
Motors . .	.	Two 2,100 h.p. Pratt & Whitney Double Wasp R–2800 C
Span . .	.	66 feet
Loaded weight .	.	28,000 lb.
Maximum speed	.	440 m.p.h.
Maximum range	.	4,000 miles

Country of origin	.	U.S.A.
Designing company	.	Northrop Aircraft Inc.
Type number	.	U.S. Army XB–35
Duty	.	Bomber (Flying wing)
Motors	.	Four 3,000 h.p. Pratt & Whitney Wasp Major R–4360
Span	.	172 feet
Loaded weight	.	180,000 lb.
Overload weight	.	209,000 lb.
Performance	.	Not available for publication

Northrop XB–35

Country of origin	.	U.S.A.
Designing company	.	The Piper Aircraft Corporation
Name and type number	.	Cub Super Cruiser, J5C
Duty	.	Private owner type
Motor	.	One 100 h.p. Lycoming
Span	.	35 feet 5½ inches
Loaded weight	.	1,550 lb.
Cruising speed	.	90 m.p.h.
Maximum speed	.	110 m.p.h.
Range	.	300 miles
Accommodation	.	Pilot and 2 passengers

Piper CUB SUPER CRUISER

Country of origin	.	U.S.A.
Designing company	.	The Piper Aircraft Corporation
Name and type number	.	Skysedan, PA–6
Duty	.	Private owner type
Motor	.	One 165 h.p. Continental E–165
Span	.	34 feet 8 inches
Loaded weight	.	2,400 lb.
Cruising speed	.	140–150 m.p.h.
Maximum speed	.	160 m.p.h.
Range	.	620 miles
Accommodation	.	Pilot and 3 passengers

Piper SKYSEDAN

259

Republic RAINBOW

Country of origin	U.S.A.
Designing company	The Republic Aviation Corporation
Name and type number	Rainbow (Civil), U.S. Army XF–12
Duty	Rainbow, Civil passenger transport; XF–12, Military photographic reconnaissance
Motors	Four 3,250 h.p. Pratt & Whitney Wasp Major R–4360
Span	129 feet 2 inches
Loaded weight	113,250 lb.
Cruising speed	400 m.p.h.
Maximum speed	Over 450 m.p.h.
Range	Up to 4,150 miles
Accommodation	40 passengers

Republic SEABEE

Country of origin	U.S.A.
Designing company	The Republic Aviation Corporation
Name and type number	Seabee, RC–3
Duty	Private owners and taxi amphibian
Motor	One 215 h.p. Franklin 6 A8–215–B7F
Span	37 feet 8 inches
Loaded weight	3,000 lb.
Cruising speed	103 m.p.h.
Maximum speed	120 m.p.h.
Range	560 miles
Accommodation	Pilot and 3 passengers

Note :—Ten thousand are on order, the first deliveries were made to Sweden and Mexico in October 1946.

Republic THUNDERJET

Country of origin	U.S.A.
Designing company	The Republic Aviation Corporation
Name and type number	Thunderjet, U.S. Army XP–84
Duty	Single-seat fighter
Motor	One General Electric TG–180 (J–35) turbo-jet
Span	36 feet 5 inches
Maximum speed	592 m.p.h.
Range	1,000 miles

Note :—An XP–84 has been attempting to set up a world's air-speed record. Single runs have been made at 617 and 619 m.p.h.

Country of origin	. U.S.A.
Designing company	. The Ryan Aeronautical Company
Name and type number	. Fireball, U.S. Navy FR–1
Duty	. Single-seat carrier-borne fighter
Motors	. One 1,350 h.p. Wright Cyclone R–1820 and one General Electric I–16 (J–31) turbo-jet
Span	. 40 feet
Loaded weight	. 9,800 lb.
Cruising speed	. 207 m.p.h.
Maximum speed	. 410 m.p.h.
Maximum range	. 1,500 miles
Armament	. Four .5-inch machine-guns

Ryan FIREBALL

Country of origin	. U.S.A.
Designing company	. Sikorsky Aircraft Division of the United Aircraft Corporation
Type number	. Sikorsky VS–316A, U.S. Army R–4B, U.S. Navy HNS–1, R.A.F. Hoverfly I
Duty	. Training helicopter
Motor	. One 185 h.p. Warner R–550–1
Rotor diameter	. 38 feet
Loaded weight	. 2,540 lb.
Maximum speed	. 75 m.p.h.
Accommodation	. Pilot and passenger or pupil

Note :—Later Sikorsky helicopters are the R–5A (Army), HO2S–1 (Navy) and the R–6A (Army), HOS–1 (Navy).

[Photo : Charles Brown

Sikorsky R–4B

Country of origin	. U.S.A.
Designing company	. The Stinson Division of the Consolidated Vultee Aircraft Corporation
Name	. Voyager 150
Duty	. Private owner type
Motor	. One 150 h.p. Franklin
Span	. 34 feet
Loaded weight	. 2,150 lb.
Cruising speed	. 125 m.p.h.
Maximum speed	. 133 m.p.h.
Maximum range	. 500 miles
Accommodation	. Pilot and 3 passengers

Stinson VOYAGER

Taylorcraft BC 12D

Country of origin	.	U.S.A.
Designing company	.	Taylorcraft Aviation Corporation
Type number	. .	BC 12D
Duty	. .	Private owner type
Motor	. .	One 65 h.p. Continental
Span	. .	36 feet
Loaded weight	.	1,200 lb.
Cruising speed	.	100 m.p.h.
Maximum speed	.	110 m.p.h.
Range	. .	300–500 miles
Accommodation	.	Pilot and passenger

Vought CORSAIR

Country of origin	.	U.S.A.
Designing company	.	Chance Vought Aircraft Division of the United Aircraft Corporation
Name and type number	.	Corsair, U.S. Navy F4U
Duty	. .	Single-seat carrier-borne fighter
Motor	. .	One 2,000 h.p. Pratt & Whitney Double Wasp R–2800–18
Span	. .	41 feet
Maximum speed		Over 400 m.p.h.
Armament	.	Six .5-inch machine-guns. Two 1,000 lb. bombs or eight rocket projectiles can be carried

Note :—Built by Brewster as the F3A, by Goodyear as the FG. The F2G–1 is powered by a Wasp Major motor.

Vought XF5U–1

Country of origin	.	U.S.A.
Designing company	.	Chance Vought Aircraft Division of the United Aircraft Corporation.
Type number	.	U.S. Navy XF5U–1
Duty	. .	Fighter
Motors	. .	Two 1,350 h.p. Pratt and Whitney Twin Wasp R–2,000
Speed range	.	20–400 m.p.h.

Note :—The aircraft illustrated is the V–173, a full-size low-powered flying model of the XF5U–1. A later version of the XF5U–1 will be powered by gas turbines and will have a top speed of over 500 m.p.h.

AUSTRALIAN . CANADIAN . CZECHOSLOVAKIAN . DANISH . FRENCH GERMAN . RUSSIAN . SWEDISH AIRCRAFT

To show a collection of world aircraft in this book as representative as those shown in the other sections would take far more space than that available, therefore a few types have been selected, mainly the products of European constructors.

Australia now has a fair-sized industry although much of its output is confined to British-designed aircraft.

Czechoslovakia has now a formidable array of civil aircraft, while France has a great variety of designs although not so many are in service.

German aircraft production has, of course, stopped and little information escapes from the U.S.S.R.

Country of origin	.	Australia
Designing Company	.	Commonwealth Aircraft Corporation Pty., Ltd.
Type number	.	CA–15, R.A.A.F. A–62
Duty	.	Single-seat fighter
Motor	.	One 1,540 h.p. Rolls-Royce Griffon 61
Span	.	36 feet
Maximum speed	.	Over 450 m.p.h.
Armament	.	Six .5-inch machine-guns and ten rocket projectiles

Commonwealth Aircraft CA–15

Country of origin	.	Canada
Designing company	.	The de Havilland Aircraft of Canada Ltd.
Name and type number	.	Chipmunk, D.H.C.1
Duty	.	Elementary trainer
Motor	.	One 140 h.p. de Havilland Gipsy Major
Span	.	34 feet 3½ inches
Loaded weight	.	1,782 lb.
Cruising speed	.	129 m.p.h.
Maximum speed	.	144 m.p.h.
Range	.	580 miles

De Havilland CHIPMUNK

[Photo : John Stroud

Noorduyn NORSEMAN

Country of origin	.	Canada
Designing company	.	Noorduyn Aviation Ltd.
Name . .	.	Norseman
Duty . .	.	Transport
Motor . .	.	One 600 h.p. Pratt & Whitney Wasp
Span . .	.	51 feet 8 inches
Loaded weight .	.	7,400 lb.
Cruising speed .	.	141 m.p.h.
Range . .	.	1,150 miles
Accommodation	.	8 passengers

Note :—Figures are for the Mk. V.

[Photo : Mraz Aircraft Construction Co.

Mraz SOKOL

Country of origin	.	Czechoslovakia
Designing company	.	Mraz Aircraft Construction Company
Name and type number	.	Sokol (Falcon), M.1A
Duty . .	.	Private owner type
Motor . .	.	One 105 h.p. Walter Minor 4–III Toma
Span . .	.	33 feet
Loaded weight .	.	1,540 lb.
Cruising speed .	.	131 m.p.h.
Maximum speed .	.	151 m.p.h.
Range . .	.	650 miles
Accommodation	.	Pilot and passenger

Note :—A three-seat version is the M–1C.

[Photo : John Stroud

S.A.I. KZ II

Country of origin	.	Denmark
Designing company	.	Skandinavisk Aero Industri A/S
Type number	.	KZ II
Duty . .	.	Elementary trainer and sports type
Motor . .	.	One 145 h.p. de Havilland Gipsy Major X
Span . .	.	33 feet 6 inches
Loaded weight .	.	1,870 lb.
Maximum speed	.	146 m.p.h.

Note :—The KZ II is in service in Denmark as a military trainer. The sports type is named the Sport. A Swedish-owned model appears in the illustration. A third version has a cabin and is named Kupe.

Country of origin	.	Denmark
Designing company	.	Skandinavisk Aero Industri A/S
Name and type number	.	Lark, KZ III
Duty	.	Private owner type
Motor	.	One 100 h.p. Cirrus Minor II
Span	.	31 feet 6 inches
Loaded weight	.	1,435 lb.
Cruising speed	.	106 m.p.h.
Maximum speed	.	115 m.p.h.
Range	.	310–500 miles
Accommodation	.	Pilot and passenger

[*Photo : John Stroud*

S.A.I. KZ III LARK

Country of origin	.	France
Designing company	.	Morane-Saulnier
Type number	.	MS.570
Duty	.	Private owner type
Motor	.	One 140 h.p. Renault Bengali 4 PEI
Span	.	34 feet 4 inches
Loaded weight	.	1,905 lb.
Maximum speed	.	165 m.p.h.
Range	.	621 miles
Accommodation	.	Pilot and passenger

Morane-Saulnier MS.570

Country of origin	.	France
Designing concern	.	Société Nationale de Constructions Aéronautiques du Nord
Name and type number	.	Noralpha, Nord 1101
Duty	.	Light touring type
Motor	.	One 240 h.p. Renault 6Q.10
Span	.	37 feet 8 inches
Loaded weight	.	3,638 lb.
Cruising speed	.	172 m.p.h.
Maximum speed	.	189 m.p.h.
Range	.	745 miles
Accommodation	.	Pilot and 3 passengers

[*Photo : S.N.C.A.N.*

S.N.C.A.N. NORD 1101

[*Photo : S.N.C.A.N.*

S.N.C.A.N. NORD 1201

Country of origin	.	France
Designing concern	.	Société Nationale de Constructions Aéronautiques du Nord
Name and type number	.	Norécrin, Nord 1201
Duty . .	.	Light touring type
Motor . .	.	One 140 h.p. Regnier 4L.00
Span . .	.	33 feet 6 inches
Loaded weight .	.	1,930 lb.
Cruising speed .	.	145 m.p.h.
Maximum speed .	.	165 m.p.h.
Range . .	.	560 miles
Accommodation	.	Pilot and 2 passengers

[*Photo : Service Cinématographique de l'Air*

S.N.C.A.S.E. LANGUEDOC 161

Country of origin	.	France
Designing concern	.	Société Nationale de Constructions Aéronautiques de Sud-Est (S.N.C.A.S.E.)
Name and type number	.	Languedoc 161
Duty . .	.	Passenger transport
Motors . .	.	Four 1,020 h.p. Gnome Rhone 14N 44–45
Span . .	.	95 feet 5 inches
Loaded weight .	.	49,423 lb.
Cruising speed .	.	251 m.p.h.
Maximum speed .	.	273 m.p.h.
Range . .	.	2,000 miles
Accommodation	.	12–33 passengers

Note :—In service with Air France.

[*Photo : S.N.C.A.S.E.*

S.N.C.A.S.E. SE 200

Country of origin	.	France
Designing concern	.	Société Nationale de Constructions Aéronautiques de Sud-Est (S.N.C.A.S.E.)
Type number .	.	S.E.200
Duty . .	.	Passenger flying-boat
Motors . .	.	Six 1,320 h.p. Gnome Rhone
Span . .	.	170 feet
Loaded weight .	.	162,800 lb.
Cruising speed .	.	189 m.p.h.
Maximum speed .	.	234 m.p.h.
Range . .	.	Nearly 4,400 miles
Accommodation	.	82 day passengers, 40 night passengers

Country of origin .	France
Designing concern .	Société Nationale de Constructions Aéronautiques du Sud-Ouest
Name and type number .	Bellatrix, S.O.3OR
Duty . . .	Passenger transport with pressure cabin
Motors . .	Two 1,750 h.p. Gnome Rhone 14R.33
Span . . .	84 feet
Loaded weight .	37,000 lb.
Cruising speed .	255 m.p.h.
Maximum speed .	342 m.p.h.
Range . .	2,110 miles
Accommodation .	30 passengers

[*Photo : S.N.C.A.S.O.*

S.N.C.A.S.O. S.O.3OR

Country of origin .	Germany
Designing company .	Junkers Flugzeug und Motorenwerke A.G.
Type number .	Ju 52/3m
Duty . .	Passenger transport
Motors . .	Three 600–750 h.p. B.M.W. 132 Z
Span . .	95 feet 11 inches
Loaded weight .	24,200 lb.
Cruising speed .	132–146 m.p.h.
Maximum speed .	165 m.p.h.
Range . .	520 miles
Accommodation .	12–14 passengers

Note :—Many of this type are still in service.

[*Photo : Alex Stöcker*

Junkers Ju 52/3M

Country of origin .	U.S.S.R.
Designer .	Sergei Iliuchin
Type number .	IL 3
Duty . .	Two-seat attack
Motor . .	One 1,300 h.p. AM–38
Span . .	49 feet
Maximum speed .	About 270 m.p.h.
Armament .	Two 23 mm. cannon and two 7.6 mm. machine-guns in leading-edge of wing, one cannon in rear cockpit and eight 56 lb. rocket projectiles

Note :—This type became known as the Stormovik from the Russian word for assault aeroplane.

[*Photo : S. Kafafyan*

IL 3

Country of origin	U.S.S.R.
Designer	Lavochkin
Type number	LA 5
Duty	Single-seat fighter
Motor	One 1,650 h.p. M–82FNW
Span	32 feet 2 inches
Loaded weight	7,400 lb.
Maximum speed	380 m.p.h.
Range	400 miles
Armament	Two 20 mm. cannon and four 110 lb. bombs

Note :—A later version is the LA 7 powered by a 2,000 h.p. motor.

LA 5

Country of origin	U.S.S.R.
Designer	Petlyakov
Type number	PE 3
Duty	Four-seat reconnaissance fighter
Motors	Two 1,100 h.p. M–103
Span	56 feet 1 inch
Loaded weight	16,930 lb.
Cruising speed	226 m.p.h.
Maximum speed	335 m.p.h.

PE 3

Country of origin	U.S.S.R.
Designer	A. N. Tupolev
Type number	PE 8
Duty	Heavy bomber
Motors	Four 1,300 h.p. AM–38
Span	131 feet 3 inches
Loaded weight	About 49,000 lb.
Maximum speed	About 235 m.p.h.
Range	2,500 miles
Armament	One 20 mm. cannon and six machine-guns. Maximum bomb load 8,000 lb.

PE 8

Note :—Known earlier as the TB 7.

268

Country of origin	U.S.S.R.
Designer	Alexander Yakovlev
Type number	YAK 9
Duty	Single-seat fighter
Motor	One M–107
Span	32 feet 10 inches
Loaded weight	About 6,000 lb.
Cruising speed	230 m.p.h.
Maximum speed	370 m.p.h.
Range	650 miles
Armament	One cannon and two machine-guns

YAK 9

Country of origin	Sweden
Designer	Bo Lundberg
Type number	J 22
Duty	Single-seat fighter
Motor	One 1,050 h.p. Swedish Pratt & Whitney Twin Wasp
Span	32 feet 10 inches
Cruising speed	280 m.p.h.
Maximum speed	360 m.p.h.
Armament	Two 13.2 mm. and two 7.9 mm. machine-guns in J 22A. Four 13.2 mm. machine-guns in J 22B

[Photo: Swedish International Press Bureau

J 22

Country of origin	Sweden
Designing company	Svenska Aeroplan A.B
Type number	B 18
Duty	Bomber reconnaissance
Motors	B 18A, two 1,065 h.p. Swedish Pratt & Whitney Twin Wasp; B 18B, two 1,475 h.p. Swedish Daimler-Benz
Span	55 feet 11 inches
Loaded weight	B 18A, 17,960 lb.; B 18B, 19,390 lb.
Cruising speed	B 18A, 260 m.p.h. ; B 18B, 300 m.p.h.
Maximum speed	B 18A, 290 m.p.h.; B 18B, 357 m.p.h.
Armament	Three machine-guns

[Photo: Svenska Aeroplan A.B.

S.A.A.B. B 18

269

[*Photo : Svenska Aeroplan A.B.*

S.A.A.B. J 21

Country of origin .	Sweden
Designing company .	Svenska Aeroplan A.B.
Type number . .	J 21
Duty . .	Single-seat fighter
Motor . .	One 1,475 h.p. Swedish Daimler-Benz
Span . .	38 feet 7 inches
Loaded weight .	9,150 lb.
Cruising speed .	324 m.p.h.
Maximum speed .	400 m.p.h.
Armament .	One 20 mm. cannon and two 13 mm. machine-guns

Note :—A jet-propelled version is the S.A.A.B 21R.

[*Photo : Svenska Aeroplan A.B.*

S.A.A.B. SCANDIA

Country of origin .	Sweden
Designing company .	Svenska Aeroplan A.B.
Name and type number .	Scandia, Saab 90
Duty . .	Passenger transport
Motors . .	Two 1,450 h.p. Pratt & Whitney Twin Wasp
Span . .	91 feet 8 inches
Loaded weight .	30,000 lb.
Cruising speed .	222 m.p.h.
Maximum speed .	251 m.p.h.
Range . .	Up to 960 miles
Accommodation .	24–32 passengers

[*Photo : Svenska Aeroplan A.B.*

S.A.A.B. SAFIR

Country of origin .	Sweden
Designing company .	Svenska Aeroplan A.B.
Name and type number .	Safir, Saab 91
Duty . .	Private owner type
Motor . .	One 130 h.p. de Havilland Gipsy Major
Span . .	34 feet 10 inches
Loaded weight .	2,200 lb.
Cruising speed .	127 m.p.h.
Maximum speed .	146 m.p.h.
Range . .	650 miles
Accommodation .	Pilot and 2 passengers

Note :—Twin floats can be fitted.

Country of origin	.	Sweden
Designing company	.	Svenska Aeroplan A.B.
Type number	.	S 17
Duty	.	Two-seat reconnaissance floatplane
Motor	.	One 980 h.p. Swedish Bristol Pegasus 24
Span	.	45 feet 1 inch
Loaded weight	.	8,430 lb.
Cruising speed	.	208 m.p.h.
Maximum speed	.	215 m.p.h.

[*Photo : Svenska Aeroplan A.B.*

S.A.A.B. S 17

SUPPLEMENT TO THE WORLD'S AIRCRAFT

DURING THE compilation of this work it was inevitable that many new types of aircraft would appear and it is for this reason that the following aircraft have been included out of their respective sections.

The Concordia is now flying but its production has been discontinued; the Merganser has also appeared and a radial-motored development—the Prince—is being built; the Aerocar is flying and a large number of orders have been placed for the type ; the Saunders-Roe A1 has given Britain the first jet-flying-boat.

In Denmark the KZ VII has taken the place of the KZ III on the production line ; the French Latécoère 631 flying-boat is now in service and is the largest passenger aeroplane in use.

Country of origin	.	Britain
Designing company	.	Cunliffe-Owen Aircraft Ltd.
Name	.	Concordia
Duty	.	Feeder line transport
Motors	.	Two 550 h.p. Alvis Leonides
Span	.	56 feet 7.6 inches
Loaded weight	.	12,500 lb.
Cruising speed	.	160–194 m.p.h.
Maximum speed	.	216 m.p.h.
Range	.	575–1,080 miles
Accommodation	.	10–12 passengers

[*Photo : Charles Brown*

Cunliffe-Owen CONCORDIA

[Copyright : Temple Press Ltd.

Armstrong WHITWORTH

Country of origin	.	Britain
Designing company		Sir W. G. Armstrong Whitworth Ltd.
Type number	.	A.W.52
Duty	.	Research aircraft
Motors	.	Two 5,000 lb. thrust Rolls-Royce Nene turbo-jets
Span	.	90 feet 11 inches
Length	.	37 feet 4 inches
Loaded weight	.	32,700 lb.
Maximum speed	.	450–500 m.p.h.
Accommodation	.	Crew of two

Percival MERGANSER

Country of origin	.	Britain
Designing company		Percival Aircraft Ltd.
Name	.	Merganser
Duty	.	Feeder line transport
Motors	.	Two 296 h.p. de Havilland Gipsy Queen 51
Span	.	47 feet 9 inches
Loaded weight	.	6,700 lb.
Cruising speed	.	150–183 m.p.h.
Maximum speed	.	193 m.p.h.
Range	.	800 miles
Accommodation	.	6–8 passengers

[Photo : John Stroud

Portsmouth AEROCAR

Country of origin	.	Britain
Designing company	.	Portsmouth Aviation Ltd.
Name	.	Aerocar Major
Duty	.	Light transport
Motors	.	Two 155 h.p. Blackburn Cirrus Major III
Span	.	42 feet 0 inches
Loaded weight	.	3,950 lb.
Cruising speed	.	141 m.p.h.
Maximum speed	.	167 m.p.h.
Range	.	About 500 miles
Accommodation	.	Pilot and 4 or 5 passengers

272

Country of origin .	Britain
Designing company .	Saunders–Roe Ltd.
Type number . .	A 1
Duty . . .	Single-seat fighter flying-boat
Motors . . .	Two 3,500 lb. thrust Metro-vick Beryl turbo-jets
Span . . .	46 feet
Weights and performance	Not available for publication

Note:—The first jet-propelled fighter flying-boat.

[*Photo : John Stroud*

Saunders-Roe A 1

Country of origin .	Belgium
Designing company .	Avions Tipsy
Name . . .	Junior
Duty . . .	Private owner and club type
Motor . .	One 60 h.p. Walter Mikron
Span . . .	22 feet 7½ inches
Loaded weight .	660 lb.
Cruising speed . .	113 m.p.h.
Maximum speed .	125 m.p.h.
Range . . .	375 miles
Accommodation .	Pilot only

[*Photo : John Stroud*

Tipsy JUNIOR

Country of origin .	Denmark
Designing comapny .	Skandinavisk Aero Industri A/S
Name and type number .	Lark, KZ VII
Duty . . .	Private owner and taxi type
Motor . . .	One 125 h.p. Continental C–125
Span . . .	31 feet 6 inches
Loaded weight .	1,911 lb.
Cruising speed . .	115 m.p.h.
Maximum speed .	125 m.p.h.
Range . . .	400 miles
Accommodation .	Pilot and 3 passengers

Photo : Charles Brown

S.A.I. KZ VII LARK

S

Country of origin	France
Designing concern	Atelier d'Études et de Constructions Aéronautiques de Toulouse
Type number	Latécoère 631
Duty	Transport flying-boat
Motors	Six 1,600 h.p. Wright Cyclone
Span	188 feet 0 inches
Loaded weight	157,300 lb.
Cruising speed	185 m.p.h.
Maximum speed	246 m.p.h.
Range	3,750 miles
Accommodation	46–100 passengers

[*Photo: John Stroud*

LATÉCOÈRE 631

Country of origin	France
Designing concern	Société d'Études et de Constructions Aéro-Navales
Name and type number	Courlis, type SUC-10
Duty	Light transport, freight and ambulance type
Motor	One 190 h.p. Mathis G8R
Span	37 ft. 9 ins.
Loaded weight	3,086 lb.
Cruising Speed	143 m.p.h.
Maximum Speed	162 m.p.h.
Range	621 miles
Accommodation	Pilot and 4 passengers

[*Les Reportages Photographiques de France*

S.E.C.A.N. COURLIS

Country of origin	Holland
Designing company	Fokker-Diepen Vliegtuigen
Name and type number	Promotor, F.25
Duty	Private owner and taxi type
Motor	One 190 h.p. Lycoming O-435 A
Span	39 feet 5 inches
Loaded weight	3,140 lb.
Cruising speed	102–123 m.p.h.
Maximum speed	136 m.p.h.
Range	377–590 miles
Accommodation	Pilot and 3 passengers

Fokker PROMOTOR

Country of origin . U.S.A.
Designing company . Douglas Aircraft Co. Inc.
Name and type number . Skystreak, D–558
Duty . . . High-speed research
Motor . . . One 4,000 lb. thrust General Electric TG–180 turbo-jet
Span . . . 25 feet 0 inches
Length . . . 35 feet 1½ inches
Loaded weight . 9,750 lb.
Maximum speed . Over 650 m.p.h.
Accommodation . Pilot only

Note :—This aircraft set up a world's absolute speed record by attaining 1,047.356 km./h. (650·606 m.p.h.) in 1947. A later development is the swept-back wing Skyrocket.

[*Photo: Central Press*

Douglas SKYSTREAK

Country of origin . U.S.A.
Designing company . The Glenn Martin Company
Type number . . Model 202
Duty . . . Passenger transport
Motors . . . Two 2,400 h.p. Pratt and Whitney Double Wasp
Span . . . 92 feet 9 inches
Loaded weight . 38,000 lb.
Cruising speed . 263 m.p.h.
Maximum speed . 293 m.p.h.
Range . . . 1,165 miles
Accommodation . 36–40 passengers

Note :—A cargo version exists.

Martin MODEL 202

Country of origin . U.S.A.
Designing company . Sikorsky Aircraft Division of the United Aircraft Corporation
Type number . . S–51
Duty . . . Commercial helicopter
Motor . . . One 450 h.p. Pratt and Whitney Wasp Junior
Rotor diameter . 48 feet
Loaded weight . 4,985 lb.
Cruising speed . 85 m.p.h.
Maximum speed . 103 m.p.h.
Minimum speed . 0 m.p.h.
Maximum range . 245 miles
Accommodation . Pilot and 3 passengers
Remarks . . British version is the Westland Sikorsky S–51 with 500 h.p. Alvis Leonides motor

[*Photo: John Stroud*

Sikorsky S–51

BOOKS & PERIODICALS

*A selection of recent books, mostly English, together with a number
of standard works on the history and other aspects of aeronautics.*

A. GENERAL

AIR MINISTRY.	Elementary Flying Training. London (H.M.S.O.), 1943.
ALLAN (W. J. D.).	Allan's Guide to the Pilot's ' A ' Licence. London (Allen & Unwin), 1945.
' FLIGHT.'	' Flight ' Handbook. 4th ed. London (Flight Office), 1945.
ODHAMS PRESS.	Air Training Manual : a Practical Guide . . . for Members of the A.T.C., etc. London (Odhams), n.d., c. 194(?).
STEWART (O.).	Air Power and the Expanding Community. London (Newnes), 1944.
VEALE (S. E.).	Guide to Flying. London (Temple Press), 1943.
WIMPERIS (H. E.).	Aviation. London (Oxford University Press), 1945.

B. GLOSSARIES AND DICTIONARIES

AEROPLANE SPOTTER.	Glossary of Flying : a Dictionary of Aeronautical Terms. London (Temple Press), 1943.
BRITISH STANDARDS INSTITUTION.	Glossary of Aeronautical Terms. London, 1940.
LANZ (J. E.).	Lanz Aviation Dictionary in Nine Languages. Pasadena, U.S.A. (Perkins), 1944.
NELSON (H.).	Dictionary of Aeronautical Terms. London, 1946.
PARTRIDGE (E.).	A Dictionary of R.A.F. Slang. London (Joseph), 1945.

C. AIRCRAFT TYPES AND AERO ENGINES (*See also* **Section E.**)

BRIDGMAN (L.).	Jane's All the World's Aircraft. (Annually). London (Sampson Low).
GIBBS-SMITH (C. H.).	The Aircraft Recognition Manual. London (Newnes), 1944.
GREY (C. G.).	British Fighter Planes. London (Faber), 1941.
GREY (C. G.).	Bombers. London (Faber), 1941.
JUDGE (A. W.).	Aircraft Engines. Vol. II (2 ed. revised). London (Chapman & Hall), 1947.

276

LLOYD (F. H. M.).	Hurricane. Leicester (Harborough), 1946.
RUSSELL (D. A.).	Aircraft of the Fighting Powers. 6 Vols. Leicester (Harborough), 1940–47.
SAVILLE-SNEATH (R. A.).	British Aircraft. 2 vols. London (Penguin), 1944.
SAVILLE-SNEATH (R. A.).	Aircraft of the United States. Vol. I. London (Penguin), 1944.
STROUD (J.).	Japanese Aircraft. Leicester (Harborough), 1946.
TAYLOR (J. W. R.) AND ALLWOOD (M. F.).	Spitfire. Leicester (Harborough), 1946.
WILKINSON (P. H.).	Aircraft Engines of the World. New York (Pitman), 1945.

D. AERODYNAMICS

BROWNE (H. F.).	Aeroplane Flight. London (Longmans), 1944.
HADDON (J. D.).	Aeronautics : a Book of Graded Worked Examples. 2 vols. London, 1945.
HEMKE (P. E.).	Elementary Applied Aerodynamics. London (Constable), 1947.
KERMODE (A. C.).	Mechanics of Flight. London (Gale & Polden), 1942.
PIERCY (N. A. V.).	A Complete Course in Elementary Aerodynamics. London (English Universities Press), 1944.
PIERCY (N. A. V.).	Aerodynamics. London (English Universities Press), 1946.

E. JET AND ROCKET PROPULSION

GRIERSON (J.).	Jet Flight. London (Sampson Low), 1946.
JUDGE, (A. W.).	Modern Gas Turbines. London (Chapman & Hall), 1947.
LEY (W.).	Rockets. New York (Viking). 1945.
SMITH (G.).	Gas Turbines and Jet Propulsion for Aircraft. New ed. London (Flight), 1946.

F. ENGINEERING, INSTRUMENTS, etc.

BARTHOLOMEW (N. C.).	Aircraft Inspection Methods. London (Pitman), 1943.
BEAUMONT (R. A. ed.).	Aeronautical Engineering : a Practical Guide for Everyone connected with the Aircraft Industry. London (Odhams), n.d., c. 194(?).
BLANDFORD (P. W.).	Practical Aircraft Rigging. London (Hutchinson), 1944.
CLANCEY (V. J.).	Chemistry and the Aeroplane. London (Nelson), 1942.
HENSHAW (J. T.).	Aircraft Mechanic's Pocket Book. London (Pitman), 1944.

JUDGE (A. W.).	Aircraft Engines. 2 vols. London (Chapman & Hall), 1945 (vol. I, 2nd ed.), 1941 (vol. II).
LEES (H. P.).	Elements of Aeroplane Hydraulics. London (Hutchinson), 1944.
MATSON (R.).	Aircraft Electrical Engineering. New York (McGraw Hill), 1943.
PRESTON (F.) AND WIL-LIAMSON (G. W.).	Aircraft Servicing Manual. London (Elek), 1945.
SLOLEY (R. W.).	[Aircraft] Instruments. 5th ed. London (Pitman), 1944.
THARRAT (G.).	Aircraft Production Illustrated. New York (McGraw Hill), 1944.
VINE (D.).	Aircraft Hydraulics Simplified. London (Newnes), 1943.
WILLIAMSON (G. W.).	Aircraft Engineer's ' C ' Licence. London (Newnes), 1946.
WILLIAMSON (G. W.).	Flight Mechanic's Handbook. London (Newnes), 1944.

G. RADIO AND RADAR

SURGEMOR (D. H.).	Radio for Aeroplanes. London (Longmans), 1944.

H. NAVIGATION

AIR MINISTRY.	Air Navigation. London, 1944.
BENNETT (D. T. C.).	The Complete Air Navigator. 4th ed. London (Pitman), 1942.
BENNETT (D. T. C.).	The Air Mariner. 2nd ed. London (Pitman), 1943.
HUGHES (A. J.).	History of Air Navigation. London (Allen & Unwin), 1946.

I. METEOROLOGY

AIR MINISTRY.	A Short Course in Elementary Meteorology. By W. H. PICK. 5th ed. revised. London (H.M.S.O.), 1945.
AIR MINISTRY.	Cloud Forms : Definitions and Photographs. 5th ed. London (H.M.S.O.), 1945.
AIR MINISTRY.	Meteorological Glossary. London (H.M.S.O.), 1944.
AIR MINISTRY.	Meteorological Observer's Handbook. London (H.M.S.O.), 1942.
CAVE (C. J. P.).	Clouds and Weather Phenomena. London (Cambridge University Press), 1943.
HUMPHREYS (W. J.).	Fogs, Clouds and Aviation. London (Baillière), 1944.

J. GLIDING

HORSLEY (T.).	Soaring Flight : the Art of Gliding. London (Eyre & Spottiswoode), 1944.

SITEK (A.) AND BLUNT (V.).	Gliding and Soaring. London, 1944.
'STRING-BAG.'	Gliding and Power Flying. London (Oxford University Press), 1946.

K. CIVIL AVIATION

FROESCH (C.) AND PROKOSCH (W.).	Airport Planning. New York; London (Chapman), 1946.
MINISTRY OF INFORMATION.	Merchant Airmen : The Air Ministry Account of British Civil Aviation, 1939–1944. London (H.M.S.O.), 1946.
STUART (F. S.) AND BIARD (H. C.).	Modern Air Transport. London (Long), 1946.
VEALE (S. E.).	To-morrow's Airliners, Airways and Airports. London (Pilot Press), 1945.
WYNN (W. E.).	Civil Air Transport. London (Hutchinson), 1946.

L. MODELS

ALLEN (G.).	Semi-scale Model Aircraft. Maidenhead (Marshall), 1947.
BOWDEN (C. E.).	Petrol-engined Model Aircraft. Maidenhead (Marshall), 1947.
COPLAND (R.) AND WARRING (R. H.).	The Model Aeronautical Digest. Mitcham (Model Pubns.), 1945.
ELWELL (J. H.).	Solid Scale Model Aircraft. Leicester (Harborough), n.d.
FORSTER (J. F. P.).	Model Aircraft Petrol Engines. Leicester (Harborough), n.d.
RUSHBROOKE (C. S.).	An ABC of Model Aircraft Construction. Leicester (Harborough), n.d.
SIZER (J. A.).	Model Flying Boats. Leicester (Harborough), n.d.
SPAREY (L. H.) AND RIPPON (C. A.).	The Model Aeroplane Manual. Maidenhead (Marshall), 1947.
WARRING (R. H.).	Indoor Flying Models. Leicester (Harborough), n.d.
WARRING (R. H.).	Model Gliders. Leicester (Harborough), n.d.
WINTER (W.).	The Model Aircraft Handbook. London (Harrap), 1946.
WOODASON (V. T. G.)	Watch and Make: the art of scale model aircraft building. London (Useful Publications Ltd.), 1944.

M. MEDICINE, LAW, etc.

ARMSTRONG (H. G.).	Principles and Practice of Aviation Medicine. London (Baillière), 1944.
FITZPATRICK (F. L.) AND STILES (K. A.).	The Biology of Flight. London (Allen & Unwin), 1944.

GEMMIL (C. L.).   Physiology in Aviation. London (Baillière), 1943.

SHAWCROSS (C. N.) AND   Shawcross and Beaumont on Air Law. London (Butter-
BEAUMONT (K. M.).   worth), 1945.

N. MISCELLANEOUS

ABRAMS (T.).   Essentials of Aerial Surveying and Photo Interpretation.
                       New York (McGraw Hill), 1944.

AYMAR (G.).   Bird Flight. London (Lane), 1936.

BRYDEN (H. G., *ed.*).   Wings: an Anthology of Flight. London (Faber), 1942.

HORTON-SMITH (C.).   The Flight of Birds. London (Witherby), 1938.

LOW (A. M.).   Parachutes in Peace and War. London (Scientific Book
                       Club), 1942.

MEACOCK (F. T.).   Aircraft Propeller Design. London (Spon), 1947.

MORRIS (C. L.).   Pioneering the Helicopter. New York (McGraw Hill), 1945.

MURPHY (C. J. V.).   Parachute. New York (Putnam), 1930.

SPAIGHT (J. M.).   Air Power and War Rights. London (Longmans), 1947.

WARREN (J. A. C.).   The Flight Testing of Production Aircraft. London (Pitman),
                       1944.

O. HISTORY

BRIDGMAN (L.).   All the World's Aircraft. (Annually). London (Sampson
                       Low), 1910 [in progress].

BREWER (G.).   Fifty Years of Flying. London (Air League), 1946.

CHANUTE (O.).   Progress in Flying Machines. New York, 1894.

DAVY (M. J. B.).   Interpretive History of Flight. London (H.M.S.O.), 1937.

DOLLFUS   (C.)   AND   Histoire de l'Aéronautique. Paris (L'Illustration), 1932.
BOUCHÉ (H.).

GIBBS-SMITH (C. H.).   Ballooning. London (Penguin), 1948.

GREY (C. G.).   A History of The Air Ministry. London (Allen & Unwin),
                       1940.

HEINMULLER (J. P. V.). Man's Fight to Fly: Famous World-Record Flights and a
                       Chronology of Aviation. New York; London (Funk &
                       Wagnall), 1944.

HODGSON (J. E.).   The History of Aeronautics in Great Britain. London
                       (Oxford University Press), 1924.

KELLY (F. C.).   The Wright Brothers. London (Harrap), 1944.

MAGOUN (F. A.) AND   A History of Aircraft. New York (McGraw Hill), 1931.
HODGINS (E.).

MARSH (W. LOCKWOOD).   Aeronautical Prints and Drawings. London (Halton), 1924.

MILBANK (J.).   The First Century of Flight in America. Princeton, U.S.A. (Princeton University Press), 1943.

REDGROVE (H. S.).   The Air Mails of the British Isles. London (Field), 1940.

ROYAL AERONAUTICAL SOCIETY.   Eighty Years of British Aviation: the Work of the Royal Aeronautical Society from . . . 1866 to . . . 1946. London, 1946.

SAUNDERS (H. ST. G.).   Per Ardua [the Rise of British Air Power, 1911–1939]. London (Oxford University Press), 1944.

SCIENCE MUSEUM.   Handbooks of the Collections Illustrating Aeronautics. By M. J. B. DAVY. I. Heavier-than-Air Aircraft. II. Lighter-than-Air Aircraft. III. Propulsion of Aircraft. London (H.M.S.O.), 1934–36.

VIVIAN (E. C.) AND MARSH (W. LOCKWOOD).   A History of Aeronautics. London (Collins), 1919.

P. THE SECOND WORLD WAR

AIR LEAGUE.   The Story of the Air Training Corps. London (Air League), 1946.

AIR TRANSPORT AUXILIARY.   Air Transport Auxiliary. White Waltham (A.T.A.), c. 1945.

ANDERSON (WING-COM-MANDER, W.).   Pathfinders. London (Jarrolds), 1946.

[ANONYMOUS.]   Arnhem Lift: The Story of a Glider Pilot. London (Pilot Press), 1945.

[ANONYMOUS.]   Fighter Pilot. London (Batsford), 1941.

BALCHIN (N.).   The Aircraft Builders. London (H.M.S.O.), 1947.

CHESHIRE (SQUADRON-LEADER L.).   Bomber Pilot. London (Hutchinson), 1943.

GIBSON (WING - COM-MANDER G.).   Enemy Coast Ahead. London (Joseph), 1946.

GREY (C. G.).   The Luftwaffe. London (Faber), 1944.

GREY (C. G.).   Sea Flyers. London (Faber), 1942.

HARRIS (MARSHAL OF THE R.A.F., SIR A.).   Bomber Offensive. London (Collins), 1947.

HILLARY (R.).   The Last Enemy. London (Macmillan), 1943.

HORSLEY (T.).   Find, Fix and Strike : the Work of the Fleet Air Arm. London (Eyre & Spottiswoode), 1945.

LEE (A.).	The German Air Force. London (Duckworth), 1946.
MACMILLAN (CAPT. N.).	The Royal Air Force in the World War. Vols. I– . London (Harrap), 1942 [in progress].
MINISTRY OF INFORMATION.	Bomber Command. London (H.M.S.O.), 1941. [Also Bomber Command Continues. 1942.]
MINISTRY OF INFORMATION.	By Air to Battle: the Official Account of the British First and Sixth Airborne Divisions. London (H.M.S.O.), 1945.
MINISTRY OF INFORMATION.	Coastal Command. London (H.M.S.O.), 1943.
MINISTRY OF INFORMATION.	Fleet Air Arm. London (H.M.S.O.), 1943.
MINISTRY OF INFORMATION.	R.A.F. Middle East. London (H.M.S.O.), 1945.
MINISTRY OF INFORMATION.	The Battle of Britain. London (H.M.S.O.), 1941.
U.S. ARMY AIR FORCES.	Target Germany. London (H.M.S.O.), 1944.

Q. PERIODICALS

Title	Place of Issue	Published
AERO DIGEST	New York	Fortnightly
AERO FIELD (Air Stamps and Air Mail News)	Sutton Coldfield, Worcs.	Monthly
AEROMODELLER	Leicester	Monthly
AERONAUTICAL ENGINEERING REVIEW	New York	Monthly
AERONAUTICAL SCIENCES (INSTITUTE OF) JOURNAL	New York	Quarterly
AERONAUTICS	London	Monthly
AEROPLANE, THE	London	Weekly
AEROPLANE SPOTTER, THE	London	Fortnightly
AIRCRAFT (Official organ Australian branch of R.Ae.S.)	Melbourne	Monthly
AIRCRAFT AND AIRPORT	Toronto	
AIRCRAFT ENGINEERING	London	Monthly
AIRCRAFT PRODUCTION	London	Monthly
AIRCRAFT RECOGNITION	London	Monthly—not on sale
AIR-LOG, THE	Sydney	Monthly
AIR MAIL (Official organ of R.A.F. Association) (previously AIRMAN)	London	Monthly

BOOKS AND PERIODICALS

AIR NEWS (*with Air Tech.*)	New York	Monthly
AIRPORTS	New York	Monthly
AIR PORTS AND AIR TRANSPORTATION	London	Monthly
AIR RESERVE GAZETTE	London	Monthly
AIR TRANSPORT	New York	Monthly
AIR TRANSPORT AND AIRPORT ENGINEERING	London	Monthly
AIR TRANSPORTATION	New York	Monthly
AMERICAN AVIATION	Washington, D.C.	Fortnightly
ASSOCIATION OF LICENSED AIRCRAFT ENGIN-EERS, JOURNAL OF	Durban, S.A.	
AVIATION	New York	Monthly
AVIATION NEWS	Washington, D.C.	Weekly
BRITISH OVERSEAS AIRWAYS NEWS LETTER	London	Monthly
CANADIAN AVIATION	Ottawa	Monthly
C.I.A.T.O. BULLETIN (*Conference of International Air Traffic Operators*)	London	Monthly
CIVIL AERONAUTICS JOURNAL	Washington, D.C.	Monthly
COMMERCIAL AVIATION	New York	Monthly
FLIGHT	London	Weekly
GUILD OF AIR PILOTS AND AIR NAVIGATORS (*Journal*)	London	Quarterly
INDIAN AVIATION	Calcutta	Monthly
INTER AVIA	London	3 issues weekly
LOG, THE (*Official Journal of the British Air Line Pilots Association*)	London	
MODEL AIRCRAFT (*S.M.A.E. Journal*)	London	Monthly
MODEL AIRPLANE NEWS	New York	Monthly
QANTAS EMPIRE AIRWAYS NEWS LETTER	Sydney	Monthly
ROCKETS (*United States Rocket Society Inc.*)	Illinois, U.S.A.	Monthly
ROYAL AERO CLUB GAZETTE	London	Monthly
ROYAL AERONAUTICAL SOCIETY (*Journal*)	London	Monthly
ROYAL AIR FORCE QUARTERLY	Aldershot, Hants.	Quarterly
SAILPLANE AND GLIDER	London	Monthly
S.B.A.C. SUMMARY	London	Weekly

' SPACEWARDS ' (*British Interplanetary Society, Journal of*). (*Also Bulletin*)	London	Quarterly
SPEEDBIRD (*House Organ of B.O.A.C.*)	London	Monthly
U.S. AIR SERVICES	Washington, D.C.	Monthly
WEATHER (*Roy. Met. Soc.*)	London	Monthly
WINGS	Johannesburg	Monthly
WINGS (*Official organ of Royal New Zealand Aero Club Inc.*)	Wellington, New Zealand	Monthly
WINGS OVER THE WORLD (*B.O.A.C.*)	London	Quarterly

INDEX